THE ORSANCO STORY

*Water Quality Management
in the Ohio Valley under
an Interstate Compact*

THE ORSANCO STORY

*Water Quality Management
in the Ohio Valley under
an Interstate Compact*

Edward J. Cleary

Published for Resources for the Future, Inc.
by The Johns Hopkins Press, Baltimore, Maryland

Foreword

In this book the experience of the Ohio River Valley Water Sanitation Commission is recorded and appraised by the man who has been the executive director and chief engineer of that organization since its establishment in 1948. Growing concern with water pollution, which in many parts of the country has come to be recognized as the most serious problem of water management, and rising interest in the interstate compact as a device for dealing with a variety of regional situations make this study particularly timely.

ORSANCO is a unique institution for water quality management with a remarkable record of accomplishment in combating water pollution throughout a large river valley. All who are concerned with pollution abatement programs are fortunate that Edward J. Cleary undertook to write this account of an operation with which he has been so intimately connected. Too rarely, at least in this country, does a successful administrator review his own experience. Can such an account be completely objective? Probably not. Certainly no one could expect Dr. Cleary, with his past and present dedication to ORSANCO's objectives and program, to be a completely neutral observer. On the other hand, given his analytical turn of mind and lively recognition of his own biases, he has written an account that is neither narrow nor partisan. In fact, one of the strong points of his study is its inside view: the reader can see ORSANCO through the eyes of one who knows the whole story and who has had a leading part in molding the institution's objectives and guiding its program.

In the evolution of the federal system in the United States, one of the most difficult tasks has been that of dealing with problems that affect more than one state but are not nationwide in extent. How can we assure appropriate representation of all interested parties in such problems and at the same time achieve effective action and administration? The inter-state compact has long offered a possible basis for establishing an inter-state agency to deal with problems of a regional nature, but the device has seldom been utilized successfully to deal with complex problems. ORSANCO is an outstanding exception: an interstate compact agency with a long and successful record of dealing with a complex day-to-day planning and operation task. Thus, this study is of special interest to students of American government interested in the evolution of the federal system. It not only details what ORSANCO has accomplished, but suggests that an interstate compact agency can serve an even broader purpose.

Irving K. Fox, vice-president of Resources for the Future, Inc., until last September, took a leading part in working out the arrangements under which this study was made, and throughout has been both advisor and sounding board for the author. Dr. Cleary perfected the design of this book, and did much of the preliminary writing during part of 1963 and 1964, when he took a year's leave of absence from his ORSANCO post and temporarily joined the research staff of RFF.

December, 1966   JOSEPH L. FISHER, President
                                         Resources for the Future, Inc.

Contents

vii

Preface

When this manuscript was finished, I began to wonder if I had told more about ORSANCO than anyone could possibly want to hear about. Would the reader feel like the reviewer of a treatise on whales who began by saying, "This book tells more about whales than I want to know." But then I gained some reassurance from the fact that during the past year my mail has been heavy with requests for all sorts of detail concerning the background, organization, program, and operations of the Ohio River Valley Water Sanitation Commission.

In large part these requests for information on an interstate compact reflect a growing interest in what has been called creative regionalism. This position was apparent in a statement by Dr. James M. Conant, president emeritus of Harvard University, urging the states to consider establishment of an interstate educational compact: "Unless the states act on school problems, and do something to meet the needs, the federal government will move in more and more with money and try to make policy in fields where it would have great difficulty with details."

Certainly in the complex business of controlling water pollution it is the "details" that pose the difficulties. This is amply demonstrated by happenings in the conduct of the Ohio Valley clean-streams program. And these experiences provide background to appreciate the difficult nature of the task confronting the federal government in seeking to advance pollution abatement on a national scale. Among other things, it is to be noted that in the effort to give vitality to legislative fiats more and more money has been requested. As a result the federal subsidy to municipalities for construction of sewage treatment plants has escalated from $50 million yearly in 1956 to an authorization in 1966 of $3.4 billion over the four-year period, 1968–71. Yet it is far from clear that even such an outlay will adequately take care of the "details." Presumably this is what prompted President Johnson to say in his February, 1966, message to the Congress on water pollution that "the development of new knowledge and new organizations to carry on the work is as crucial as our dollars."

It is to research on matters of this kind—probing the virtues and shortcomings of institutional arrangements—that Resources for the Future, Inc., has been addressing much of its attention. Thus it was that in 1963, Irving K. Fox, then vice president of RFF, talked to me about writing an account of why and how eight states in the Ohio Valley adopted an interstate compact to promote a regional program of pollution control, and what years of experience—now nearly twenty years—revealed about such an operation. Although I was enthusiastic about undertaking such an assignment, I felt that my emotional involvement would preclude me from acting as a detached observer. After all, as my wife puts it, I've had a love affair with ORSANCO. And who can be dispassionate in writing about the object of his affections?

Mr. Fox disposed of this question by saying I was not expected, nor should I try, to develop the kind of exposition that might emanate from one who had been insulated from the day-by-day stimulations and frustrations of ORSANCO affairs. Further, he foresaw possibilities of broadening my one-dimensional viewpoints if I would be responsive to the judgments of reviewers that would be selected by RFF to comment on the initial draft of the manuscript. To this I readily assented, and as a result I find myself greatly indebted to those who lavished so much attention on the first draft. For whatever deficiencies now exist in the final document only I can be held accountable.

Among the reviewers to whom I am grateful, there is Richard H. Leach, department of political science, Duke University. Professor Leach, who is co-author of a book on interstate compact agencies and an advocate of their wider use, displayed such zeal in pointing out ways of improving my text that I devoted many days in an endeavor to match his aspirations.

Only a degree less demanding but equally provocative was the critique from Albert Lepawsky, department of political science, the University of California, Berkeley. In fact, Professor Lepawsky came to Cincinnati to inspire further attention to matters that he regarded as significant by virtue of having attended some of the early meetings of the ORSANCO compact negotiating committee in 1936–37. He inclines to the view that the late Senator Robert A. Taft played a more decisive role in influencing the drafters of the compact to include federal representation than the records available to me indicated, or on which I could elaborate from the recollections of several participants in the negotiations.

Dr. Mitchell Wendell, legal counsel for the Council of State Governments, reined in my tendency to generalize about interstate compacts. "Too much should not be claimed," he cautioned, "for general conclusions which inevitably must be based only on the single example of ORSANCO." This admonition, along with his clarification of certain legal points, received appropriate consideration.

Somewhat more difficult was the attempt to satisfy the criticism of Dr. Norman Beckman, assistant director of the Advisory Committee on Intergovernmental Relations, Washington, D. C., who felt that "the weaknesses, failings or disappointments with respect to ORSANCO are only briefly touched." But in the rewrite I sought to remedy this deficiency, along with a number of others to which he called attention.

The comments of Henry C. C. Weinkauff, chief of the civil-works planning division, U. S. Corps of Engineers, pointed up aspects of river quality management as viewed from the standpoint of the largest water-resources construction agency in the Ohio Valley. They were given cognizance and served as a source of valuable reference in restructuring the final draft.

A long-time friend and counsellor, Gordon M. Fair, professor emeritus of sanitary engineering, Harvard University, provided further evidence of his generosity by halting work on a book he had going to press in order to review my manuscript. His commentary reminded me of the story of the critic of the small-town band who told the bass drummer, "You don't make good music." To this the drummer modestly retorted, "That may be so, but I sure can drown out a lot of bad." Since no such convenient cover-up could be offered by me, I applied myself to matters that Professor Fair decreed should be more harmoniously blended.

Other friends who were invited by RFF to review the manuscript and kindly provided comments included: Maurice LeBosquet, Jr., U. S. Public Health Service, retired; Grant A. Howell, assistant chief engineer, U. S. Steel Corporation, retired; R. R. Balmer, E. I. du Pont de Nemours Company; and Dr. Abel Wolman, professor emeritus, The Johns Hopkins University. Robert K. Horton, assistant director of ORSANCO, and John E. Kinney, a former staff member, were also enlisted as reviewers.

But this does not exhaust the list of those who were involved at one stage or another in offering assistance. Commissioner Hudson Biery and Secretary F. H. Waring, whose intimate association with events related to ORSANCO dates back more than thirty years, checked the manuscript for historical accuracy. Dr. Allen V. Kneese, director of the water-resources program of RFF, was a close companion during the period in which much of this book was written, and one of my severest but most appreciated critics.

Henry Jarrett, director of RFF publications, was frequently sought out for solace and he never failed to provide cheering counsel, some of which I interpreted as meaning, "Either put some fire into your writing or vice versa." Since in some passages I feared I was unable to do either, it was pleasing to learn that this option would be delegated to the editorial skill of Nora Roots. One of those who may be suspected of concluding at times that a fire would be the best place for the manuscript was Ruth Bergmeyer who toiled endlessly in typing revised drafts.

On the basis of this recital one might ask what was left for the author to contribute aside from pampering his pride and prejudice? My patient wife and children could provide one answer by saying that it was time— a commodity they had occasions to believe might have been more equitably distributed among such pursuits as attending the theatre, mending screens, and cruising on the river. It may be small recompense to them, but I would inscribe the names of Adelaide, Ellen, Daniel, Kathleen, and Rogers as participators in this project.

EDWARD J. CLEARY

Cincinnati, Ohio
December, 1966

Part I

The Setting

"The promise of any land
lies in the streams that water it."
Theme of the 13th annual report of
the Ohio River Valley Water Sanitation Commission,
December 1, 1961.

1

A Panoramic View

In a message to Congress on conservation and pollution on February 23, 1966, the President of the United States asserted that what the nation needed was new watershed organizations. He proposed a "Clean Rivers Demonstration Program" to foster experimentation with agencies designed to unite all pollution-control activities within the confines of a single river basin.[1] And he called attention to the use of interstate compacts to provide this kind of partnership among state, local, and private interests and the federal government. The President's message coincided with the final stages of this case history of the Ohio River Valley Water Sanitation Commission, which is just such a partnership.

The story of this interstate compact agency begins some thirty years ago when a group of citizens in the Ohio Valley became interested in a regional approach to water pollution problems. In 1948 their efforts were rewarded when the Governors of Illinois, Indiana, Kentucky, New York, Ohio, Pennsylvania, Virginia, and West Virginia met in Cincinnati to bind these eight states to an agreement pledging co-operation in pollution abatement through the establishment of an interstate agency. They had been empowered to do this by prior action of their legislatures, and with approval of the Congress of the United States.

Thus was launched an enterprise that provided an opportunity to give trial to the potentialities of an interstate compact agency for advancing a regional clean-streams program. The results have been gratifying.[2] Simply creating a compact agency did not solve the pollution problem.

1. Thirty years ago the Advisory Committee on Water Pollution of the National Resources Board made a similar proposal. See chap. 7.
2. Congressman James C. Wright, Jr., of Texas, a member of the House Public Works Committee, assesses the Ohio River experience in his new book and reaches this conclusion: "Great accomplishments have been registered. Greater ones are needed. In any event I shudder to think what conditions on the Ohio would be today, if ORSANCO had not been created." See *The Coming Water Famine* (New York: Coward-McCann, Inc., 1966), pp. 150–56.

3

But it did provide a useful mechanism for activating the people who could. It generated the "contagious force of example and leadership." Several thousand municipalities and industries were motivated to invest more than a billion dollars—nine-tenths of which was locally financed— in the construction of pollution-control facilities. Most of this was done, incidentally, during a period when other areas in the nation were waiting on federal aid for this purpose. What is equally important is that experiences in the Ohio Valley have illuminated ways in which future interstate agencies may be harnessed for more effective performance, notably in the practice of regional management of water quality. This involves the application of new concepts and techniques, some of which have already been pioneered in the Ohio Valley. Two innovations specifically mentioned in the President's message—programming discharges in accord with variability of streamflow and continuous monitoring of river quality —are already in operation. The concept of proportioning wastewater discharges to river flow was adopted for salt control in 1958. And the world's first robot monitor system was developed by the interstate commission and placed in operation on the Ohio River in 1960.

But to get back to the beginning of the story. First let us consider precisely what an interstate compact is. It is a unique instrumentality made available in our form of government for the conduct of co-operative undertakings among states. It is as old as the United States itself, provision for its use stemming from Article I, Section 10, Clause 3, of the Constitution of the United States. Here recognition was given to a mechanism that had been effectively employed by the American colonial governments for solving problems of mutual concern—mostly boundary adjustments—through the appointment of a joint commission. The Ohio Valley compact was designed to co-ordinate and supplement the resources and the police powers of the signatory parties in resolving mutual problems of stream pollution abatement. The principal focus was on the 981-mile Ohio River. Six states border its shores. And from within these states and several others adjacent to them, nineteen major tributaries drain into the main stem. (See Appendix 1 for data on the major tributaries of the Ohio.)

Over the years the utility of the Ohio River and many of its tributaries as sources of water supply and for other uses had progressively deteriorated because of expanding and indiscriminate discharges of raw sewage and industrial wastes. The deleterious consequences were regional in their impact. Rivers despoiled by pollution in one state affected the welfare of adjacent states as they progressed through the drainage district.

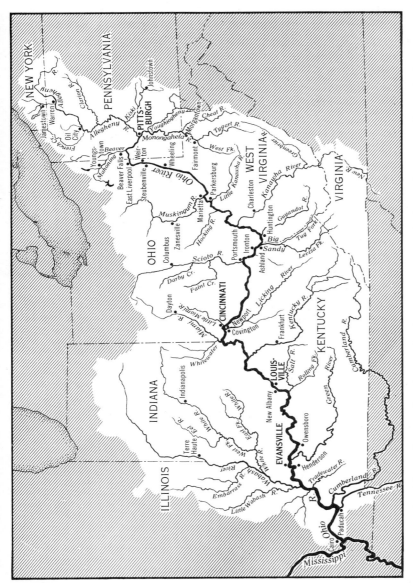

Figure 1. The Ohio River Valley Water Sanitation Compact district embraces portions of eight states and covers an area of 155,000 square miles.

In brief, the degradation of water quality in the Ohio Valley was wide-spread and interstate in character. This indeed was typical of the situation in many other parts of the nation. And with little progress being manifested in devising means to deal with interstate pollution, a growing advocacy for federal intervention began to assert itself in the 1930's.

However, the notion of federal control in matters pertaining to state water resources was not a popular doctrine. There had been a long record of sporadic overtures to the Congress for national legislation to curb water pollution. But in every instance opposition from the states on constitutional grounds, coupled with the resistance of industrial interests to federal restraints on discharging wastes to streams, discouraged congressional support. Public opinion was apathetic. Few people were informed about pollution and fewer still were inspired to shoulder responsibility for its abatement.

Throughout the valley, frustrated public health officials and conservation organizations had long been deploring water pollution and the inadequacy of measures to check it. But they lacked a rallying point. In 1935 the situation changed, and leadership appeared from an unexpected source. The Cincinnati Chamber of Commerce, aroused by the increasingly degraded condition of the Ohio River as it flowed past the "Queen City," decided to spearhead a campaign for regional co-operation in pollution control.[3]

Circumstances appeared auspicious at that time to experiment with institutional innovations for river-basin development. Much of this may be credited to President Roosevelt's creation of a planning and advisory council of cabinet officers in 1933, called the National Planning Board (later called the National Resources Board). Among other things, this board directed attention to the opportunities for state-established regional agencies to assume leadership for advancement of local, state, and national welfare. This philosophy nurtured the aspirations that were being voiced in the Ohio Valley concerning a regional approach to pollution control. And within a short time the Cincinnati crusaders took the lead in promoting negotiations that ultimately led to the compact creating the Ohio River Valley Water Sanitation Commission, now more popularly known as ORSANCO.

3. Reminiscing on this development, the leader of the Chamber of Commerce activities, Hudson Biery, was quoted in the *Cincinnati Enquirer* of March 6, 1948, as follows: "It was a new page in the book for a chamber of commerce to support such a movement. It helped break the opposition of industries, which normally would not have favored it, and bring support from quarters which otherwise might not have participated."

Although the Ohio Valley group pinned its hopes for action on an interstate compact, it was not indifferent to enlisting the resources of the federal government in furthering pollution-control efforts. In fact, it played a significant role in sponsoring legislation for expanding federal research and services to the states, which later was incorporated in the first national water pollution control act of 1948. But it was not convinced that extension of federal jurisdictional authority offered an appropriate or efficient way to control water pollution—at least not in the Ohio Valley.

The culmination of legislative efforts both regionally and nationally to get started on pollution control came—by mere coincidence—on June 30, 1948, the day on which the first federal anti-pollution act went into effect. While the Governors were putting their signatures on the compact documents in Cincinnati, they received a telegram from President Truman that he was signing the first federal law.

Over the years the federal act has been amended four times—in 1956, 1961, 1965, and 1966—each time expanding both federal authority and commitment of funds to hasten stream cleanup. Among the states this rapid proliferation of federal activity has created perplexing problems of adjustment to change. A prevailing attitude among state administrators is that federal jurisdictional activities are attenuating rather than strengthening execution of state responsibilities. Yet, with respect to the resolution of interstate pollution problems it appears that too few states have shown a disposition to equip themselves with appropriate mechanisms— such as interstate compacts—to handle such matters. And it might be added that state budgets for pollution control are not realistically scaled to the increasing burdens being faced in matching capability to needs.

Within the federal establishment, too, there are reasons to believe that the administration of the national effort has not been as productive as might be expected. The program has been beset by the not unexpected difficulties associated with rapid expansion of personnel and activities and the attempt to be responsive to the proddings of those who harbor illusions that the mere issuance of fiats should result in "instant" pollution abatement. It would be fair to say that conditions within the federal bureaucracy during the past decade have not been favorable for harmonizing state-federal relationships or for attaining mutual objectives. At least, this is what one might read into the President's message wherein he announced his intention to reorganize the federal effort by transferring administration of pollution control from the Department of Health, Education, and Welfare to the Department of the Interior. And, as was stated earlier, he also intends that greater reliance for securing action should be reposed in regional and watershed organizations whose jurisdiction would embrace river basins.

This background sketch is the prelude to an account of why and how the ORSANCO compact came into being, what was done under its auspices, and what may be learned from this pioneer effort in cleaning up a river basin. The book is divided into four parts. This first section portrays the setting. It describes the salient features of the Ohio Valley and outlines the nature and complexities of the pollution problem. It then goes on to tell of the search for solutions and how the compact was negotiated. The final chapter in this section outlines the conclusions of a federal committee set up to survey pollution problems in the Ohio Valley. Mention is made here of a 1935 proposal to establish a demonstration area for a study of the interstate compact as a "promising method" for administration of river-basin pollution control. Fortuitously, records of these early events, the correspondence associated with them, along with a stenographic transcript of the deliberations of the negotiating delegates, as well as a collection of news and magazine clippings were preserved. These records, coupled with my thirty-year acquaintanceship with many of the people associated with the endeavor, aided immeasurably in reconstructing what had transpired.

The second section is divided into nine chapters that describe how various components of the ORSANCO program were conceived and developed. Beginning with the business of organizing the Commission and establishing policies, these chapters detail the trials and satisfactions in advancing control of municipal and industrial wastes, motivating public support, devising means to minimize the effects of accidental spills, and developing a river-quality surveillance and robot monitor system.

In the third section an attempt is made to provide perspective on the performance of the interstate undertaking. For obvious reasons this cannot qualify as a dispassionate assessment of its performance. Included in this part of the book is a brief discussion of the legal scope and validity of compacts, which is specifically referenced to an uncharted area into which ORSANCO was thrust when one of the signatory states sought to withdraw from the regional agreement. This resulted in a Supreme Court review, the decision on which was vital not only to the existence of ORSANCO but to the status of other compacts as well.

The final section, titled "Prospects for Tomorrow," summarizes significant changes that have taken place in the social, economic, and political aspects of water pollution control. It outlines the evolution of federal policies and actions in the field of water-quality control, and the impact they have had on state and interstate relationships. And it discusses the role of the compact-type agency in the future scheme of things. Institutions of this kind can be effective in implementing regional plans and actions for managing water quality and in co-ordinating this challenging task with related water and land resource developments. The ORSANCO experience provides some clues as to how they can serve this purpose.

2

Reconnaissance of the Region

In one of the public-education films produced by ORSANCO, the narrator points out with poetic practicality that the promise of any land lies in the streams that water it. He continues: "Here beside the Ohio many people have found their promised land; and here they have built their towns, their shops and their lives." Here also, as the film then portrays, man and his activities have placed many demands upon the streams. One of these is for the carriage of wastewaters, the indiscriminate practice of which produces pollution. From this film emerges the message that streams despoiled in quality cannot continue to fulfill their promise.

It is the purpose of this chapter to tell something about the promise of the land in terms of its geographic and hydrologic characteristics, population distribution, industrial activity, and physical development. All of this has a bearing on the pollution problem and on the shaping of arrangements for its correction.

The Ohio Valley

In the district encompassed by the Ohio Valley sanitation compact live some 19 million people—almost one-tenth the population of the entire United States. Since the turn of the century, however, population has increased at only one-half to two-thirds the national rate. The trend is described as one evidencing a stabilized growth, and characteristic of a region reaching maturity.[1]

The streams that water this district drain an area of 155,000 square miles, which is about 5 per cent of the area of the United States mainland.

---

1. What occurred during the past decade is not untypical. Population in the valley increased 9 per cent as contrasted with the national average of 18.5 per cent. In that part of the district occupied by two of the signatory states (Virginia and West Virginia) population actually declined by 7 per cent. This decline was offset by gains of almost 21 per cent in Ohio, 16 per cent in Indiana, and an average in the remaining four states of 5 per cent.

For comparison, it can be noted that the district under the purview of the Ohio Valley compact is slightly larger than the area of all of Germany and the Netherlands combined.

The Ohio Valley begins some 200 miles from the Atlantic seaboard on the western slopes of the Appalachian Mountains. Its main axis is the Ohio River, which flows in a southwesterly direction to the Mississippi River. The drainage district embraced by the compact is about 700 miles in length, and it averages about 220 miles in width.

The easterly portion, characterized by the rough hills and highlands of the Appalachians, is an industrialized region, dominated by steel manufacturing and coal mining. But here also there are a variety of agricultural pursuits. The central section, north of the Ohio River, is levelled over with thick deposits of glacial drift. South of the river the terrain is one of rugged hills and steep valleys, the recreational potential of which is only now becoming apparent. Both banks of the Ohio are bordered with hills interrupted occasionally with flood plains. In many places the scenic aspects are reminiscent of the Rhine River country in Germany. The southern region is largely agricultural, but scattered throughout are sizable communities, concentrations of industry, and centers of coal mining. The western portion of the district, featured by the low hills of an interior plateau, is principally rural in character.

As might be concluded from this description, population is distributed in a far from even way. Density ranges from less than 50 people per square mile in the southwest portion to more than 600 in the eastern area around Pittsburgh. The average population for the compact district is 120 per square mile.

The urban population, more specifically that provided with sewer systems discharging directly to streams, is 11,400,000. The remaining 40 per cent of the people reside in rural areas or in small communities without sewers, the effects of whose drainage from cesspools or septic tanks is generally localized.

Over the years the Ohio Valley has emerged as an industrial empire. Behind this development lie the variety and abundance of the area's natural resources including water; a skilled labor supply; good transportation facilities, including an inland waterways system; and proximity to markets for manufactured products.

Three-quarters of the bituminous coal reserves of the nation are located in five states of the valley. The coal seams are buried in the Appalachian highlands on the east, but they also underlie substantial parts of Indiana, Illinois, and Kentucky in the west.

Limestone, the predominant rock in much of the region, and abundant underground deposits of salt and brines provide basic components for a burgeoning chemical industry.

Oil was first discovered in the United States at Titusville, Pennsylvania, in 1859, near the headwaters of the Allegheny River. Later it was found in other parts of the valley, and even today new discoveries of oil are being made, notably in Ohio and Kentucky. These local reserves supplemented with crude oil transported by barge and pipeline from Texas have promoted growth of refining facilities to serve the region.

Steelmaking has dominated the industrial scene. But papermaking, metalworking, machine-tool fabrication, assembly of electrical equipment, whiskey production, food processing, and brick and ceramic manufacture are among the older major industries. The newest include petrochemical plants, aluminum production facilities, and, most recently, atomic-energy installations.

The world's first full-scale nuclear power plant devoted exclusively to civilian needs is located on the Ohio River at Shippingport, Pennsylvania, a few miles below Pittsburgh. In addition, the Atomic Energy Commission has located major gaseous-diffusion and uranium refining plants in the valley, one at Paducah, Kentucky, on the lower Ohio, another near the mouth of the Scioto River above Portsmouth, Ohio, and a third on the Great Miami River not far from its junction with the Ohio River.

Some of these nuclear processing installations require enormous quantities of electrical energy for their operation and this, in turn, has promoted the installation of several huge steam-generating power plants along the Ohio. (One of these is shown in Figure 2.)

The Dirtied and Dammed Ohio River

For reasons that are still valid the Ohio River was called "La Belle Rivière" by French explorers. Since those early days other distinctions have been associated with the river. Where it begins at Pittsburgh, there has developed the greatest concentration of population and industry in the valley. And navigation dams have transformed the free-flowing stream into a series of slackwater "pools." Therefore, it was not inappropriate to describe the Ohio as dirtied from its very beginning and dammed throughout its entire length. Each of these aspects has influenced, and in some instances complicated, the application of remedial measures for pollution abatement. Regarding this, more will be said later.

Figure 2. Clifty Creek plant of the Ohio Valley Electric Corporation was built at Madison, Indiana, to produce power for the Atomic Energy Commission's gaseous-diffusion facility near Portsmouth, Ohio. Surplus power is distributed to the fifteen electric companies who combined to build the plant. At times, as much as one-quarter of the entire volume of the Ohio River at low flow is required for condenser cooling purposes at this plant. (*U. S. Corps of Engineers.*)

Birth and burden. The Ohio River is born full grown. Its progenitors are the Allegheny and the Monongahela rivers. These two streams drain widely separated portions of the western slopes of the Appalachian Mountains. They merge and lose their identities at Pittsburgh to create the tenth longest river in the United States. From its source the Ohio wends a meandering course southwesterly for 981 miles to join the Mississippi River at Cairo, Illinois.

The Allegheny has a length of 325 miles from its headwaters in north-central Pennsylvania. Flowing northwest into New York State, it then loops around to the southwest to continue in this direction through Pennsylvania. Two-thirds of the annual flow of the Ohio at Pittsburgh is contributed by the Allegheny.

The Monongahela, which is 128 miles in length, flows from the south. It originates from tributaries that reach far down in West Virginia. But half of its watershed is in Pennsylvania.

Unlike many rivers which begin their journey to the sea unsullied by contact with the activities of man, the Ohio is denied an origin of pristine purity. Clustered at its source at Pittsburgh is an urban population center of 1,400,000 people as well as the most heavily industrialized zone in the valley. Furthermore, the two tributaries that give it birth bring waters that are burdened with the wastewaters from upstream communities and industries, and with the acid drainage from active and abandoned coal mines.

Thus the Ohio River may lay claim to the unfortunate distinction of having its greatest concentration of pollution at its very beginning where dilution capacity is the least. And for the first 100 miles downstream there is no surcease from this travail. On both banks of the river from Pittsburgh to Wheeling there is virtually a continuous succession of industrial activities. It was this spectacle of mighty steel mills and coke plants that led foreign observers many years ago to refer to the upper Ohio Valley as "The American Ruhr." Actually the Ruhr Valley in Germany is diminutive in comparison with this area.

Some 150 miles farther downstream, in the Ashland, Ironton, Portsmouth area, there is another great concentration of steel mills, oil refineries, and chemical plants. And then at intervals of about 130 miles emerge the metropolitan centers of Cincinnati and Louisville. Between these cities—and notably so below Louisville—the settlement along the banks of the Ohio is relatively sparse. For almost half the latter part of its length the river traverses a rural region during which it is swelled in volume by relatively clean tributaries.

Rainfall and runoff. As with many of its gifts to the Ohio Valley, Nature is generous in the matter of rainfall. The mean annual precipitation for the district is about 45 inches. It ranges from 35 inches in the extreme northwest and northeast, to 50 inches in the southwest, and up to 80 inches in the mountains of the southeast.[2]

---

2. For comparative purposes it can be noted that the yearly rainfall averages about 30 inches over the entire Mississippi drainage basin, of which the Ohio forms part. For the entire United States, the average rainfall ranges from 5 inches in the arid southwest to as much as 100 inches in the Pacific northwest.

Of course, there are extremes. Precipitation as high as 6.5 inches in 48 hours was recorded over an area of 37,000 square miles in March 1913. On the other hand, minimum monthly rainfalls of as low as 1.7 inches have persisted for six months at a time over much of the valley.

Rainfall and runoff generally are at their highest from January through April when the ground is cold and plant life is dormant. Rates of runoff in this period may be as high as 90 per cent of rainfall. If temperatures at such periods are favorable to snow melt in the mountainous sections, widespread flooding occurs on the tributaries and the main stem of the Ohio.

The magnitude and frequency of these floods are revealed from records maintained since 1858 by the U. S. Weather Bureau office at Cincinnati. The Ohio is considered to be in flood at Cincinnati when the river stage reaches a height of 52 feet. "Normal" pool level as maintained by the new navigation dams is 26 feet. The highest flood officially recorded occurred in January, 1937, when the river crested at 80 feet. The second highest was in 1884, with a stage of 71.1 feet. In the 108 years (1858–1965) for which official records are available, the river exceeded flood stage seventy-eight times; and on seventeen occasions there were two floods each spring.

Flood control occupies a position of high priority in water-resources development for the valley. In a comprehensive plan submitted to the Congress in 1935, and as later modified, the Corps of Engineers proposed among other things the construction of 99 flood-control reservoirs on various tributaries in the drainage basin. Thus far 40 have been completed and 23 more are under construction.

Of more recent concern is the question of "drought control," generally referred to as low-flow regulation. In 23 of the 63 flood-control reservoirs completed or under construction by the Corps of Engineers, additional storage capacity has been provided. The purpose is to impound excess water during periods of high flow. Water can then be released to supplement streamflows during annual low-flow periods.

Flow in the Ohio River is generally at its lowest during September and October, the months of least rainfall. Deficiencies in rainfall with consequent diminishment of river flow seldom exceed a duration of a few months. Since 1927, when continuous gauging of the Ohio River at Louisville, Ky., was initiated, droughts of greatest severity and duration have occurred in cycles of about eleven years: 1930–31, 1941–42, 1952–53, and 1963–64.

With respect to variations in runoff, the following extracts from discharge records[3] of the Ohio River are significant. Flows are shown in terms of cubic feet per second (cfs), one cubic foot per second being the equivalent of 0.646 million gallons per day.

Lowest Flows (Daily)	
At head of river	1,800 cfs
Near the mouth	20,600 cfs
Highest Flows (Daily)	
At head of river	574,000 cfs
Near the mouth	1,850,000 cfs
Ratio of Maximum to Minimum Flows	
At head of river	319 to 1
Near the mouth	90 to 1

Canalization of the river. Over the years the river has been canalized throughout its entire course, as have some of its tributaries. This navigation improvement was started in a modest way in the 1880's and completed in 1929 by the U. S. Corps of Engineers. The successive construction of 46 locks and dams converted the river into a series of elongated pools with a minimum channel depth of 9 feet. Boats moving from Pittsburgh to the confluence with the Mississippi River are lowered a total of 430 feet.

Most of the dams are of the so-called "wicket" type, consisting of a row of stoutly fabricated wood panels fastened with a hinge to a concrete foundation sill on the bottom of the river between its banks. The wickets are designed to be pulled upright to an almost vertical position where they are held in place against the current of the river with a downstream iron strut angled against them. When the wickets are raised they form a continuous barrier or dam. A lock structure for raising and lowering boats is located at one end of the dam.

During periods of low flow (generally from May to December) the wickets are raised to maintain the navigation pool. Excess runoff may be permitted to spill over the top of the dam or it may be diverted through a concrete regulating weir located at the end of the dam opposite to the lock. During high water the wickets are lowered and lie flat on the bed of the river, where they offer no obstruction to flow. Barge traffic then moves on an "open river."

Navigation pools and pollution. Conversion of the Ohio into a series of slackwater pools both relieved and aggravated the influence of pollutional discharges. During low-flow periods, the dams retard river velocity.

3. U.S. Geological Survey, Water Supply Paper No. 1725 (Washington, D. C.: U.S. Government Printing Office, 1964).

Figure 3. New Cumberland Dam on the Ohio River at Stratton, Ohio. This high-lift structure, which replaced wicket dams, 7, 8, and 9, creates a slackwater navigation pool that extends 23 miles up the Ohio River to the Montgomery Island dam and lock at Industry, Pennsylvania. Barge traffic saves as much as 4 hours in locking time through this reach of the river. (*U. S. Corps of Engineers.*)

Suspended solids in wastewaters discharged to the slow-moving river settle out to form deposits of sludge and thus tend to localize pollution close to its source. However, when the dams are lowered and river velocities are increased during freshets, a scouring of accumulated deposits takes place, and the downstream water-purification plants are burdened momentarily with excessive pollution.

Further improvement of navigation facilities is now under way. Over the next two decades the Corps of Engineers plans to replace the 43 existing wicket dams with 16 fixed dams, 6 of which are already in place.[4] Some of the slackwater pools created by the new dams are as much as 100 miles in length; the former pools averaged about 22 miles in length. The new pools are deeper, being as much as 50 feet at the dam sites in

4. The six dams completed since 1960 are New Cumberland, Pike Island, Greenup, Meldahl, Markland, and McAlpine. Engineering plans are being completed or construction has been started on nine other fixed dams.

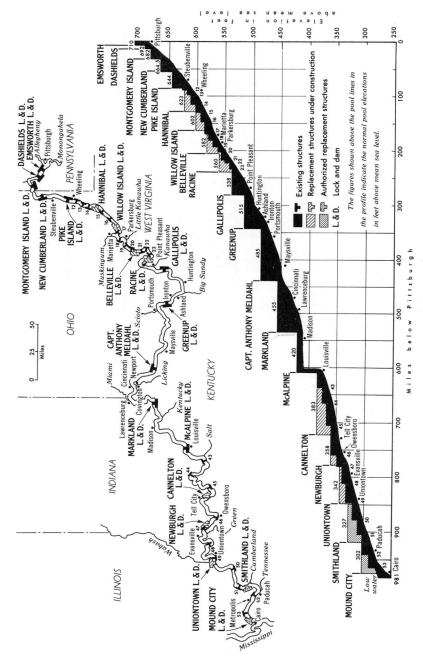

Figure 4. Navigation map of the Ohio River. (*Map based on U. S. Engineers, Ohio River Division, General Plan, January 1966*).

order to provide a depth of at least 9 feet at the head of the pool; and maintenance dredging may actually produce a 12-foot depth.

The precise effect of this change in river regimen on quality conditions is not predictable. Studies have been initiated looking toward an evaluation of ecological changes, an assessment of river re-aeration changes, as well as the effect of the deeper, longer pools on dispersion and stratification of wastewater effluents.

From this reconnaissance of the region one may gather that it is richly endowed with natural resources, not the least of which is an abundance of water. But there is also an abundance of centers of population and industry whose activities place an ever-increasing burden of wastewater carriage upon streams of the valley with consequent degradation of their quality. In fact, the intensification of water use and reuse gave rise to a fiction that the volume of waste discharges had reached the point where the flow in the Ohio River at Cincinnati had already been used in homes or factories at least *four times* over. Actually, the wastewater component in the river is less than 1½ per cent of the average flow.[5] But even this fraction of untreated sewage and industrial residues in a stream can jeopardize its usefulness by impairing both the quality and the appearance of the water, as was evidenced by conditions that finally inspired the creation of ORSANCO.

Because many of the streams in the Ohio Valley cross state lines—the Ohio River alone touches on the borders of six states—the jurisdictional problems of controlling water pollution offered a challenging exercise for regional co-ordination of effort. This situation is described in the following chapter.

5. E. J. Cleary, R. K. Horton, and R. J. Boes, "Reuse of Ohio River Water," *Journal of American Water Works Association,* Vol. 55, No. 6 (June 1963), p. 683.

3

Perplexities of
Interstate Pollution

A letter addressed to the Ohio River Valley Water Sanitation Commission shortly after its establishment illuminates one aspect of the interdependencies of pollution control on interstate streams. It came from a county health officer in Ohio who asked:

> Who should take what action against a hog farmer in my county who finds it most convenient to dispose of his diseased, dead animals by throwing them into the Ohio River? Although the farmer lives in the State of Ohio he is outside my jurisdiction when he dumps things into the river because the river belongs to the Commonwealth of Kentucky. While nobody in Kentucky has as yet complained about the hogs floating around, a lot of squawks could come from a municipality downstream in Indiana if these dead animals ever get into a waterworks intake.

The question posed by this puzzled doctor provides an elementary illustration of the reason why eight states in the Ohio Valley combined their police powers and resources for the resolution of interstate river pollution problems which escaped the jurisdictional powers of any one state and, at that time, the purview of the federal government. Occasional disposal of a dead pig, however, was the least of the problems. Infinitely more perplexing was the task of halting the degradation of streams brought about by indiscriminate discharge of sewage, oils, acids, salts, solids, and every other form of debris from several thousands of municipalities and industries situated in several states.

A dismal picture of the situation was presented by Congressman Brent Spence, a representative of the Commonwealth of Kentucky and chairman of the House Banking and Currency Committee. In testimony[1] given dur-

1. "Pollution of Navigable Waters," *Hearings* before the Committee on Rivers and Harbors, House of Representatives, 74th Cong., 2nd Sess., May 20, 1936, p. 20. Hereafter cited as *Hearings*.

ing a 1936 Congressional hearing on the pollution of navigable waters he said:

> The Ohio River is a cesspool. . . . My district consists of nine counties and eight of these border the river. They extend from 40 miles above Cincinnati to almost the corporate limits of Louisville [about 150 miles], and the river is the source of water supply for almost all these people [in the area]. I remember when the river had great recreational value. I remember when migratory waterfowl stopped to rest on the river; you never see them do that any more. . . . I think that the only flying thing, if conditions continue as they are, that will be interested in the Ohio River will be the buzzard.

At the same hearing, Dr. A. T. McCormack, who had been state health commissioner of Kentucky since 1913, made a plea for regional action and had this to say, in part:

> We know that the Ohio River, from Pittsburgh to Cairo, is an open sewer. The purification of those waters [for domestic uses] has been kept safe for cities like Cincinnati and Louisville only at an enormously increasing expenditure because of the . . . concentration of . . . sewage —industrial and human—emptied into the river at various points. . . . Now, this problem cannot be solved by Cincinnati or by Louisville. It would not make any difference what was done by one community.

Perhaps the earliest evidence of frustration and stalemate in dealing with interstate pollution is reflected by an action of the Ohio state legislature in 1908. A statute (the Bense Act) adopted at that time—and not superseded until after the interstate compact was executed—exempted every Ohio village and municipality along the Ohio River from installing sewage-treatment works *until similar facilities were provided by all municipalities upstream from it.*[2]

The existence of this statute prompted Hudson Biery, a leader in Cincinnati in the fight for clean waters, to remark: "Such a situation has just about as much logic as an old railroad operating rule which read: When two trains meet at an intersection neither one shall proceed until the other has passed."

Agreement on Phenol Control

The implications of the Bense Act and other matters prompted discussion among several states bordering the Ohio River about the desir-

---

2. This provision is found in Sect. 6111.11, Revised Code of Ohio. The change was made in 1951; see Sect. 6111.01, Revised Code of Ohio.

ability of joint action on pollution-abatement measures,[3] but no important steps toward co-operation were taken until 1924. By then the steel industry was well along in applying new technology to the recovery of valuable by-products from the gases formed when coal was converted to coke for blast furnaces. Heretofore, the gases were simply wasted to the atmosphere. Not the least of the "by-products" were phenolic compounds, large amounts of which escaped in liquid form to contaminate streams. Even minute quantities of phenol imparted a medicinal, carbolic acid taste and odor to water supplies. And this characteristic was greatly accentuated when municipal supplies were disinfected with chlorine in order to reduce bacterial contamination.

The resulting unpalatability of drinking water caused so much consternation among the citizenry that an informal agreement was reached among the health authorities in the states of Pennsylvania, Ohio, West Virginia, Kentucky, New York, Illinois, Maryland, Indiana, Tennessee, and North Carolina, to act in concert for control of phenol discharges from by-product coke plants.

Details of this early agreement on phenol control may be found in the final report of the Ohio River Valley Compact Negotiating Committee.[4] Here we learn that at a conference attended by the health commissioners of states in the Ohio Valley, U. S. Public Health Service personnel, and representatives of industry in Pittsburgh on April 14, 1924, industries agreed to co-operate in eliminating their objectionable wastes.

At a second conference on November 17, 1924, the health commissioners of the states of Ohio, Pennsylvania, and West Virginia declared their intention to "co-operate in carrying out a policy for the conservation of the interstate streams in these states, including the correction and prevention of undue pollution thereof, to the end that said streams may be

3. Some light is shed on the motivation for the Bense Act in a communication dated October 10, 1965, to the author from F. H. Waring, retired chief engineer of the Ohio State Health Department, who wrote: "At this 1908 session of the Ohio legislature, it also adopted a resolution creating a 'Joint Ohio River Sanitary Commission' and calling upon the states of Pennsylvania, West Virginia, Kentucky, and Indiana to cooperate with Ohio by similar legislative enactment. The resolution provided for appointment of three members from each state, '. . . to confer and act with one another to the end that a plan may be recommended whereby the several states interested may jointly protect the Ohio River against sewage and other pollution. . .' Five different meetings of the Commission were held during 1909, 1910, 1911. The Commission at its second meeting recommended that municipalities using the river water 'take immediate measures to discontinue the discharge of unpurified sewage into the stream and to purify the water taken therefrom and supplied for the use of their citizens.' "
4. *Proceedings,* Fifth Conference of Delegates Appointed to Draft an Ohio River Valley Water Sanitation Compact, October 11, 1938, Appendix III.

rendered and maintained as suitable sources of public water supplies."
Two years later Kentucky, New York, Maryland, and Illinois became
parties to this declaration.

Although the agreement had no legal status, it was reported to have
resulted in concerted action by industries in eliminating taste-producing
wastes. This agreement, however, did not produce any results in reducing
pollution from sewage or other industrial waste discharges.

Drought and Disease

In 1930 the Ohio Valley received a grim reminder that pollution conditions were worsening. This was a year of drought. And in the Ohio
River the flow "became so low that some of the pools formed by government navigation dams became virtually open cesspools."[5]

During the latter part of the drought period and extending into early
1931, a succession of epidemics of gastroenteritis occurred in several
parts of the valley. The first outbreak came late in October, 1930, in
Charleston, West Virginia. State health officials estimated that among the
city's 60,000 inhabitants there had been from 4,000 to 7,000 cases.
Fortunately, there were no deaths.

The outbreak soon abated but six weeks later, on January 1, 1931,
cases with exactly the same symptoms began to appear in Huntington,
West Virginia, and Ashland, Kentucky. These cities are on the Ohio
River (43 miles and 57 miles, respectively) below the confluence with
the Kanawha.

At Ironton, Ohio, a short distance downstream from Ashland, residents
experienced the ailment about the same time as those of Ashland. And at
Portsmouth, Ohio, somewhat further downstream, a similar event
occurred. Then on January 15 cases began to appear 200 miles down
river in Cincinnati. Ten days later and 140 miles further on the illness
descended on the citizens of Louisville, Kentucky.

Details of the epidemic were documented by M. V. Veldee, a surgeon
of the Public Health Service, who began an investigation after the outbreak started in Charleston.[6] "Charleston's population became ill in the
brief period of two weeks. This indicates a rapid dissemination of the
causative agent throughout the city, irrespective of economic, color or
social barriers. The presence of so many cases within the city and the

5. *Ibid.*
6. M. V. Veldee, "An Epidemiological Study of Suspected Water Borne Gastroenteritis," *American Journal of Public Health and The Nation's Health,* Vol. 21,
No. 11 (November 1931), p. 1227.

complete absence in the communities immediately surrounding further restricts the causative agent to some channel which did not extend beyond the city boundaries in the Charleston area. . . . However, the appearance approximately two months later in at least six Ohio River cities of an ailment that in all of its clinical manifestations corresponded with the Charleston cases makes it appear that the causative agent was contained in some vehicle which also was common to these latter cities. . . ."

"The evidence strongly suggests," concluded Dr. Veldee, "that the acute gastrointestinal symptoms were brought about by the presence in the water of some chemical irritant whose physiological action simulated a strong purgative. The evidence does not show whether this chemical irritant was a cleavage product of bacterial action, a new chemical produced by bacterial synthesis, or the result of increased chemical concentration in the water brought about by a decrease in the diluent. There is at least a slight suggestion from the evidence that the toxic substance originated in the Great Kanawha River and was released into the Ohio when the [navigation] dams were lowered on the Great Kanawha late in December, thereby releasing the pent-up wastes in a concentrated form which affected the public supply of each city as it moved downstream."

Bacterial pollution problems. It was not only a drought that dramatized health hazards associated with sewage pollution. During the flood of 1937 the water purification plants serving municipalities along the Ohio River were burdened with an unusually high bacterial content in the river. This was attributed to the scouring action that takes place in the early stages of a rapidly rising river and the consequent flushing of sewage deposits that had accumulated behind the navigation dams.[7] So long as sewage was not processed for removal of solids prior to discharge, a similar situation could be expected whenever high water occurred and the dams were lowered, which might be several times a year.

A quantitative measure of quality degradation was provided by Alfred Le Feber, consulting engineer of Cincinnati, in testimony before a Congressional committee.[8] Detailing experiences in operating the waterworks at Ashland, Kentucky, he said the bacterial count in the Ohio River had increased by 80 times from 1921 to 1934. Speaking of difficulties in producing a palatable water, Mr. Le Feber noted that costs for purification chemicals alone had trebled in the period 1925 to 1936. "What we are doing in effect, is paying for sewage treatment through the medium of purifying our water supplies."

7. *Proceedings, op. cit.,* p. 96.
8. *Hearings, op. cit.,* p. 43.

Mr. Le Feber reported that treatment costs for chemicals alone had gone up to $48 per million gallons, which he considered unusually high. His view was confirmed by a report on river pollution by the National Resources Board, in which it was said that water purification operating costs at plants receiving a "severely polluted raw water" could be expected to be as high as $16 per million gallons. This was contrasted with a cost of $9.30 for treating water from a so-called "normal stream."[9]

An over-all picture of the pollution situation prevailing in the Ohio Valley in 1935 is to be drawn from the facts and viewpoints developed by the late Harold W. Streeter. Mr. Streeter, a sanitary engineer in the Public Health Service, had been studying pollution of the Ohio River since 1913 as a staff member of the federal Stream Investigations Station in Cincinnati, of which he eventually became the director. A few years after he retired in 1948 he was retained as a consultant by ORSANCO. From conversations with him and review of his notes, this picture unfolds:

The Ohio River, as is true of virtually all streams, has been called upon to serve in a dual but conflicting role—as a source of water supply and as a means for sewage disposal. River water thus became a vehicle for the transmission of intestinal-borne diseases, notably typhoid fever. The sanitary engineer in his development of water-filtration techniques provided, however, an effective means for purifying polluted water. Thus, in the first two decades of the present century, cities along the Ohio began to install filtration plants[10]—and water-borne typhoid fever soon thereafter began to disappear.

But pollution of the river was increasing and so were difficulties in providing satisfactory water supplies. These difficulties included: greater concentration of sewage-associated bacteria, the magnitude of which caused engineers to question whether their filter plants could deal adequately with this excessive burden; pronounced tastes and odors whose intensification was related to phenolic compounds and to the decomposition of organic materials and microscopic organisms; and conditions of excessive hardness and acidity during periods of low flow, which contributed to scale formation in steam boilers, corrosion of pipes, and increased fuel consumption.

Finally, there were sporadic outbreaks of gastrointestinal disorders, all of which displayed characteristics of being water-borne ailments. While

9. "Water Pollution in the United States," House Doc. No. 155, 76th Cong., 1st Sess., 1939.

10. Examples include Cincinnati, which began pumping water from the Ohio River in 1821, but did not provide filtration until 1907, and Steubenville, where filters were installed in 1915 after pumping from the river since 1835.

the specific cause of the ailments was not defined, the evidence suggested that they might be due to a toxic substance capable of penetrating the defenses of water-purification processes.

Particularly serious by 1935 were the effects of pollution on water supplies in the Pittsburgh-Wheeling and the Huntington-Portsmouth sections of the river. In the uppermost stretch, the primary difficulties were those associated with excessive hardness and corrosiveness resulting from the presence of free acids and the acid salts of iron and manganese in the river. However, pointed out Mr. Streeter: "Were it not for the bactericidal and coagulating effects of the acids and iron salts, this section of the river probably would also have been highly offensive." What in effect happened was that the acid acted as a "pickling" agent to retard the decomposition of organic waste materials until they were carried further downstream.

The cumulative effect of this retarded decomposition of upstream sewage, combined with heavy local pollution, was regarded as the reason why the Huntington-Portsmouth section was the zone with the highest bacterial pollution of any stretch of the river. In order to produce a supply safe for domestic use, a combination of all of the resources of water-purification technology had to be utilized, including double-stage coagulation, long periods of sedimentation, heavy chlorination, and the use of activated carbon.

Even halfway down the river near Cincinnati where natural-purification influences might otherwise have been expected to bring about improved quality, the water treatment plants were overburdened, notably in their efforts to deal with taste and odor problems.

In brief, concluded Mr. Streeter, the deterioration of water quality had reached the point where despite the application of every technique then known in water purification, the margin of safety at cities like Cincinnati and Louisville was relatively narrow and appeared to be growing smaller each year.

Suggested remedial measures. From a technical standpoint it seemed obvious to Mr. Streeter what steps were required to restore the safety, the palatability, and the general suitability of river water. His recommendations in 1935 were:

—Install sewage-treatment plants along the Ohio and its major tributaries, designed to reduce pollution of the river at the various water intakes within a safe margin for subsequent purification.

—Control acid mine-drainage by continuation of sealing activities, which in the 1930's had been initiated by the federal government as an unemployment-relief measure.

—Promote efforts for the elimination of odor-forming, taste-producing, and other contaminants from industrial sources.

—Operate flood-control reservoir projects in a manner to stabilize flow conditions on the Ohio, especially in providing more dilution water during periods of low river stages.

—Install ample raw-water storage facilities at all existing water-purification plants.[11] Aside from additional storage and perhaps the use of lime or lime-soda water-softening facilities, he believed that water-purification systems along the Ohio had been developed practically to the highest possible degree of efficiency.

Pollution-control scientists and engineers—at least in 1935—generally were not concerned with matters that were outside the realm of their technical specialization. But Mr. Streeter clearly perceived that solution of the Ohio Valley pollution problem did not hinge on development of technology but on the assertion of political statesmanship. He said:

> The principal obstacles now standing in the way of an intelligent and comprehensive program of river sanitation in this drainage area appear to be legal and administrative, as the necessary engineering data are fairly complete and well established. . . . The remedy lies in the hands of the several states bordering the river, in cooperation with the federal government, which also has a rightful interest in the broader interstate aspects of the problem. The more narrow local and commercial interests involved in this problem, however, must give way to the common good of all and place themselves solidly behind these governmental agencies before any real progress can be made toward its permanent solution.[12]

There were some others in Cincinnati who shared similar views. Who they were and what they did in giving form and substance to execution of a remedial program is told in the next chapter.

11. It was common practice along the Ohio at the larger plants to provide storage basins that would hold as much as a four days' supply of river water. The function of these storage basins was to settle out mud, to enhance the natural purifying effects of sunlight and oxygen, to permit bacterial die-away, and to otherwise improve quality of the river water. Furthermore, with storage facilities it was possible to temporarily halt pumping from the river when slugs of excessively polluted water were passing the intake.

12. H. W. Streeter, "The Ohio River: Its Future as a Water Supply Source," *Engineering News–Record*, May 2, 1935, p. 612.

4

The Clean-Stream Crusaders

On a spring evening in 1934 twenty men constituting the "Clean-up and Beautify Week" committee of the Cincinnati Chamber of Commerce were gathered for their final meeting. Representing interests allied to sanitation, real estate, garden club, school, church, and civic betterment, they had assembled to tally results of an annual campaign sponsored by the Chamber. Committee members were enveloped with pride as the chairman enumerated accomplishments: 82,086 yard and basement clean-ups; 71,289 rubbish removals and house repairs; 54,941 flower and shrubbery plantings; 31,248, houses, fences and outbuildings painted—a grand total of 239,564 completed tasks!

"Is there anything else that needs to be cleaned up?" quipped the chairman. "Yes," came an unexpected reply, "The Ohio River." Noting some incredulity on the part of his listeners, the speaker continued: ". . . citizens of Cincinnati don't want to be reminded everytime asparagus is served for supper in Pittsburgh or some other upstream community. The time is at hand for someone to provide a rallying point for control of water pollution in our valley. Cincinnati has a big stake in this. Why shouldn't our Chamber of Commerce spearhead the move?"

And why not? This unpremeditated appeal by Hudson Biery, director of public relations for the Cincinnati Street Railway Company, started a fire, and far into the night the committee members fueled it with ideas. Stream pollution was a menace to health. It caused bad taste and odors in the water supply. It destroyed recreational opportunities. Should not the federal government, which was then embarked on a huge public-works program to bolster a depressed economy, earmark some of these funds to make rivers healthy, too? And how about doing something locally to halt discharge of sewage into streams by Cincinnati and surrounding communities? Finally, what was the matter with the "constituted authorities" who permitted this continued pollution? This was but a sampling of the views incorporated in a resolution hastily drafted that night by the committee for presentation to the Chamber of Commerce.

Never was a resolution more appropriately timed for generating public discussion. President of the Chamber of Commerce was William F. Wiley, the militant editor of the Cincinnati *Enquirer,* one of the most influential newspapers in the valley. Over the years his paper had carried an increasing number of stories and editorials on the degradation of streams by pollution. Mr. Wiley not only was prepared for action on stream cleanup, but he had the personality and prestige to command it.

And by June of 1935—less than a year after the idea was born—a Stream Pollution Committee of the Cincinnati Chamber of Commerce was a reality. Its cadre of thirty-six members included men in legal, governmental, sanitation, and industrial affairs—men who were distinguished for their talents and for knowing how to get things done. Just a few names will illustrate the caliber of the committee: Robert A. Taft, who later became a U. S. Senator from Ohio; Myers Y. Cooper, a former governor of Ohio; Walter Schmidt, then president of the National Association of Real Estate Boards; and Alexander Thomson, president of the Ohio Chamber of Commerce and chairman of the board of the Champion Paper and Fiber Company.

Nearly all the members of the committee started out as neophytes in matters relating to the administrative and technical aspects of water pollution control. Perhaps that was their greatest strength. In 1935, many people were under the illusion that pollution existed because we had not advanced far enough with research and technological know-how. The committee was not mesmerized with such notions. It proceeded on the assumption that, if there was a will to do, a way could be found to curb pollution. Consequently, its efforts were oriented toward awakening public demand for reform and guiding development of political action to satisfy it. The choice of Hudson Biery as chairman was a happy one. He was perceptive, he was persuasive, he was optimistic, and he was indefatigable; in brief, not only was he a man with a mission, but he was endowed with the imagination and conviction to bring about its accomplishment.

The Need for Leadership

The Cincinnati Chamber of Commerce was not the first or only group in the Ohio Valley concerned with pollution control. Health authorities, sanitary engineers, conservation organizations (notably the Izaak Walton

League), and boating enthusiasts had long been agitating for corrective measures.

But the impact of these groups left something to be desired. Either their range of influence was too localized or they were too parochial in their views. For example, those concerned with the preservation of fish life seldom made common cause with those who viewed polluted water primarily as a public health hazard. And even the sanitation authorities who had to deal with the taste-and-odor crisis that followed the introduction of by-product coke ovens after World War I had limited their efforts to only one phase of industrial-waste control, namely, the curbing of phenol discharges.

Nor must it be overlooked that some of the states in the valley had been gearing up for action. Indiana, for example, revamped its legislation in 1935 to strengthen legal compulsions and to allow municipalities greater latitude in financing sewage works with revenue bonds. And Pennsylvania was involved in revising its clean-stream laws and administrative structure (the revisions being adopted in 1937).

Important as these developments were, none of them represented the thrust from which might emanate an integrated, regional attack on pollution problems. Furthermore, there were widely differing philosophies as to how such a job should be tackled.

For example, there was the issue of federal versus state control. Over a period of fifty years, more than 100 bills had been introduced in the Congress of the United States calling for one form or other of federal intervention in water pollution matters. Under the Commerce clause of the Constitution—through which Congress exercises certain control over navigable waters—legislation was enacted in 1899, prohibiting the discharge of refuse matter; and later, the Oil Pollution Act of 1924 prohibited discharge of oil in coastal navigable waters. But there was little disposition in the Congress to extend federal jurisdiction in an administrative area in which the states were solidly entrenched.[1] The states, of course, were unalterably opposed to whatever might be construed as pre-emption of their sovereignty through federal action.

Industrial interests were traditionally and vehemently opposed to any extension of federal control, a viewpoint that has been sustained to this day. In their view, pollution is a problem involving local interests and

1. See H. G. Baity, "Aspects of Governmental Policy on Stream Pollution Abatement," *American Journal of Public Health and The Nation's Health,* Vol. 29, No. 12 (December 1939). Reprinted in *Hearings* before the Committee on Rivers and Harbors, House of Representatives, 79th Cong., 1st Sess., November 13–20, 1945, p. 205.

should be handled by the level of government most responsive to these interests, namely, the state. To industry, the concept of an interstate agency endowed with powers to deal with pollution control on a regional basis was almost as unattractive as federal control.

Conservation groups, on the other hand, espoused federal control as the only solution to the problem. Pointing to deficiencies in state programs and the absence of satisfactory arrangements to deal with interstate pollution, these interests felt that too much was being left to local decision in a matter that had more than local impact. The conservationists stated it was their experience that, when the interests of fishermen conflicted with those of the industrialists, the fishermen came out second best at the hands of state regulatory authorities. A review of some state laws on pollution control and the problems associated with their enforcement would seem to sustain the views of the conservation groups.

Even if the question of state or federal control had been absent, there was a further point on which viewpoints clashed. In one camp were those who felt that "prohibition-type" laws, combined with heavy penalties and aggressive use of injunction-type proceedings, were the only way to bring a halt to pollution. Others, who believed themselves to be more sophisticated in the conduct of human affairs, pointed to the national liquor prohibition law, which had only recently been repealed as unworkable, and said that the abatement of stream pollution called for something more than legislation. They claimed there were already too many laws on the subject. What was needed, in their opinion, was motivation to secure compliance—a procedure that would involve generating public demand for clean streams, co-ordination of control efforts by interstate agreement, and the application of financial incentives.

This case against prohibition was succinctly enunciated by Ellis S. Tisdale, state sanitary engineer in West Virginia, in testimony before a 1936 Congressional committee. "I do not believe that you will ever get this [water pollution] problem solved simply upon the principle of trying to penalize and saying that none of these wastes shall be discharged into the streams. That has been the program which has been attempted for the last 100 years—fifty years anyway—without success. . . ."[2] Mr. Tisdale's words undoubtedly reflected the frustrations he had experienced during two decades of endeavor in his state.

This, in brief, was the situation when the Cincinnati Chamber of Commerce committee tackled the problem: sporadic, unco-ordinated efforts

2. "Pollution of Navigable Waters," *Hearings* before the Committee of Rivers and Harbors, House of Representatives, 74th Cong., 2nd Sess., May 20, 1936, p. 49.

by various official and unofficial entities, but no one group in a position to generate the enthusiasm and sustain the impact needed for a regional approach; differing philosophies on the appropriate role of state and federal governments; and, finally, uncertainty as to whether the legislation best suited to expedite compliance was outright prohibition with heavy penalties or "reasonable" legislation with provision for grants-in-aid, and for promotion of public education, research, and institutional incentives to stimulate action.

Genesis of the Cincinnati Program

Prior to the formal organization of the Cincinnati Stream Pollution Committee in the summer of 1935, the Chamber of Commerce crusaders established contact with many of the groups in the Ohio Valley and became acquainted with their viewpoints. Having thus "felt the pulse" of those with whom it sought to make common cause, the Chamber appointed its committee. It was charged with planning a comprehensive program of action that included:

(1) Encouraging municipalities to seek federal aid for the construction of sewage-treatment plants (grants-in-aid were then being offered for public works projects);

(2) Advocating an interstate compact among the states bordering the Ohio River which would have the power to punish violators;

(3) Introducing federal legislation to facilitate the creation of basin authorities for stream pollution control.

All of this was outlined in a directive of June 26, 1935, to Hudson Biery when he was appointed chairman. He was instructed further that the committee was to "act as the liaison group between the Chamber of Commerce and other organizations joining in the movement to purify our rivers."

In brief, what this charge suggested was an amalgam of local, state, and federal efforts for combating pollution on a regional basis. Finding the way toward such an accomplishment was to be the committee's task. What this involved is detailed in the following chapter.

5

Searching for Solutions

One month after its formation, the Cincinnati Stream Pollution Committee announced its plans. It had concluded that solutions to the problem were local in character but regional in scope. And it was convinced that local action would not be forthcoming until there was assurance of regional co-operation.

The preamble to the program said: "We hold that the streams of the Ohio Valley were not intended to serve as sewers and that they should be restored to their proper use in the fields of public health, conservation, commerce and recreation. This committee will: promote legislation to control pollution of streams of the Ohio Valley; encourage the construction of disposal plants; conduct a general program of education; and coordinate, so far as possible, all local efforts to accomplish these ends."

Subcommittees were assigned to undertake the following tasks:

(1) *Legislation*—Investigate present laws of states regarding stream pollution; draft a model state law based on this investigation; study interstate compacts relating to water resources; and finally, draft proposals for any federal legislation that appears desirable.

(2) *Research and planning*—Inspect sewage disposal plants now operating and those under construction; collect information for educating the committee and to provide material for publicity purposes; develop a statement of the policies to be espoused by the committee.

(3) *Federal emergency and relief activities*—Investigate policies in Washington on work-relief projects in general, with the possibility of having a federally-sponsored survey made of the region, or at least in the Cincinnati area.

The committee contemplated setting up a subcommittee to present proposed legislation to governors, legislative committees, and other state or municipal authorities, as well as to enlist the support of Chambers of

Commerce throughout the Ohio Valley for the proposed legislation. It seemed probable that another subcommittee would be needed to solicit the co-operation of all organizations concerned with recreation. And, if events dictated the need, still another subcommittee would be organized to consult with health and sanitation boards in the general effort to promote construction of sewage-treatment plants.

Action on Three Fronts

The comprehensive nature of the campaign, with its separate but related thrusts on several fronts, prescribed the strategy that action be taken on all fronts simultaneously. The committee recognized that realization of some of its objectives would depend on developments on the national scene, while other actions would require painstaking negotiations locally as well as on a state and regional level.

The local focus. In promoting local action, the committee stressed conditions in the so-called Cincinnati Pool, a twenty-two mile stretch of the Ohio River between navigation dams No. 36 and No. 37. It was from the upper end of this pool that Cincinnati and several Kentucky cities on the opposite bank drew their water supply.

Not far downstream from these water intakes, there began a succession of some 90 sewer outfalls on both sides of the river. The 60 emanating from Cincinnati alone discharged an estimated 350 tons of human excrement daily. To make matters worse, a polluted Ohio tributary, the Little Miami River, entered the pool a short distance below the municipal water intakes, and during periods of slack water in the Ohio River the influx from the Miami moved upstream in the vicinity of the intakes.

Two reasons were advanced by the committee "for cleaning up our own front yard": (1) Self-interest in protecting the source of water supply in the metropolitan area, as well as restoring recreational opportunities; and (2) providing an example to communities up and down stream on the Ohio River of the willingness of at least one major metropolitan area to do its part in keeping the river clean. Accordingly, a campaign was started on both sides of the river to arouse citizen support for construction of treatment works.

In Kentucky, the Covington Chamber of Commerce stimulated negotiations that ultimately led to the formation of the 17-community Northern Kentucky Sanitation District No. 1. (This district, incidentally, was the second municipal authority on the main stem to construct sewage treatment works and place them in operation to comply with terms of the interstate compact after its adoption in 1948.[1])

In Cincinnati, the committee spurred a campaign to arouse action from the city and some 24 adjacent communities in Hamilton County. As part of this program, the committee publicized a report of the Cincinnatus Association (an organization of civic leaders and professional people), which had been prepared a year earlier by a group of engineers and doctors. This report documented the unhappy conditions associated with local pollution and its potential hazards to public health.

The committee used newspaper publicity and a variety of activities to dramatize the evils of stream pollution and arouse citizen support for its elimination. Boat clubs were encouraged to provide waterfront tours in which citizens were shown where sewers spewed their ugly contents into the river. Fishermen were urged to report fish kills.

A bacteriologist was retained by the *Cincinnati Post* to analyze samples of river water from a popular bathing point on the Ohio. The results showed coliform counts of 10,000 to 462,000 per milliliter,[2] a count greater than 10 per milliliter being regarded by many health authorities as questionable for swimming. However, no official action was taken, and people continued to swim in the rivers. On August 6, 1935, two victims of typhoid were hospitalized. Physicians checking the history of both men were convinced they had contracted the disease from swimming in polluted water—one in the Little Miami River and the other in the Ohio River a short distance below Cincinnati. This prompted Dr. F. K. Harder, acting city health commissioner, to issue a warning on June 3, 1936: "I would recommend that anyone contemplating swimming in rivers here be vaccinated against typhoid fever." And then he had forty signs posted along the river which said: "Danger, Typhoid Fever. Do not swim in the river."

Across the river at Newport, Kentucky, City Manager John T. Rawlings placed a ban on swimming in the Ohio River on July 23, 1936. Despite horrendous headline articles in the local papers (sample: "90,800 deadly germs lurk in each pint of Ohio River water")[3] and the posting of official warnings, the news stories of that day also revealed "the river

1. The first sewage treatment works to go into operation on the main stem was the Little Miami plant completed by the City of Cincinnati in October, 1953. The Kentucky plant went into operation in October, 1954.
2. Coliform bacteria are a normal inhabitant of the intestines of warm-blooded animals. Their presence in river water is presumptive evidence of sewage pollution. (A milliliter is about 16 drops of water.)
3. *Cincinnati Post*, July 23, 1936.

was crowded during the recent heat wave with thousands of persons seeking relief."

The menace of pollution was supported by Dr. Hugh Leavell, director of health at Louisville, Kentucky. He reported (Nov. 20, 1936) that: "Ten per cent of our typhoid cases originate in persons who have been swimming in the Ohio River. Although none of the increasing number of germs in the water bear the design 'Made in Cincinnati,' yet I am sure that we do get quite a lot of Cincinnati's pollution and germs, just as Cincinnati gets some from Pittsburgh and other points above the city."

Before long, virtually every civic, social, health, recreational, and religious group in the metropolitan area of Cincinnati, found reason to ally itself with the aims of the pollution-control crusaders. There was an outpouring of resolutions and offers of support to the committee. They came from such diverse interest groups as the Cincinnati Landscape Association, the Ohio Teachers Association, the YMCA Men's Club, the Federated Civic Clubs, and the B'nai B'rith.

Also supporting the campaign were the Master Brewers Association of Greater Cincinnati, the Federated Garden Clubs, the Ohio Valley Conference of Food, Drug, and Health officials, the Ohio Division of the Izaak Walton League of America, the Cincinnati Council of the Boy Scouts of America, and the Cincinnati Automobile Club. The latter, looking at polluted streams from the viewpoint of the tourist, went beyond enlisting automobile clubs up and down the Ohio Valley, and sought to interest the American Automobile Association in promoting a national campaign against pollution.

With such a rallying of followers, it is not surprising that when Chamber President Wiley called a meeting of officials from three neighboring states (Indiana, Kentucky, and West Virginia) on July 31, 1936, to invite their co-operation in stream cleanup, he declared: "We are engaged on what amounts to a holy crusade of public health. This is no local campaign, nor is it a movement for the people of Ohio or Kentucky alone."

The specific aim of the committee with regard to home-front affairs was to develop citizen support to finance installation of municipal sewage-treatment facilities. And for the next two years, without diminishing its efforts to promote interstate and federal action, it hammered away on this issue.

On November 8, 1938, the local efforts paid off. In Cincinnati a $1 million municipal bond issue for sewage treatment was approved by the voters. The committee was jubilant. It had spared no effort to put the bond campaign across, under the slogan: "Let's take the dead horses out of the river." This slogan derived from a rather original calculation, whereby the sewage load from the Cincinnati area was translated into the equivalent of a daily addition of 720 dead horses, or one floating past the city every two minutes of the day.

The favorable response to the bond issue paved the way for the city to do something tangible to eliminate pollution, and the committee declared that such action would stimulate the advancement of regional co-operation. "Cincinnati now can show the other states that this city means business and calls upon them to do their part."[4]

State and interstate developments. While one unit of the committee was thus engaged in promoting local action, the legislative subcommittee was probing aspects of federal participation in pollution control and the potentialities of an interstate agreement for the conduct of a regional program.

An embryonic form of interstate co-operation had made its appearance as early as 1924 in the Ohio Valley when several state health departments agreed to combine their efforts to curb the discharge of phenolic wastes from coke plants. Although the agreement had no formal legal status, this display of interstate action did bring some pressure upon the steel industry to apply corrective measures.

Several factors motivated enthusiasm for a regional compact. Not the least of these was the thinking of the National Resources Board, which was then seeking to promote co-ordination among the states and the federal government in water-resources developments.

The NRB occupied what was then a unique role in national affairs. It was constituted by President Roosevelt in 1933 as a top-level planning and policy-recommending body composed of the Secretaries of War, Agriculture, Labor, Commerce, and Interior, and the administrator of Federal Emergency Relief, and three citizen members. Backed with a professional staff of planners, economists, and engineers, and supplemented with consultants, the NRB was engrossed, among other things, with the possibilities of promoting regional co-operation in the conservation and development of resources.

The NRB was leaning strongly to the view that the states and the regions concerned should develop and conduct their own programs.[5] And it favored the interstate compact procedure for the Ohio Valley. In fact, the secretary of the NRB, Charles W. Eliot, visited Cincinnati and urged that the Chamber of Commerce group try its hand in drafting an inter-

4. *Cincinnati Times and Star,* November 9, 1938.
5. Statement of Charles W. Eliot II, Secretary, National Resources Board, in *Hearings* before subcommittee of the Committee of Commerce, U.S. Senate, 74th Cong., 2nd Sess., February–May, 1936, p. 128.

state compact. He called attention to one currently being discussed by the states of New York, New Jersey, and Connecticut for pollution control in New York Harbor. "It is important," said Mr. Eliot, "that the NRB see several proposals so that a national policy may be suggested to Congress."[6]

In response to this invitation to participate in an endeavor that might be helpful in guiding national policy, the Cincinnati committee produced a draft of a suggested compact. The draft, prepared by Robert A. Taft and his law-firm colleague, Leonard A. Weakley,[7] was destined to provide a framework for the Ohio River Valley Water Sanitation Compact.[8]

Thus was the stage set for opening negotiations among the Ohio Valley states looking toward the adoption of an interstate agreement.

Federal relationships. The Cincinnati committee's action in drafting a compact did not mean, however, that it was committed to this instrumentality alone for achieving desired ends. It was not overlooking the desirability of having the federal government participate more fully in pollution-control affairs. In particular, it felt that the federal role should be one of providing technical leadership and financial assistance to the states regardless of whether or not a compact came into existence. (As a matter of fact, the committee had attempted with limited success to obtain federal funds for installing sewage treatment works. What it got was a work-relief grant of $70,000 for a sewerage survey of the county.)

Because of uncertainty at that time as to the agency to which Congress might designate pollution-control responsibilities, the committee asked Mr. Taft to prepare two bills. One of these called for creation of a division of stream pollution control in the Public Health Service; the other placed such responsibility under jurisdiction of the Chief of Engineers in the War Department. In submitting these bills the committee said:[9] "Our position is neutral, so either plan is acceptable. We want action by one agency or the other and we have full confidence in both."

At the same time the committee promoted sponsorship of federal legislation that would permit the Ohio Valley states to undertake formal negotiations for a compact (based on third clause of Section 10 of Article I of the Constitution, which requires the consent of Congress

6. *Cincinnati Enquirer,* September 21, 1935.
7. In 1948, Mr. Weakley was appointed legal counsel for the compact commission and has continuously held this post since then.
8. See Committee on Stream Pollution, Cincinnati Chamber of Commerce, Doc. No. 15, draft No. 3, February 20, 1936, Archives of ORSANCO.
9. "Pollution of Navigable Waters," *Hearings* before the Committee on Rivers and Harbors, House of Representatives, 74th Cong., 2nd Sess., May 20, 1936, p. 13.

before states may enter into agreements).[10] The consent request later became an amendment to an earlier and similar request from certain New England states who likewise entertained ideas about a compact. This parliamentary maneuver helped to speed approval, which was granted on June 8, 1936.

Not so speedy, however, was Congressional action with respect to a national water-pollution control bill. For at least fifty years the federal lawmakers had been confronted with this issue. Always a deadlock had ensued. Generally, the federal bills were of a "prohibition type" and most of them never reached the stage of serious consideration.

The Ohio Valley proposal was presented to Congress at the same time as two other propositions. One of these, introduced by Senator Augustine Lonergan of Connecticut[11] who was sympathetic to the views of the Izaak Walton League, called for assumption of authority by the national government to exercise pollution control through injunction proceedings in the federal courts. The other, endorsed by the Conference of State and Territorial Health Officers, paralleled the Ohio Valley proposal. It called for: establishment of a division of pollution control in the Public Health Service to render technical assistance; provision of a federal grant of $700,000 annually to aid the states in expanding their activities; and a continued vesting of regulatory authority in the states alone.

It was on the issue of federal regulatory authority versus state jurisdiction that the battle lines were drawn on water pollution control legislation.[12] Throughout the period from 1936 to 1948, when a federal law finally was passed, the Ohio Valley group was active in this controversy as protagonist for those who favored the following principles: recognition that the primary responsibility for control resided with the states; establishment of compacts for pollution control on interstate streams; conduct of investigations and research by the Public Health Service, which would also provide technical services to the states; appropriation of federal funds

10. Mitchell Wendell, counsel of the Council of State Governments, made this observation to the author in a communication dated October 15, 1965: "By settled judicial construction some compacts do not need consent. Since the Federal Water Pollution Control Act of 1948, water pollution compacts need consent. Prior to that time it is at least arguable that the Ohio Valley compact was of a sort not needing consent."

11. The philosophy embodied in these proposals set forth in "Stream Pollution and Stream Purification," a report by Senator Lonergan, published as Senate Doc. No. 16, 74th Cong., 1st Sess., January 30, 1935.

12. For an excellent exposition of the conflicting viewpoints, see Herman G. Baity, "Aspects of Governmental Policy on Stream Pollution Abatement," *American Journal of Public Health and The Nation's Health,* Vol. 29, No. 12 (December, 1939).

to aid municipalities in constructing sewage-treatment plants and to provide loans to industry for installation of waste-control works.

These principles found expression in Public Law 845, the first Federal Water Pollution Control Act, which was passed in 1948. Everybody seemed to be satisfied with the outcome except the Izaak Walton League, which had fought for a bill that would give dominant enforcement authority to the federal government. The League had little confidence in the capability of the states to match performance with needs. It thought even less of the potentialities of compact commissions for resolving interstate problems. And it saw no virtue in the federal government being restricted primarily to investigations and planning on a matter that "already had been studied to death."

The only provision in P.L. 845 that might be viewed as a concession to the League was that a federal court action for abatement might be initiated under limited circumstances on interstate streams—but only with the consent of the state in which pollution was alleged to originate. This prompted a League spokesman to observe: "It looked like the Public Health Service had been told to go to bat in a ball game with a feather duster instead of a stout piece of hickory."[13]

As a matter of historical background, the 1948 act turned out to be the embodiment of what the Cincinnati group and the national Association of State and Territorial Health Officers proposed in 1936. The sponsors of the legislation from its initiation to final passage, were senators and representatives from Kentucky and Ohio, beginning with Senator Alben Barkley (D., Kentucky) and Representative John B. Hollister (R., Ohio); followed by Senator Barkley and Representative Fred Vinson (D., Kentucky), and finally Senator Robert Taft (R., Ohio) and Representative Brent Spence (D., Kentucky). It can be appreciated, therefore, why the Ohio Valley group believed it had played an important role in guiding national policy. With various refinements over the years this legislation had captured the backing of more than 100 organizations representing state, municipal, industrial, and professional groups. By many, the 1948 act was regarded as a practical compromise—it preserved state authority in the matter of enforcement but it also provided for federal leadership and participation.

President Harry S Truman signed the measure on June 30, 1948. And on that same day the governors of eight states met in Cincinnati and put their signatures on the document that created the Ohio River Valley

13. "Water Pollution Control—1966," *Hearings* before a subcommittee of the Committee on Public Works, U.S. Senate, 84th Cong., 1st Sess., April 22, 25, and 26, 1955, p. 100.

Water Sanitation Compact. The Cincinnati committee had now achieved two more of its major objectives: establishment of a regional agency, and the initiation of federal participation. Equally gratifying was the fact that Public Law 845 authorized construction of facilities in Cincinnati for studies on water pollution and the training of personnel. When this facility was dedicated on April 8, 1954, it was named the Robert A. Taft Sanitary Engineering Center.

From this thumbnail sketch of the committee's participation on three fronts of activity—local, state, and national—we now turn to a more detailed account of how matters progressed with regard to negotiating a compact for regional co-operation.

6

Negotiating the Compact

Thirty years ago the interstate compact was an untried institutional device for regional co-operation on pollution control. However, to those who were seeking in 1935 to rehabilitate the streams of the Ohio Valley, this mechanism for regional co-operation seemed to offer the greatest promise. It represented an alternate to federal intervention, which the states did not want and which many individuals rejected on ideological grounds as an undesirable extension of centralized authority. "We should not have to run to Washington every time we want to flush the toilet," was the way one spokesman characterized the prevailing sentiment.[1]

Industrial interests abhorred the notion of any change in the status quo. What the states were doing—or more accurately, what they were unable to do in curbing interstate pollution—was not unsatisfactory so far as industry was concerned. Industrial interests pleaded an unfair competitive situation if one state sought to be aggressive in pollution control, while others were laggard. At the same time, industrial lobbyists opposed proposals for any federal laws that would promote uniformity of enforcement, saying that water pollution was so intimately related to local conditions that the only logical arbiter for dealing with it was a state agency.

One such incident was described by Philip J. G. Platt before a Congressional hearing in 1945.[2] Mr. Platt, who identified himself as a former member of the Pennsylvania Sanitary Water Board and as an officer of the Izaak Walton League, said: "During the 1935 session of our [Pennsylvania] legislature, a manufacturer's representative appeared at a committee hearing and said in effect: 'We are in sympathy with the lofty purpose of this bill, but its adoption would place Pennsylvania industry at an unfair competitive disadvantage. If drastic pollution legislation is to be fair, it must be national in scope to provide for uniformity.' " Con-

1. Statement of Hudson Biery, Chairman of the Committee on Stream Sanitation of the Cincinnati Chamber of Commerce, in "Pollution of Navigable Waters," *Hearings* of Committee on Rivers and Harbors, House of Representatives, 79th Cong., 1st Sess., November 1945, p. 183.
2. *Ibid.,* p. 155.

tinued Mr. Platt: "This argument helped to defeat pending legislation of that time, but there was an interesting sequel. This same individual checked his bags and appeared at a later hearing before the Commerce Committee of the United States Senate and said, in effect: 'We are in sympathy with the lofty purpose of this proposed legislation, but it is just none of the business of the federal government how Pennsylvania conducts its pollution problem.' "

That pollution problems of the Ohio Valley might be resolved by unilateral action on the part of the states concerned was an unrealistic possibility in view of the facts. The Ohio River (except for the first 40 miles) belongs to two states—Kentucky and West Virginia.[3] However, neither of these states could enforce action to curb discharges into the river from municipalities and industries in Pennsylvania, Ohio, Indiana, and Illinois, except by recourse to the U.S. Supreme Court.

In the face of this dilemma—widespread opposition to an extension of federal control and the lack of legal and institutional capability of individual states to resolve regional problems—the logical alternative was a compact. But commitment to this alternate represented an act of faith. In 1936 there was no record of experience as to the possible effectiveness of an interstate agency in the realm of regional pollution control. And for precedent as to the appropriate scope and content of such an agreement, there was only the recent pioneering effort of New York and New Jersey. These two states, joined later by Connecticut, had completed negotiations in 1935 for an interstate agreement to abate pollution in New York Harbor and adjacent waters.

But the Ohio Valley group had great faith. And as events proved, they had need of it. At first, progress toward an interstate agreement moved along rather swiftly under the drive of Mr. Wiley and his Cincinnati team. The bill seeking Congressional consent for the states in the valley to negotiate a compact was introduced on March 31, 1936, and by June 8 approval was granted. Governor Martin L. Davey of Ohio then issued an invitation to the governors of the other Ohio Valley states to appoint delegates to consider the details of the sanitation compact.

3. In 1789, the Commonwealth of Virginia ceded part of its western lands for the formulation of a new state—Kentucky. At that time, the northern boundary of the Virginia territory was the low-water mark on the northern bank of the Ohio River. When Kentucky was admitted to the Union in 1792, it inherited this boundary mark, which has a length of about 700 miles along the Ohio River. Similarly, at a much later date when West Virginia was created out of part of Virginia territory, it also inherited as its northern boundary the original low-water mark on the far side of the Ohio River.

Six states sent representatives to a meeting in Cincinnati on November 20. Governor Davey appointed F. H. Waring, chief sanitary engineer of Ohio, to welcome the delegates and to outline the purpose of the meeting, which was to organize for negotiation of an "Ohio Valley Treaty." The conferees elected W. F. Wiley as chairman, and appointed Mr. Waring as secretary. The representatives were then given copies of a proposed draft of a compact, prepared by the stream pollution committee of the Cincinnati Chamber of Commerce.

Not the least interesting aspect of this first meeting was the view held by a number of delegates that much more than stream sanitation should be included in the proposed interstate agreement. In fact, a delegate from Kentucky said that his governor and several members of the legislature had instructed him to advance the proposition that three matters—flood control, soil conservation, and pollution abatement—should be considered as integral components of the compact. Another delegate advanced forestry management as a laudable component. It took considerable persuasion to dampen these enthusiasms and to convince the group that the single task of co-ordinating stream cleanup would in itself represent a challenging assignment without the addition of subsidiary matters.

The practicality of this view became apparent when the delegates were confronted with the details of what should constitute an appropriate agreement for executing pollution abatement within a regional context. One of the complex and difficult aspects, from a technical standpoint, was the manner of specifying requirements for sewage and industrial waste control. Inherent in this was the problem of setting standards of water quality, applying them, and at the same time meeting the need for flexibility. This indeed is the very question that thirty years later was debated with respect to amending the federal law for establishment of quality standards.

The final business of this first meeting was appointment of a subcommittee consisting of the chief sanitary engineers of the states along with representatives of the U.S. Public Health Service to clarify and expand basic ideas set forth in a tentative draft of the compact. The composition of the subcommittee reflected the view that those who were administering state pollution-abatement measures should be best able to advise how an interstate program might be conducted.

This subcommittee produced a revised working draft of the compact on December 18, 1936, but a year elapsed before formal discussions were resumed with all the negotiators. During that time the states along the Ohio River were preoccupied with flood-contol matters, which assumed priority when the record-breaking high water inundated the valley in

January, 1937. Some of the states, however, did make provision through their legislatures for formal designation of commissioners to consummate an agreement.

Eight states joined in the negotiations when they were reopened in 1938, and meetings were held on January 17, on May 24, on June 13, and on October 11. At the last three meetings, representatives of the Council of State Governments were invited to contribute to the deliberations.[4]

The negotiators included not only men who were skilled in legislative affairs but also experts in the engineering and administrative aspects of stream sanitation. Among them were veterans from many a skirmish in the arena of state politics. As a consequence, every item in the draft document was not only scrutinized from the standpoint of its legal and technical validity, but examined in terms of how it might be interpreted in legislative hearings.

The October, 1938, meeting produced a final document which was then submitted to the states for ratification, together with a draft of what was regarded as appropriate enabling legislation.

By 1940, legislatures of six states had adopted the compact, and the Congress had granted approval for its execution. Indiana, Illinois, New York, and Kentucky approved the agreement without any reservations. But Ohio conditioned its adoption on ratification by its upstream and adjacent neighbors, Pennsylvania, West Virginia, and New York. And West Virginia, feeling that there was little value in becoming a signatory to the compact unless upstream states were bound by the agreement and unless there were some assurance that Pittsburgh would be required to abate the discharge of raw sewage, made its adoption contingent on New York, Pennsylvania, Ohio, and Virginia becoming parties to the agreement. For varying reasons, Pennsylvania, Virginia, and Tennessee had taken no action.

In Pennsylvania, little headway was being made in securing legislative approval. Some observers felt that the reluctance of the Pennsylvania

4. The Council of State Governments is a service organization designed to strengthen state relationships. In the middle thirties it co-operated with various "Commissions on Interstate Cooperation" created by the states, one of which was activated in the Ohio Basin in January, 1937. This commission included three representatives from each state in the basin (one from the House, one from the Senate, and one appointed by the governor of the state). The objective of the commission was to study matters of mutual interest and make recommendations to their legislatures for unified action. The Ohio Basin group became interested, of course, in the movement to negotiate a compact for pollution abatement. Chairman of the group was State Senator James O. Monroe of Illinois, who made many practical contributions in developing the ORSANCO compact.

legislature to act on the compact stemmed from the attitude of two groups. City officials in Pittsburgh were not yet prepared to accept the idea that they should create a tax burden in order to construct multimillion dollar sewage-treatment facilities primarily for the benefit of down-river neighbors. And industrial interests, who had continually exhibited their opposition to federal intervention in stream pollution, considered a regional authority as only a degree less onerous than a "big stick" wielded by the federal government. (The action of West Virginia in insisting that Virginia must become a party to the compact was likewise viewed as a subtle method of industrial lobbyists to scuttle possible establishment of a regional agency.) Whatever validity may be attached to these views, another more potent influence brought a temporary halt to legislative consummation of the agreement. This was the advent of World War II. With every effort in the nation in the early forties directed toward winning the war, such matters as pollution prevention were relegated to the background. During these years there was tremendous industrial expansion in the Ohio Valley, and stream conditions, already considered bad, became far worse.

By 1944 it appeared propitious to push again for interstate action. Mr. Wiley called a conference of the negotiating delegates in Pittsburgh, but before the meeting was convened on December 7, he died. The call to order, as was the case with the first meeting of the group eight years earlier, became the responsibility of Secretary Fred Waring.

Hudson Biery, the man to whom Mr. Wiley had entrusted day-by-day responsibility in the fight for the compact, was unanimously elected as chairman. He was thoroughly prepared to press the point that Mr. Wiley had planned to make: either the states show alacrity in taking steps to control pollution on a regional basis or the federal government would have to intervene. Responding to assertions that nothing short of a federal action could solve the problem, he said: "There are those who feel that our compact has been a failure. This compact hasn't had a chance to be anything."[5]

Following election of the new chairman, a report was presented that provoked the delegates into action. It was a resumé of findings that had just been presented to the Congress from a survey of Ohio basin pollution conducted by the Corps of Engineers and the U.S. Public Health Service. In summary the situation pictured was this: Practically all streams in the Ohio River Basin were polluted by domestic and industrial

5. *Proceedings,* Sixth Conference of Delegates Appointed to Draft an Ohio River Valley Water Sanitation Compact, December 7, 1944, p. 5. Hereafter cited as *Proceedings,* Sixth Conference.

wastes, and some had severe corrosive characteristics imparted to them by acid mine-drainage. Thirty public sources of water supply were endangered by pollution in the Ohio River. In a number of tributaries the situation was at least as severe as in the worst reaches on the main Ohio River. (Details of the survey are given in Chapter 7.)

If the delegates—notably those from Pennsylvania—harbored any illusion that their task was not of an urgent nature, the notion was dissipated by the facts in the report. The meeting ended with a resolution urging the Pennsylvania and Virginia legislatures to adopt the compact.

A few months later (April 2, 1945) Pennsylvania did vote approval with the reservation, however, that West Virginia, Ohio, and New York would also be parties to the agreement.

Now all that remained was to secure Virginia's approval. Virginia was in much the same position as New York in that it had no upstream benefits to gain from participating in the Ohio Valley program because its drainage area constituted one of the headwater regions of the watershed. In fact, no delegates from Virginia participated in the negotiations of the compact. But since the compact—and the promise it offered as a substitute for federal intervention in regional affairs—could not become effective without Virginia, the legislature was inspired to give it support, and on March 5, 1948, Virginia approved the compact.

Although Tennessee was among those states named in the Congressional act to participate in negotiating the compact, like Virginia, it played no active role in the drafting of the compact itself. But, unlike Virginia, it chose not to become a signatory. The Tennessee situation, which raised some interesting issues, is discussed separately, later in this chapter.

Nature and Scope of the Agreement

At a time when interstate compacts had not yet been widely used for regulatory purposes, devising an agreement for regional pollution control that would be acceptable to eight state legislatures could be regarded as an exercise in ingenuity and political acumen. The Ohio Valley covenant was more than a declaration of co-operative intent. It established standards of performance and, in addition, provided for their enforcement under defined conditions. (See Appendix 2 for text of compact.)

By some it was declared to be an experiment in American government because it provided the institutional framework for a co-ordinated regional attack on pollution. Others, who were cynically inclined, dubbed the agreement as nothing more than an expression of "pious hopes and paper dreams."

It is of interest, therefore, to examine the nature and scope of the agreement. First, in Article I, each of the states pledged to each other:

> . . . faithful cooperation in the control of future pollution in and abatement of existing pollution from the rivers, streams and water in the Ohio River Basin which flow through, into or border upon any such signatory States, and in order to effect such object, agrees to enact any necessary legislation to enable each such State to place and maintain the waters of said basin in a satisfactory sanitary condition, available for safe and satisfactory use as public and industrial water supplies after reasonable treatment, suitable for recreational usage, capable of maintaining fish and other aquatic life, free from unsightly or malodorous nuisances due to floating solids or sludge deposits, and adaptable to such other uses as may be legitimate.

Composition of membership. The agreement provided for creation of the Ohio River Valley Water Sanitation Commission, an agency, "which shall be a body corporate with the powers and duties set forth herein." There were to be three commissioners from each state appointed by the Governor of the state and three federal commissioners appointed by the President of the United States.

Making provision for federal representation gave recognition to the importance of facilitating exchange of viewpoints and co-ordination with federal agencies already involved in Ohio Valley water resources utilization. Although specific federal agencies were not named in the compact, the negotiators felt that it would be logical to include the Public Health Service, the Corps of Engineers, and the Fish and Wildlife Service.

In a critique of the compact made in 1943 (see Chapter 7), it was recommended that the three commissioners representing the United States Government be given "voting power equal to that of the commissioners representing the States."[6] It should be noted, therefore, that the negotiators had discussed this matter and decided that a quorum for the transaction of business should consist of "one or more commissioners from a majority of the *member states* . . ." (Article V).[7] When one delegate asked if this ignored the federal members, the chairman answered, "Federal members do not count in a quorum; and if we make some requirement with respect to their participation, we will encumber the compact unnecessarily. . . ."

6. Report of the Ohio River Committee, House Doc. No. 266, 78th Cong., 1st Sess., August 27, 1943, p. 67.
7. *Proceedings,* Fifth Conference of Delegates Appointed to Draft an Ohio River Valley Water Sanitation Compact, October 11, 1938, p. 10. Hereafter cited as *Proceedings,* Fifth Conference.

While the federal commissioners were thus excluded from voting on matters relating to enforcement actions they were accorded an equal voice with the signatory states on both the executive and engineering committees, as well as in the conduct of other formal business. There is nothing in the record, nor is there any reason to believe, that the federal members ever felt that the lack of a vote on enforcement measures deprived them of either status or influence.

These membership arrangements were reached only after much discussion by the negotiators. The recently enacted New York–New Jersey–Connecticut compact provided for five commissioners from each state. If this number had been applied to the Ohio Valley situation, it would have meant five times eight, or forty state members, and possibly five federal representatives. A commission of this size was considered to be too awkward for effective transaction of business. Accordingly, it was agreed that three from each state should be the limit.

Since public-health issues were regarded to be of paramount concern in pollution abatement, there was strong support for the health commissioner from each state being an ex-officio member. While this was considered acceptable, it did pose the question whether any other specific interests—fisheries, industries, and municipalities, for example—should likewise be given mandatory representation. Finally it was decided that to bind the states in this fashion with regard to making appointments would be unwise. "Furthermore," said one negotiator, "we would not want industries represented because they are potential violators, and we do not want them in to vote against enforcement of regulations against themselves."[8] The same reasoning might have been applied, of course, with respect to municipal representation.

To minimize possibilities of debate among state legislators on matters of detail, the manner of appointment of commissioners was set forth not in the compact itself, but in the model enabling act submitted to the state legislatures along with the compact.[9]

The enabling act also covered the matter of whether a health officer commissioner, or any commissioner for that matter, would designate an alternate. ". . . With the exception of the issuance of any order under the provisions of Article IX of the Compact, said ex officio commissioner may delegate, from time to time, to any deputy or other subordinate in his department or office the power to be present and participate, including

8. *Proceedings*, Fifth Conference, *op. cit.*, p. 63.
9. Model enabling act adopted October 11, 1938, by the Fifth Conference of Delegates Appointed to Draft an Ohio River Valley Water Sanitation Compact.

voting, as his representative or substitute at any meeting of or hearing by or other proceeding of the Commission. . . ." The provision was enacted as a part of the enabling legislation by all the signatory states except Virginia, which has no ex officio member. No state legislation provides for proxy representation except for the ex officio commissioner.

This model act served as a guide and aided greatly in securing uniformity of state practice in appointment of commissioners. It is the practice in all states except Virginia for the chief health officer to be designated as a member, ex officio, and for two other members, generally of opposite political parties, to be appointed for six-year terms with eligibility for reappointment. In Virginia, three members of the State Water Control Board are appointed. The federal members have been the Surgeon General of the Public Health Service, a civilian staff representative from the Ohio River division of the Corps of Engineers, and a staff member of the Fish and Wildlife Service of the Department of the Interior.[10]

Formula for appropriations. Difficulty was experienced in evolving a rational procedure for securing appropriations to operate the commission and to provide for equitable apportionment among the states. Prior practice among most interstate compact agencies had been to establish a budget not to exceed a given amount, and then to prorate the total according to some fixed percentage.[11]

Such a procedure did not appeal to the negotiators of the Ohio Valley compact, and they rejected the notion of attempting to establish a fixed budget. Not only was there little experience to suggest what might be adequate, but if a fixed amount were written into the compact, it could not be changed without legislative action by all the signatory states. The negotiators recognized, however, that state legislatures would not commit themselves to an obligation to provide unlimited funds and would insist on some means for internal review and approval of budget requests.

To preserve this prerogative among the states and at the same time provide the commissioners with flexibility, it was finally agreed that "The

10. There has been stability among the membership; at the end of 10 years more than half the commissioners first chosen to represent the states and the federal government were still active; three commissioners had died and ten had been replaced because they were no longer residents in their states. At the end of 15 years, one-third of the original members retained their affiliation.

11. The New York-New Jersey-Connecticut (Tri-State) Compact provided that New York and New Jersey each contribute 45 per cent, and Connecticut 10 per cent, with the limitation that New York and New Jersey obligate themselves only to the extent of $15,000 and Connecticut not more than $3,333 annually. A four-state compact on the Delaware River provided that New York and New Jersey would pay ¼ each, Pennsylvania ⅜, and Delaware ⅛ of the budget.

Commission shall submit to the Governor of each State, at such time as he may request, a budget of its estimated expenditures for such period as may be required by the laws of such State for presentation to the legislature thereof."[12] This procedure permits a governor to screen a budget request and to convey his views regarding it to the legislature prior to its adoption. In turn, it provides opportunity for the Commission to make adjustments in accordance with needs and to prepare whatever justification might be requested by either the governor or members of the legislature.

However, this arrangement did not resolve the question of how to prorate the budget among the states. The idea that the states should share alike in the expenses was rejected as inequitable because of the substantial differences in both the area and population of those portions of the various states lying within the Ohio Valley drainage district. This led to the notion that operating costs might be assessed in accord with "benefits" received. However, so many imponderables were involved in developing such a formula that it was abandoned as impractical. Also dismissed was a proposal that the size of the industrial-waste load generated in each state should be given "due regard" in allocating appropriations. In turn, consideration was separately given to proportioning expenses on the basis of sewered population or on the size of drainage area and these were also rejected.

It was not until the fourth conference of the negotiators that a "rational scheme" was advanced by Wayne D. Heydecker, director of state planning in New York.[13] Here is what he said:

> Mr. Holmquist [at that time chief engineer of the New York State Health Department] and I have been giving considerable thought to Article X [dealing with appropriations]. It seems to us that the legislatures will want to know specifically the amount of financial participation which may be expected of the states they represent, instead of leaving the determination of that financial participation to the Commission and approval by the governors of the signatory states, and we have this suggestion to make.
>
> We did some experimentation with the population and area figures of the basin, believing the problem was directly related to both those factors. The volume of flow within the basin, generally speaking, is roughly proportionate to the area of the states affected thereby. The sewage problems and the water supply problems generally are proportionate to the population; and as the population shifts, these problems

12. See Article V of the Compact.
13. *Proceedings,* Fourth Conference of Delegates Appointed to Draft an Ohio River Valley Water Sanitation Compact, June 13, 1938, p. 24. Hereafter cited as *Proceedings,* Fourth Conference.

grow in one state or decline in another. It seems to us that the compact should recognize these changing conditions in the financial formula. I therefore offer for your consideration the following suggested addition. The section is so short that I would like to read it as it is proposed to be amended: "The signatory states agree to appropriate for the salaries, office and other administrative expenses, their proper proportion of the annual budget, as determined by the Commission and approved by the governors of the signatory states, one half of such amount to be prorated among the several states in proportion to their population within the district at the last preceding federal census, the other half to be prorated in proportion to their land area within the district."

Now, actually it works out this way: Illinois—5.20; Indiana—16.25; Kentucky—18.60; New York—1.10; Ohio—21.20; Pennsylvania—14.90; Tennessee—10.40; and West Virginia 12.35.

If we were to take either area or population solely as a basis, it seems to me there would be wide discrepancies which might result in practical injustice; but by taking the two factors which counteract one another and giving them equal weighting, I believe we arrive at an equitable arrangement.

The Heydecker-Holmquist proposal—regarded as "the most practical solution of an otherwise apparently hopelessly complex problem"—was subsequently adopted. Then came the question of what might constitute a likely amount for the total budget. Each negotiator was eager to apply the formula to learn what it might cost his state. The "guesstimates" varied between $100,000 and $250,000 annually. Using the lowest amount, the assessments varied from a low of $1,100 for New York to a high of $21,200 for Ohio.

The amounts appeared reasonable to all except Clarence W. Klassen, chief engineer of the Illinois State Health Department. He was disturbed in trying to reconcile a contribution of $5,200 from Illinois to an interstate agency for pollution abatement when the amount earmarked in his state budget for this purpose amounted to only $15,000. Other states also might have shared Mr. Klassen's feeling of imbalance because in 1938 state legislatures were not concerned over water pollution because this issue had little public support. But, as pointed out by State Senator James Monroe, also of Illinois: Was this the fault of the legislatures or was it more properly a failure on the part of the pollution-control administrators to gain public understanding of the importance of their programs?[14] Senator Monroe said he regarded the objectives of the compact and its budget requirements as realistically geared to needs that had been neglected. He argued that the budget proposal for the compact should

14. *Proceedings,* Fifth Conference, *op. cit.,* p. 38.

aid the state agencies in securing greater attention for pollution-control activities and the funds to pursue them.

The matter of assessment was finally resolved with adoption of the pro rata area and population formula advanced by the New York delegates. It might be added that this formula has since been employed in other compacts.

Establishing Pollution-Control Standards

The first draft of the compact contained only a generalized statement on what the interstate agency was expected to do. It called for creation of a commission to "make a complete plan for the reduction of stream pollution," and to consult with municipalities and industries on their problems, "particularly with respect to construction of plants for the disposal of sewage, industrial and other wastes."[15]

Dissatisfaction with this phraseology led to appointment of a subcommittee of state sanitary engineers and representatives of the U.S. Public Health Service to draft a more explicit directive. However, the lawyer members of the negotiating team cautioned the committee that from the standpoint of legal draftmanship and the desire to maintain flexibility to adapt to changing conditions, there was some doubt that the compact should specify standards. It would be better, they argued, if technical matters of this kind could be resolved free from any statutory requirements set forth in the compact.

However, the engineers had a different outlook. Working as they did under state laws that lacked uniformity either in principles of approach to pollution abatement or in procedures for enforcement (to wit: some states required that a condition of nuisance must exist before any remedial actions could be instituted), they wanted the compact to: (1) enunciate a regional pollution-control policy; and (2) specify that under no circumstances would the discharge of any raw sewage be permitted regardless of the size, condition, or location of a waterway.

They gave expression to their views with this statement:

> It is recognized by the signatory states that no single standard for the treatment of sewage or industrial wastes is applicable in all parts of the district due to such variable factors as size, flow, location, character, self-purification, and usage of waters within the district. The guiding principle of this compact shall be that pollution by sewage or

15. *Proceedings,* First Conference of Delegates Appointed to Draft an Ohio River Valley Water Sanitation Compact, p. 19.

industrial wastes originating within a signatory state shall not injuriously affect the various uses of the interstate waters as hereinbefore
defined.

With respect to sewage discharges it was concluded that the least to be
required from every community was "primary treatment." This technical
term describes a basic type of processing wherein settleable solids and
floating materials are removed, and which in large measure would satisfy
aesthetic necessities as well as reduce by about one-third the oxygen-
consuming characteristics of the sewage. Primary treatment facilities are
requisite to whatever other additional purification might be undertaken.

In order to provide a basis for interpretation by the courts of this
minimum requirement, it was written into the compact in this form: "All
sewage . . . shall be so treated . . . to provide for substantially complete
removal of settleable solids, and the removal of not less than forty-five
percent (45%) of the total suspended solids. . . ."

This stipulation was accompanied with the proviso "provided that, in
order to protect the public health or to preserve the waters for other
legitimate purposes . . . in specific instances such higher degree of treatment shall be used as may be determined to be necessary by the Commission after investigation, due notice and hearing."

Virtue of the standard. This statutory interstate requirement was
intended to satisfy several necessities. It established the discharge of raw
sewage as *prima facie* evidence of pollution and thus subject to abatement without the necessity of time-consuming litigation in the courts. At
the same time it recognized that certain situations might require a higher
degree of treatment. But in such cases it placed upon the regulatory
agency the restraint of making appropriate investigations for justifying
this action. And the provision for public hearings on such matters was
designed to solicit views of parties who might be affected and thus permit
the commissioners to weigh the merits of all factors bearing on a decision.

The attitude of the state sanitary engineers was probably best expressed
by C. A. Holmquist of New York, when he told the negotiators: "I have
had some quarter of a century experience in the control of pollution, and
I welcome that clause. We have had two or three municipalities in our
state that are discharging sewage and we have failed to get them to put in
proper treatment works. They are creating quite a serious nuisance. But
in our state we have to prove injury to health, which is pretty difficult to
do. We have to prove that some persons actually got sick of some disease
because sewage is put into that stream. Under the compact, the Commis-

sion would only have to prove they were violating the compact—that they were discharging raw sewage—and court action could be started."[16]

When it came to the question of prescribing standards for industrial-waste control, the engineers were on less certain ground. It was not practical, they concluded, to establish a minimum treatment measure similar to that set forth for sewage discharges. Therefore, they agreed with the lawyers that here was a situation wherein the intent of regulation should be broadly stated with the details to be resolved later by the Commission itself.[17] The intent was phrased in this manner:

> All industrial wastes discharged or permitted to flow into the aforesaid waters shall be modified or treated, within a time reasonable for construction of the necessary works, in order to protect the public health or to preserve the waters for other legitimate purposes, including those specified in Article I, to such a degree as may be determined to be necessary by the Commission after investigation, due notice and hearing.

In this statement one might not ordinarily linger over the word "modified." It was not in the original proposal of the engineers, which specified only that wastes shall be treated. Its incorporation is another example of the diligence and perspicacity of the negotiators. Alfred Bettman, a lawyer of Cincinnati, raised the point by asking: "Are there not preventive methods in the case of industrial wastes which ought to be within the power of this Commission to make recommendations on, which are not treatment? The word 'treatment' may cover what I have in mind, but are there not modes of operation within the plant which do not constitute treatment of flow, whereas the language here seems to limit the Commission to things which are treatment of water flow itself, of the water that goes into the flow?"[18]

16. *Proceedings,* Second Conference of Delegates Appointed to Draft an Ohio River Valley Water Sanitation Compact, p. 50. Hereafter cited as *Proceedings, Second Conference.* It might be noted that while the New York negotiators enthusiastically endorsed this principle for inclusion in the Ohio Valley compact, the state itself failed to adopt it to facilitate conduct of its pollution-control endeavors. Quite to the contrary, the New York legislature in 1949 adopted a "stream-classification" program, which made it incumbent upon the regulatory agency to classify all streams with respect to usage as a prerequisite to any enforcement action for abatement of pollution. These detailed classification studies and the public hearings associated with them generally required years for completion. In the meantime, nothing could be done despite the visible evidence of obvious pollution.

17. It took some three years of study and debate by the Commission to work out the details of "industrial waste control policy and procedures," which are set forth in a following chapter.

18. *Proceedings,* Second Conference. pp. 44–45.

The addition of the word "modified" was a happy one in that it did provide for great flexibility in devising measures to satisfy pollution abatement necessities. There are, in fact, many ways in which industrial waste discharges may be modified. Changes of industrial processing or manufacturing methods may achieve this end. And so will the practice of proportioning discharges to streamflow—a technique ultimately prescribed by the Commission for regulation of salt content in streams. None of these alternatives constitute "treatment" per se. But under appropriate circumstances they will prevent pollution.

One of the troublesome side issues that arose in connection with control requirements concerned the application of Commission regulations to streams that were not interstate themselves but which drained into interstate waters. There was no disposition on the part of the negotiators to permit the Commission to extend its jurisdiction to intrastate streams. However, they felt it should be recognized that failure to curb pollution on a tributary could influence the quality of interstate waters. Accordingly, they wrote the following provision:

> All sewage or industrial wastes discharged or permitted to flow into tributaries of the aforesaid waters situated wholly within one state shall be treated to that extent, if any, which may be necessary to maintain such waters in a sanitary and satisfactory condition at least equal to the condition of the waters of the interstate stream immediately above the confluence.

The intent of this provision was to allay fears that the Commission would seek to exercise authority on tributaries situated wholly within a state. If the Commission were clothed with such power, so the argument ran, then the regional agency would have a status superior to a state on matters that might be far removed from interstate implications. It was reasoned that no state legislature would agree to such an arrangement.[19]

All of this, however, was simply the prelude to discussion of precisely what authority the Commission should have and how it might be exercised without improper infringement on the sovereignty of the states.

How Much Enforcement Authority?

There was general agreement that the Commission should be armed with a "big stick"—the power to enforce compliance with its decisions and orders. But there were many different views on how big the stick should be and where and under what conditions it could be wielded.

19. *Proceedings,* Fourth Conference, *op. cit.,* p. 22.

Having conceded that the compact must be something more than a "gentleman's agreement," the negotiators tackled these two questions: How much authority could be granted to a regional agency without incurring the risk of confusion and conflict within a state? What safeguards could be placed on the exercise of such authority? The state regulatory agencies saw virtue in having a strong regional body that could be depended on to back them up in pursuing mutual objectives. But what would happen on occasions when the desires of the regional agency might be incompatible with individual state interests?

To some of the legal-minded negotiators the discussion on enforcement power was regarded as academic. Their argument was that with or without an explicit clause on enforcement, the compact established in fact a superauthority whose decisions were enforceable by the Congress of the United States. They cited an opinion of Mr. Chief Justice White of the U. S. Supreme Court (in *Virginia* v. *West Virginia,* 246 U.S. 565) in which he said: "It follows as a necessary implication that the power of Congress to refuse or to assent to a contract between the states carried with it the right, if the contract was assented and hence became operative by the will of Congress, to see to its enforcement."[20]

This did not satisfy those negotiators who were concerned primarily with drafting an interstate agreement that would be acceptable to eight state legislatures. They insisted that if the enforcement provisions could not be clearly defined—that if they did not provide opportunity for a signatory state to register some influence over the actions and authority of its regional agency—then it would be futile to seek approval of any type of compact.

The negotiators persevered and found a way to endow the Commission with enforcement powers, and in a manner calculated to satisfy the states that exercise of such authority would be judiciously safeguarded. The procedure as described in Article IX of the compact is as follows:

> The Commission may from time to time, after investigation and after a hearing, issue an order or orders upon any municipality, corporation, person, or other entity discharging sewage or industrial waste into the Ohio River or any other river, stream or water, any part of which constitutes any part of the boundary line between any two or more of the signatory States, or into any stream any part of which flows from any portion of one signatory State through any portion of another signatory State. . . . No such order shall go into effect unless and until it receives the assent of at least a majority of the commissioners from

20. *Proceedings,* Second Conference, *op. cit.,* p. 58.

each of not less than a majority of the signatory States; and no such
order upon a municipality, corporation, person or entity in any State
shall go into effect unless and until it receives the assent of not less
than a majority of the commissioners from such State.

In other words, issuance of an order by the Commission would require
approval of two commissioners from each of five states (or a total of ten
favorable votes), coupled with approval of at least two of the commissioners from the state affected by the order.

Although some felt that this grant of enforcement power was condi-
tional and left something to be desired, they conceded that in this form
there was greater likelihood of winning approval for the compact from
state legislatures. Furthermore, and as a practical matter, the agency
established by the compact was not conceived as a policing organization but as an institution that would induce co-operative action and
supplement the efforts of the states in working toward common objectives.
The imposition of orders, it was held, must be regarded only as a last
resort. Effectiveness of the Commission would be measured in terms of
its ability to accomplish its aims through education and persuasion and
not by the number of orders it sought to enforce.

In supporting adoption of this clause, one of the negotiators, State
Senator James Monroe of Illinois, made this observation: "I am thinking
not only of the mere matter of getting this compact concurred in by the
assemblies, but I am also thinking in broader terms. In legislative matters
it is better to proceed slowly, step by step, and accomplish small things
which can be accepted by the people and used as progressive steps to
other things, rather than to do revolutionary things. This compact affair,
while it has been provided for from the beginning of our government, is
new, and in that sense revolutionary; and it will be looked upon with
some apprehension, not only by the assemblies of the states, but by the
people themselves. Furthermore, the whole business of government in a
democracy relies on good faith and political responsiveness on the part
of those designated for administrative and legislative positions. . . ."[21]

The negotiators felt they had devised a workable procedure—a view
that was not shared by the Ohio River Committee, which was appointed
several years later by the President of the United States to make recommendations on interstate pollution control. (The activities of this committee are detailed in the following chapter.) In its report made in 1943,
five years before the compact was signed by all of the states, the President's committee made the following observation about the enforcement

21. *Proceedings,* Fifth Conference, *op. cit.,* p. 31.

clause: "It is obvious that under this compact any municipality, corporation, person or entity in any one State can block action of the Commission within that State if it controls a majority of the commissioners (2 out of 3 as now proposed) from the State in which the municipality, corporation, person or entity resides or conducts its business."[22]

The pessimism of the Ohio River Committee proved groundless. The record since 1948 shows that in all cases where the Commission exercised enforcement action it was with the unanimous concurrence of the three commissioners of the states involved.

A more sanguine assessment of the compact's enforcement provision was displayed by Willard Cowles, professor of law at the University of Nebraska, in a seminar paper presented before the Academy of International Law at The Hague, Netherlands, in 1949. He cited the Ohio River Valley Water Sanitation Compact as having been "born with perhaps the strongest teeth of any American interstate organization, indeed stronger than any international organization." And he predicted that "the Commission's power to invoke the strong sanction of enforcement is the best guarantee that only rarely will it have to exercise it." Later events established the validity of this prophecy, as will be described in Chapter 10.

What Happened to Tennessee

Tennessee, though one of the parties named in the 1936 grant of consent from the Congress[23] to negotiate the interstate agreement, played no active role during the drafting of the compact. Nor was it prepared to become a signatory when the document was executed on June 30, 1948.

Representatives from Tennessee attended only two of the six meetings of the negotiating committee,[24] and then primarily as observers. Nothing further transpired until early in March, 1948, when Hudson Biery wrote to Governor James N. McCord to inform him that approval of the compact by Virginia had cleared the path for eight states to effectuate the agreement. He said these states would warmly welcome participation of Tennessee, particularly since it was one of the original group receiving Congressional assent for this purpose.

22. See House Doc. No. 266, *op. cit.,* p. 51. When negotiators of the compact were made aware of this comment some of them considered it to be a naive assumption that any group or individual could control a majority of the commissioners in a state.

23. Public Res. 104, 74th Cong., 2nd Sess., approved June 8, 1936.

24. The Third Conference on May 24, 1938, and the Fifth Conference on October 11, 1938.

Governor McCord replied that he was referring the matter to his state Stream Pollution Control Board for study and recommendations, and if it appeared that Tennessee "will benefit by such ratification or that we may be in a position to materially assist a neighbor, consideration may be given to referring the question to our next General Assembly, which will meet in January 1949."[25]

Conditions placed on entry. Apparently the Tennessee Pollution Control Board did find merit in joining the compact because in February, 1949, the legislature authorized the governor to "execute any and all agreements necessary to enable this State to become a member. . . ."[26] However, exercise of this broad authority was conditioned by three limitations, namely, (1) that Alabama and North Carolina also become signatories to the compact; (2) that the governor retain the prerogative "to determine if and when it shall be for the best interest of the State of Tennessee to withdraw from said compact if permitted by its terms;" and (3) that the contribution of Tennessee not exceed $10,000 annually.

These reservations were disturbing to Chairman Biery who, in the months preceding enactment of the Tennessee bill, had endeavored to guide its sponsors. Among other things he had sounded out Alabama, and, discovering there was little favorable sentiment in that state to becoming a party, he had urged Tennessee to omit any reference to Alabama. With respect to North Carolina he had reason to be more sanguine.

Concerning appropriations, he had informed Tennessee that it was using an erroneous calculation of pro rata distribution in figuring the Tennessee share to be $10,100 based on a then proposed $100,000 budget. The amount should have been $15,000. However, Mr. Biery pointed out the enabling legislation should not be tied to a specific amount because the budget might change as time went on and the compact did require each state to assume its proportionate share.[27]

The provision for withdrawal from the compact was added by the legislature, and had not been anticipated by the sponsors. When the Tennessee bill was presented to the ORSANCO commissioners in 1949 they asked for legal advice from Mr. Weakley. Here is what he said:[28]

25. Letter of March 24, 1948, from Governor McCord to Hudson Biery, chairman, Ohio Valley Compact Negotiating Committee.

26. Tennessee Public Acts of 1949, Chapter No. 27. Passed February 16, 1949; approved by Governor Gordon Browning, February 18, 1949.

27. Letter to R. P. Farrell, Director, Tennessee Division of Sanitary Engineering from Hudson Biery, December 2, 1948.

28. ORSANCO, minutes of meeting, April 6, 1949, p. 29 (bound vol., p. 243).

Since the compact itself contains no language whatever that permits a withdrawal or re-entry, it seems to me that whole section is meaningless. We gather from what we have heard that perhaps that section was put in to satisfy the people in the state or legislature who may have been objecting to the entry of Tennessee into the compact. But as I read the section it is made meaningless by the language 'if the compact permits it by its terms'. . . . In view of the fact that it would be extremely desirable to have Tennessee join into the compact, it seems to me that it would be unwise to raise any serious objections to the entry of Tennessee with that particular language in the act of acceptance. I see no reason why we should go back to Tennessee and ask them to amend the act by having that withdrawn.

However, another provision is a little bit more difficult. . . . The State of Tennessee is authorized to make contributions to the Commission in sums not to exceed $10,000 per annum. That places a ceiling upon the amount of money that the State of Tennessee may contribute. The language of the compact is drawn in such a fashion that any member State assumes the obligation of contributing a sum which is determined upon a formula that is set out in the compact, and even though the dollars and cents difference may not be great in amount, I question very seriously whether the authorization of the Tennessee act is really an authorization of the compact, since it deviates in a material sense from the compact. However, the basic intent of the Tennessee legislation was one of adopting the compact and accepting it as the law of Tennessee. So you have the peculiar situation of the legislature accepting the terms of the compact as it stands—which inferentially is acceptance of the financial contribution formula in the compact itself—and at the same time they turn around and set a limitation upon the ability of the State of Tennessee to contribute to the finances of the compact. There seems to be a very definite conflict in the legislation itself.

Debate on state appropriations. Mr. Weakley's views on the exercise of a state limitation on financial contributions were not convincing to at least one commissioner, Henry Ward, who had served in both houses of the Kentucky Legislature. This early difference in viewpoint is worth recording because it later became a matter at issue with the State of West Virginia that claimed the attention of the Supreme Court of the United States.[29]

The following is a partial transcript of the colloquy that ensued:[30]

Mr. Ward: It may be of interest to investigate the law of Kentucky. We are in exactly the same shape. The General Assembly of Kentucky each biennium makes an appropriation. There is no such thing as some-

29. *State of West Virginia* ex rel. *Dyer* v. *Sims* (1950) 341 U.S. 22, 95 L. Ed. 713. Details are given in Chapter 18.
30. ORSANCO, minutes of meeting, April 6, 1949, p. 31 (bound vol., 243).

one determining that Kentucky can pay fifteen thousand or twenty-five thousand and so forth. The way we are doing it now is the legislature appropriates money to the Governor's emergency fund and he has the decision to decide how that shall be spent and we are getting our part out of the Governor's emergency fund, but in the future there must be a specific appropriation by the legislature.

Mr. Weakley: The difficulty here is that the legislature of Tennessee has attempted to write an amendment into the Compact by placing a limitation upon any contribution that the State of Tennessee must be making.

Chairman Biery (Ohio): The adoption of the Compact itself by the legislature of Kentucky was not so conditioned. It was without any reservation whatever. It was the only State that did enact it exactly right.

Mr. Ward: Don't think the Kentucky General Assembly is going to vote an unlimited amount of money.

Mr. Weakley: That isn't the question, Senator. I appreciate the point you are making. No legislature can commit the funds of the State beyond the period of the biennium, but that is a different problem from this particular provision that is in the Tennessee Act, by which they purport to adopt the Compact but then write into the Compact a separate provision of its own, limiting for all time, in effect, the amount.

Mr. Ward: I think you are worrying about something that isn't important and that you are going to cause trouble if you raise a question about these limitations, because I can well understand why they wrote it in there.

Chairman Biery: They haven't accepted the Compact as the other eight States have. All the other States have agreed to enact such provisions as the Compact calls for.

Mr. Ward: That didn't mean a thing in the world. Kentucky agreed in 1940 and it wasn't until 1948 that any money was made available and if the Governor in 1948 hadn't been cooperative the mere fact that the legislature of 1940 approved it wouldn't have meant a thing in the world.

Chairman Biery: We are somewhat convinced that we haven't anything to worry about with Kentucky.

Mr. Ward: I wouldn't say that at all. No one can tell you what the fiftieth session of the Kentucky legislature is going to do. The point I think important is you don't want to create the impression you are not going to permit a legislature to put a limit on how much the State can spend.

Chairman Biery: Any State could refuse to appropriate any money if it felt it didn't want to go ahead with its obligations under the Compact.

Mr. Ward: And that, incidentally, would be a very effective withdrawal from the Compact.

Chairman Biery: It would be an embarrassment but it wouldn't necessarily destroy the Compact.

This exchange of views ended with a motion by the Commission that further consultation be held with Tennessee looking toward amendment of the enabling legislation. The discussions did not prove fruitful and at the meeting on July 6, 1949, the commissioners decided that the appropriate next move would be to invite the governors of Tennessee, North Carolina, and Alabama to send observers to meetings of ORSANCO. It was hoped that this opportunity to become acquainted with the work of the Commission would reveal the merits of participation in the compact.

For the next year or so a representative from Tennessee and one from North Carolina occasionally attended meetings. In the spring of 1952,[31] the North Carolina representative informed the commissioners that he would no longer participate because "the unstudied opinion" of the Attorney General's office was that the North Carolina constitution would not permit the state to join in the compact. However, he added that this question would be given more careful study.

Meantime, the Governor of Tennessee had created a stream pollution study commission. In July, 1950, it made a report, which stated, among other things: "As Kentucky and Virginia are already compact [Ohio River Valley Water Sanitation Compact] members and water from these states drains into Tennessee, there is much to be gained from Tennessee participating, with or without the joint approval of North Carolina and Alabama. It is recommended, therefore, that Tennessee reconsider the 1949 action and join the compact as an individual state."[32]

It was also recommended that, since Tennessee constitutes 60 per cent of the area in the Tennessee River Basin, the state should take the lead in forming a Tennessee River Basin Compact. The report put it in these words: "Even though all the states in the Tennessee River Basin are eligible for the Ohio Valley Compact, it is believed that these states operating under a separate compact could work out more efficiently the specific problems of the Tennessee River Basin as a separate entity rather than functioning as a subordinate member of the Ohio Valley Compact."

After two years had passed the Tennessee representative informed the Commission that the state Stream Pollution Control Board concluded that since neither Alabama nor North Carolina had indicated interest in join-

31. Letter to author, from Fred V. Doutt, governor's representative from North Carolina, April 24, 1952.
32. Summary and Conclusions from the Report of the Stream Pollution Study Commission, State of Tennessee to Governor Gordon Browning, July 1, 1950, prepared by Lincoln Caffall, Wainwright, Ramsey, and Lancaster, New York, New York.

ing the Ohio River Valley Compact, "that possibly we would be better off to form a Tennessee River Basin Compact."[33]

By this time ORSANCO was deeply involved with public hearings, promulgation of regulations, and other matters related to the control of pollution in the district already embraced by the compact. Further, the commissioners concluded that for the time being the least of their concerns was the Tennessee River; not only did it enter the Ohio River far downstream, but at this point it offered no significant interstate pollution problem on the Ohio itself.

It should be noted that the Tennessee River flows from Tennessee through part of Kentucky before it enters the Ohio River. And so does the Cumberland River, another major tributary to the Ohio. But whatever pollution these streams carried as they crossed the state line appears to have been of no apparent nor immediate concern to Kentucky. Consequently, there was no pressure from this state for ORSANCO to urge Tennessee to participate in the compact.

Those most closely identified with pollution-control administration in Tennessee have continued in the view that there was probably much to be gained in being part of an interstate compact "family." Although circumstances conspired to deny participation in the ORSANCO group, Tennessee did succeed in negotiating a Tennessee River Basin Water Pollution Control Compact. Eligible to join with it are Kentucky, Mississippi, Alabama, Georgia, North Carolina, and Virginia. In March, 1963, Kentucky and Mississippi formally enacted the compact along with Tennessee. As of this writing, none of the other states had taken such action nor has the compact become operative.

33. Letter to Hudson Biery from R. P. Farrell, Director, Tennessee Division of Sanitary Engineering, dated June 9, 1952.

7

Diagnosis and Therapy

for a Sick River

In the period between submission of the compact to the states and its adoption, an event took place that made it possible for ORSANCO, once established, to make an immediate start on an action program. This was the publication in 1943 of a 1,368-page, three-volume pollution control survey by the Ohio River Committee.[1] This federal committee conducted one of the most thorough investigations ever made of water pollution in a major river basin. A staff of about one hundred spent three years in field studies, and the resulting report was much more than an assemblage of facts. It also diagnosed the ills and prescribed the kinds of therapy—technical, financial, and administrative—that might be employed to deal with the situation.

Origin of the Ohio River Committee Survey

As with many other aspects of the Ohio Valley crusade for clean streams, the impetus for the survey may be traced to the Cincinnati Chamber of Commerce Committee on Stream Pollution. Early in its deliberations the committee conceived the need for a general plan as a prerequisite to basinwide action. That the federal government might be enlisted in such an undertaking first became apparent when the Cincinnatians learned in the autumn of 1935 that the President's National Resources Board was thinking about subsidizing a river "demonstration project."

One of the members of the NRB advisory committee on water pollution, which was charged with drafting recommendations on national policy, made a speech in the Ohio Valley[2] in October, 1935, wherein he

1. Report of the Ohio River Committee, authorized in Section 5 of the Rivers and Harbors Act, which was approved August 26, 1937. Published as House Doc. No. 266, 78th Cong., 1st Sess., August 27, 1943.
2. Statement of R. E. Tarbett, U.S. Public Health Service, in *Proceedings*, Ohio Valley Improvement Association, October 15–16, 1935.

disclosed that: "While the formation of interstate compacts aided by the federal government has not been attempted, [the advisory committee] felt that this was the most promising method. However, before any definite plan of procedure is adopted . . . the committee is of the opinion that a demonstration area should be established where studies in *administration* [italics added] may be made and which can furnish the training ground for personnel. Any drainage area which might be taken for this demonstration study should be relatively small in area, should not involve the expenditure of too great an amount of money, should have a drainage area in at least two states, and should have problems common to all streams . . ."[3] He said that the area that the committee was prepared to recommend was the Potomac River watershed.

Here was a development that not only encompassed but went beyond what the Cincinnati group had believed to be possible at that time. The committee jumped into action, and sent a document to Secretary of the Interior, Harold Ickes, detailing a formidable array of reasons why the Ohio Valley should be chosen as the demonstration area. This document was also circulated among the governors, U. S. senators and congressmen, chambers of commerce, and newspapers in the valley with an appeal that they aid in pressing the Ohio Valley claim for priority. Secretary Ickes occupied a strategic position. Not only was he chairman of the National Resources Board, but as head of the Public Works Administration he was also overseer of the allocation of federal grants for financing projects.

It might be added that Secretary Ickes previously had been approached by the Cincinnati group on the prospects of providing federal aid in cleaning up the Ohio River. At that time he pointed out that funds from the pump-priming activities of PWA could be made available to a municipality or regional authority only on a matching basis—with the federal government advancing 45 per cent if the local or regional body provided 55 per cent of the cost of projects. Since there was no legally constituted regional agency in the Ohio Valley to finance its share of a pollution-control program, Mr. Ickes had offered this two-part suggestion: develop a compact among the states to provide the legislative basis for joint action on interstate streams; and establish an authority or agency composed of municipalities on the Ohio River, with taxing power to make assessments

3. Thirty years later, in a February 23, 1966, message of the President of the United States on conservation and pollution, a similar proposal was made. The President called for a "Clean Rivers Demonstration Project," to foster experimentation with new organizations to unify pollution-control activities in single river basins. This is discussed more fully in Chapter 22. See *New York Times*, February 24, 1966, for a transcript of the President's message.

based on general benefits to the area. Possessing such authority, the agency could issue revenue bonds and thus satisfy the requirements of meeting 55 per cent of the cost of municipal treatment works, which would make the agency eligible to request the balance from federal PWA funds.[4]

While this suggestion dashed hopes for obtaining immediate federal aid, it did fortify the notion that, regardless of what the future might hold, the requisite for a regional cleanup campaign was a formal agreement that would unite the affected states in a common effort.

It is to be wondered, however, why the second part of the suggestion—establishment of an authority to plan, finance, and construct sewage-treatment facilities—received no further attention. Yet, here was a practical institutional arrangement that could have been employed to facilitate installation of treatment works throughout the valley.

But coming back to the proposal that the federal government might subsidize the cleanup of an entire valley as a "demonstration project," there is this to add: despite intensive drum-beating for the proposal, which included resolutions from scores of groups in the Ohio Valley,[5] visits to Secretary Ickes by governors of the states and the support of Congressmen, the demonstration-project proposal died aborning. Obviously it was too ambitious a scheme at that time, both politically and financially, even for the smaller Potomac Basin where the estimated price tag for stream cleanup was $15 million. For the Ohio Valley at that time, the cost was estimated at $200 million.

The National Resources Board dropped the "demonstration" idea and turned to a program of setting up regional committees to promote the conduct of studies and recommendations for basinwide planning on a variety of matters, including pollution control. One of these was the Ohio Valley Regional Planning Board, which was organized in December, 1935, with representatives from five states—Pennsylvania, Ohio,

4. *Cincinnati Enquirer,* July 13, 1935.
5. The resolution adopted in November, 1935, by the Ohio Chamber of Commerce (see *Cincinnati Enquirer,* November 9, 1935), which was already on record as opposed to any federal control, was interesting. It said: "We favor continuation of the efficient supervision by the State Department of Health in the problem of correcting pollution of Ohio streams, and we oppose any form of regulation that would menace or unreasonably burden the state's industries. We urge the board of directors and the executive officers of the Chamber to support the general effort now being made to interest the federal government in establishing its demonstration unit for stream purification on the Ohio River. We urge the State of Ohio to cooperate with adjoining states in an effort to solve these features of pollution that are of an interstate character."

West Virginia, Indiana, and Kentucky. Its object was to stimulate co-operation among the states and the federal government in planning.

Disturbed by the possibility that establishment of this new planning committee might lessen the zeal of those in the Ohio Valley already primed for an action program, the *Cincinnati Enquirer* editorialized on December 7, 1935, as follows:

> . . . The Ohio River Valley Regional Planning Board . . . will be only a planning body, with advisory powers and nothing more. There is nothing in this new agency to insure action. There are but few men in it able to press for decisive action on the part of cities and states. It is essentially a group of experts in the field of public planning whose services are very useful but strictly limited.

> . . . The great need of the Ohio Valley is yet to be supplied. If we are to see a vigorous and intelligent attack on the problem of river pollu-tion, we shall require a river authority, with positive governmental powers, created either by interstate compact or by act of Congress alone. Such an agency would be a unit of government, with well de-fined power, able to require the construction of sewage-disposal plants, competent to issue orders to stop the pollution of streams, in pursuance of state and federal laws. . . .

The Cincinnati committee now centered its attention on one of the elements of the original NRB demonstration proposal—the conduct of a basinwide survey of pollution. The outcome was that under the sponsor-ship of Representative Brent Spence, of Kentucky, a rider was attached to the 1937 Rivers and Harbors Omnibus Bill. This rider directed the Secretary of War to make a report on pollution in the Ohio Basin and appropriated $600,000 for the purpose.[6]

6. As approved August 26, 1937, Section 5 of the Rivers and Harbors Act, read as follows: "That the Secretary of War is here and now authorized and directed to cause a survey to be made of the Ohio River and its tributaries to ascertain what pollutive substances are being deposited, directly, or indirectly, therein and the sources and extent of such deposits, and with a view to determining the most feasible method of correcting and eliminating the pollution of these streams.

"The survey herein authorized shall include comprehensive investigations and studies of the various problems relating to stream pollution and its prevention and abatement. In making these investigations and studies, and in the development and formulation of corrective plans, the Secretary of War may, with the approval of the Secretary of the Treasury, secure the cooperation and assistance of the Public Health Service, and may allot funds from the appropriation hereinafter designated to pay for such cooperation and assistance. The survey shall be com-pleted as soon as practicable after the passage of this act, and the Secretary of War shall report the results thereof to the Congress, together with such recom-mendations for remedial legislation as he deems advisable.

"The cost of the survey and such incidental expenses as may be necessary in connection therewith, shall be paid from appropriations heretofore or hereinafter made for examinations, surveys and contingencies of rivers and harbors."

The Cincinnati Stream Pollution Committee was jubilant when this rider was accepted in the passage of the general appropriation bill in 1937. One of the committee's basic aims was to garner help in having a survey made of conditions in the valley so that if a compact agency came into existence it might be spared the time-consuming and expensive task of assembling factual information for reference and as a basis for action. The committee had already learned that the states had no records that were adequate for this purpose.

The National Resources Board was likewise pleased with this development because it felt that such a survey properly conducted could focus on the regional aspects of pollution control and thus in part, at least, "demonstrate" what needed to be done.

When President Roosevelt signed the Rivers and Harbors bill, he was apparently not unfamiliar with the sentiments of his National Resources Board. He requested the Secretary of War and the Secretary of the Treasury (who had jurisdiction at that time over affairs of the Public Health Service) to jointly name a three-man "Ohio River Committee" to supervise the survey.

The members chosen were Brigadier General Max C. Tyler (later replaced by Major General Thomas M. Robins, assistant chief of engineers) to represent the Corps; Sanitary-Engineer Director Ralph E. Tarbett to represent the Public Health Service; and Abel Wolman, consulting engineer of Baltimore, to represent interests outside the federal government. At that time Dr. Wolman was chairman of the NRB Advisory Committee on Water Pollution, and Mr. Tarbett was a member of that committee. Thus, a basic interest of the NRB Committee in developing information on a river basin was nicely dovetailed into the Ohio Valley study.[7]

The task given to the Public Health Service was to determine the magnitude and characteristics of major sources of pollution, to measure the effects of pollution on receiving waters, to outline procedures for abatement by treatment, low-flow augmentation, or other means that might be economically justified, and to prepare a comprehensive program for correction, including estimates of cost. Assigned to the Corps of Engineers was the responsibility for hydrometric surveys (river discharge and velocity measurements).

7. This was not the only instance wherein the NRB played a role in advancing the Ohio Valley program. It had a regional office in Cincinnati to promote interstate and intercity co-operation on public-works planning, the operations of which were directed by Alfred Bettman, a Cincinnati lawyer and city planner. Mr. Bettman proved to be one of the active collaborators in drafting the Ohio Valley interstate compact.

Earlier pollution studies on the Ohio River by the Stream Investigations Station of the U. S. Public Health Service (established at Cincinnati in 1913) were primarily of scientific interest, but they did establish the basic principles for quantitative assessment of the characteristics of natural self-purification in streams and the behavior of rivers under varying conditions of pollution and flow regimen.[8] Personnel trained at the Cincinnati station were made available to conduct the Ohio Basin study. They included H. R. Crohurst, J. K. Hoskins, and H. W. Streeter, who were also advisory members of the Cincinnati Chamber of Commerce Stream Pollution Committee, and whose contributions to sanitary-engineering had long attracted international attention. The task of compiling and editing the report was assigned to Maurice LeBosquet, who later became a sanitary-engineer director of the Public Health Service and is now retired. Edgar W. Landenberger, now chief of the basin planning and formulations branch of the Corps of Engineers, compiled the summary of findings and recommendations of the committee.

The Ohio River Committee survey can be regarded as one of the classic water pollution inquiries. Its geographical focus may be gauged from knowledge of the drainage area it encompassed, which was some 204,000 square miles. Of the six major divisions of the Mississippi River watershed, only the Missouri River Basin is larger. The northeast-southwest axis of the Ohio Basin is 800 miles extending from the Mississippi River to New York State; the shorter axis at right angles to this is 500 miles in length reaching from Georgia to Indiana. The entire basin contains about 7 per cent of the area of the United States, and includes portions of fourteen states, namely, Alabama, Georgia, Illinois, Indiana, Kentucky, Maryland, Mississippi, New York, North Carolina, Ohio, Pennsylvania, Tennessee, Virginia, and West Virginia. (The district embraced by the compact includes only eight of these states: Illinois, Indiana, Kentucky, New York, Ohio, Pennsylvania, Virginia, and West Virginia with a total area of 5 per cent of the United States.)

---

8. These studies included the following (now out of print): W. C. Purdy, "The Plankton and Related Organisms," *Public Health Bulletin No. 131* (December 1922); Frost, Hoskins, Tarbett, and Streeter, "Report on Surveys and Laboratory Studies," *Public Health Bulletin No. 143* (July 1924); H. W. Streeter and E. B. Phelps, "Factors Concerned in the Phenomena of Oxidation and Re-aeration," *Public Health Bulletin No. 146* (February 1925); and H. R. Crohurst, "A Resurvey of the Ohio River Between Cincinnati, Ohio, and Louisville, Ky., Including a Discussion of the Effects of Canalization and Changes in Sanitary Conditions since 1914–16," *Public Health Bulletin No. 204* (May 1933).

Some Major Findings

During the survey, information was assembled from 3,700 munici-palities and 1,800 industries. Laboratory analyses were performed on 71,000 river samples collected from 2,000 points, and this required 131,000 individual determinations.

The population of the eight states eventually embraced by the com-pact district was close to 15,200,000. Of this number, some 7,830,000 people lived in sewered areas.[9] However, only one-third of the sewered population was provided with treatment facilities. Subsequent inquiry revealed that less than one per cent of those living along the banks of the Ohio River were provided with treatment facilities.

With respect to industrial-waste discharges, the pollution load from establishments in the eight states of the compact district had a "popula-tion equivalent" of nearly 8,500,000, which represented an organic load greater than that from domestic sources. The three largest contributors of organic wastes were the chemical, the paper, and the distillery indus-tries with population equivalents of 1,180,000, 1,659,000, and 1,000,-000 respectively.[10]

Severe pollution from acid mine-drainage was said to be a compara-tively recent problem, the magnitude of which was increasing in pro-portion to the cumulative tonnage of coal extracted. It was estimated that the equivalent of some 1,800,000 tons of acid annually (calcium carbonate equivalent), was reaching the streams from abandoned and active mining operations.[11] The acid load was expected to increase unless corrective measures were undertaken because less than 5 per cent of the coal resources of the basin had thus far been mined. The measurable annual damages from corrosion and increased hardness to water supplies caused by the mine acid was calculated to be $2 million for the upper Ohio Valley and $3 million for the entire basin.

9. The population is derived from House Doc. No. 266, *op. cit.,* Table 2, p. 11, by subtracting from the total population (18,816,000) the population on the Cumberland and Tennessee basins (3,620,000). The sewered population is derived from Table 1 of a presentation made by Maurice LeBosquet, Jr., to the delegates of the Ohio River Valley Water Sanitation Compact on December 7, 1944. Here the sewered population for the entire basin is given as 8,561,000; from this figure has been subtracted 730,000, which is the sewered population of Tennessee, North Carolina, Alabama, Georgia, Maryland, and Mississippi.

10. The "population equivalent" figure is derived from House Doc. No. 266, *op. cit.,* Table 5, p. 22, which shows that the industrial load from all the states in the basin was 9,974,000. Subtracted from this is the load from Alabama, Georgia, North Carolina, and Tennessee, which totaled 1,522,000. No industrial-load data were given for Maryland or Mississippi.

11. House Doc. No. 266, *op. cit.,* p. 23.

Concerning low-flow regulation, the report stated that reservoirs already built and those under construction would produce an increase in minimum flows of 220 per cent at the head of the Ohio River and up to 140 per cent at Cincinnati, the midpoint. Releases of water from reservoirs during periods of low river flow were considered in many cases to be an effective adjunct of sewage treatment and, in connection with construction of flood-control reservoirs, conducive to efficient use of water resources.

Recommended Objectives for Pollution Control

In its final report the Ohio River Committee did not confine itself to an evaluation of the technical findings, which by itself would have represented a substantial achievement. Under the leadership of its chairman, Abel Wolman, the committee concerned itself also with the administrative, political, and financial aspects of pollution-control, along with recommendations for a program of action. In brief, the report constituted a treatise on the fundamentals of water-quality management. The following points made in the report are illustrative of its scope.[12]

> The aim of public authorities charged with pollution-control programs should be to insure conditions that will permit the best social and economic use of the nation's water courses. In determining best use, however, public opinion must be considered.
>
> Because of physical and economic considerations complete elimination of wastes from streams is a manifest impossibility. Curtailment of the disposal of wastes by dilution would result in a needless sacrifice of the self-purification capacity of streams, which capacity is itself a valuable resource. The most effective social and economic use of public waters would not accrue if vital domestic and industrial activities were unduly curtailed by arbitrarily restricting the waste-disposal function of streams for the benefit of desirable uses, such as recreation.
>
> However, while use of streams for disposal of wastes has become an important factor in the economic existence of the people, it is unlikely that the public welfare has been best served in the Ohio River Basin when numerous sources of public water supply are dangerously polluted, important tangible damages to other vital water uses can be demonstrated, and aquatic recreational facilities, specifically bathing and fishing, have been virtually destroyed for mass enjoyment.
>
> Use of the streams of the basin for waste disposal has progressed to a point where the propriety of using them for water sports has disappeared.
>
> The conclusion seems inescapable that irresponsible dumping of wastes, which has been the rule in the past and continues to be in

12. *Ibid.*, pp. 45–47.

many sections of the basin, has not resulted in the most effective use of the public waters of the Ohio River Valley, and does not accurately reflect present public opinion or desire in the matter of pollution control.

In view of these facts, it appears that higher standards of stream quality should be maintained. The most nearly applicable set of standards for a specific stream reach must be established in light of the uses of the reach, each use being weighted with consideration for its relative importance to public welfare. Since streams can assimilate a certain amount of pollution without undue adverse effects on their established or desired use, the program for improvement should contemplate the removal of only that part of pollutive substances which the streams cannot assimilate.

The limiting minimum water-quality characteristics set forth below should be considered a desirable goal in localities where the maintenance of these standards will be of benefit to present and probable future water uses:

Coliform bacteria (per milliliter)—Not over 200 in more than 5 per cent of samples; monthly average not over 200.

Dissolved oxygen (parts per million)—Monthly average not less than 5; daily average not less than 3.0. In limited zones a minimum of 4 would be acceptable.

Biochemical oxygen demand (five-day value at 20 degrees C. in parts per million)—Monthly average not over 5.0.

pH value—Not less than 4.0 and not more than 9.5

Phenol content (parts per billion)—Not over 10.0.

Where present conditions were such that a reasonable degree of pollution control would make recreational use of streams available to large centers of population, it was recommended that these standards should be raised.

The Ohio River Committee than summarized its position as follows: "The objective of a pollution-control program should be the regulation of waste disposal into public waters, such that standards of water quality may be maintained which are commensurate with stream use in specific localities, to the end that the greatest possible yield of public benefits will accrue."

Difficulties to be Overcome

Pointing out that the difficulties hampering pollution abatement are technical, financial and administrative, the Ohio River Committee addressed itself to each of these components in turn:

Technical difficulties. Problems of a technical nature are associated mainly with industrial-waste control. These arise because there are no known satisfactory methods of treatment for some wastes and because others, including acid mine-drainage, require complex treatment; or the methods must be so extensive as to render control extremely tedious and frequently only partially effective. However, most wastes including both domestic and industrial, are amenable to treatment by well-established and not unduly expensive methods. Designation of a governmental agency to act as a clearinghouse for information on treatment methods and to conduct research would help to effect an early solution of remaining technical problems.

Difficulties also result because of practical and economic limitations on the degree of control that can be applied in specific cases. Many pollution damages and the benefits from abatement are not susceptible to evaluation and, as a result, a satisfactory comparison between the cost of abatement works and anticipated benefits cannot be set forth.

However, such difficulties were not considered unusual, and it was pointed out that in the United States they are customarily met by providing, as equitably as possible, an opportunity for all persons concerned to express their views by direct vote or by public presentation of supporting information. It appeared to the committee that this aspect of the problem must find its solution in administrative arrangements that would permit the public to choose between using certain streams for controlled waste disposal or curtailing activities.

Financial difficulties. Financing problems stem basically from the fact that the readily evaluated benefits of pollution control are generally but a small part of the cost. Furthermore, those who might reasonably be expected to bear the cost of control are usually not the recipients of the benefits realized. For example, it is the downstream user who benefits if the upstream plant or municipality treats its waste before discharging it into the stream. Conversely, it is the downstream user who bears the cost if the upstream user does not treat the water.

Under these conditions, polluters have no economic incentive to solve their own problems, and it is difficult for those damaged by pollution to obtain relief. Damages usually are difficult to evaluate and prove. And the courts have recognized that a well-established community or industry is favorable to the public welfare, even though it may be a gross polluter. The result, more often than not, is that such polluters are not disturbed, or they are required to pay only relatively small damages, neither of which alternative accomplishes pollution abatement.

The committee did not regard statutory limitations on the bonding and taxing power of many communities as a basic difficulty. This matter could be taken care of when the public felt it had an incentive to control pollution.

Several considerations underlying the problem of equitably distributing the cost of pollution-control works were cited. For example, where it is contended that industries exist only in response to public demand for their products, it might be concluded the public is indirectly responsible for all pollution, both industrial and domestic, and ultimately should bear the cost of abatement, either by direct expenditures or by a combination of direct expenditures and higher prices for industrial products.

It was observed in the report that, had the beginnings of waste disposal and its regulation been concurrent, each polluter would probably have borne the burden of compliance and a thoroughly equitable distribution of costs would have resulted. From this it might be concluded that an equitable distribution of costs would result if each polluter were now made to stand the full cost of correcting his own waste discharges. However, this was not regarded as entirely true. A reversal of public waste-disposal policy at this late date would work a hardship on communities and industries that had established their location without regard to ease of waste-disposal correction.

The committee felt that no useful purpose was served by arbitrarily declaring that a riparian owner has a right to clean streams above all else, and that others must therefore pay to make them clean. If there has been any benefit to the nation as a result of the unregulated discharge of wastes, it has been in the form of aid to national expansion, and this would benefit all, including riparian owners. On the other hand, where damages occur as a result of pollution, a policy that permits irresponsible waste discharge is of economic benefit to polluters in an amount at least equal to the cost of providing a minimum of treatment. The committee said it was logical to conclude that an equitable distribution of abatement costs should contemplate their division between the polluter (who has a definite responsibility in this connection) and the beneficiaries of the improvements. The present status could be recognized as a starting point, and the financial burdens could be apportioned equitably between these entities in proportion to their responsibilities and requirements. The lack of a provable economic basis for providing abatement works was not considered to be a serious obstacle, provided costs were apportioned among several entities and not charged to only one.

Governmental financial aid could be expected to hasten completion of a comprehensive program for the Ohio River Basin. However, there were no components in such a program, with the possible exception of mine sealing and supplemental low-flow control, which could not be accomplished without governmental aid, providing public demand supported such accomplishments.

Administrative difficulties. Because of the interstate character of many pollution problems in the Ohio River Basin, the most challenging aspect of executing a remedial program was that of devising an appropriate administrative unit for regional co-ordination and for promoting more effective application of state laws. While many states had laws intended to regulate pollution, they have had varying but not outstanding success. Cases of ineffectiveness in state control were ascribed partly to lack of public demand for clean streams and lack of public willingness to bear the cost of regulation.

Administrative difficulties inherent in interstate pollution had been recognized by many states, some of which had entered into compacts or agreements. The committee regarded these arrangements as of doubtful efficacy because they, too, had to contend with public indifference and difficulties associated with securing compliance with regulations. The Ohio River Committee was pessimistic about the effectiveness of Article IX of the Ohio Valley Compact dealing with enforcement powers, as detailed in Chapter 6. It concluded that "The possibility of solving Ohio River pollution problems by the present interstate compact does not appear good."

Recommended Improvement Program

The remedial measures recommended by the committee were based on the premise that every damaging source of pollution is now susceptible to some degree of abatement. Findings from the survey led to these conclusions:

> Improvement measures should contemplate the initial construction of primary sewage-treatment plants at all significant sources of pollution from domestic wastes where the quality of water downstream therefrom is adverse to the safe and established use of the stream as a source of water supply;
> Contributors of industrial wastes located in close proximity to the significant sources of domestic waste pollution should concurrently provide approximately equivalent treatment to their wastes; and
> If the inhabitants of the basin as a whole are to secure maximum available benefits for a given expenditure, the program should contemplate: (a) Construction of secondary facilities to improve the degree of treatment at some sources of pollution; (b) construction of secondary facilities at many existing plants; (c) construction of new primary and secondary treatment plants at many other locations and

(d) construction of industrial waste-treatment facilities throughout the basin giving a degree of treatment approximately equal to that provided in nearby community plants.

Control of pollution by acid mine-drainage calls for continuance of the sealing program started under auspices of the federal emergency work-relief program in the late thirties. To prevent future sources of acid discharge, state mining laws should be correlated to the end that mining procedures be adopted that would be favorable to sealing operations.

Low-flow regulation of streams might be satisfactorily and most economically accomplished as an incidental feature of the operation of reservoirs provided primarily for other purposes, such as flood control and the production of hydroelectric energy. Under such circumstances, the low-flow improvement could be obtained at comparatively slight cost. Provision of reservoir capacity for the sole purpose of flow regulation was not considered economically feasible at this time.

On the basis of 1942 prices it was estimated that the total cost for pollution abatement in accordance with the recommended program would be $179 million for the basin as a whole (fourteen states): $75 million for municipal treatment works, $85 million for municipal interceptor sewers, $13.5 million for independent industrial waste-treatment works, and $5.5 million for mine-drainage control. These estimates were said to reflect recent cost experience in the eastern United States.[13]

Conclusions of the Ohio River Committee

In summarizing its views, the Ohio River Committee concluded that practically all streams in the Ohio River Basin were polluted by domestic and industrial wastes and that some had severe corrosive characteristics imparted to them by acid mine-drainage. The degree of pollution was described as varying from gross nuisance conditions with menace to life and health to conditions adverse to special uses of the stream such as swimming. Pollution in the Ohio River alone had reached the point where thirty sources of public water supply, serving about 1,660,000 people, were endangered. Pollution in a number of tributaries was at least as severe as in the worst reaches on the main-stem river.

It was conceded that the federal government had a decided interest in the protection of public health and in wildlife conservation, as well as in the protection and development of commerce and navigation, but it was

13. When the program actually reached the construction stage in the mid-1950's, prices had risen considerably. Two comparisons provide a vivid illustration. The Pittsburgh metropolitan area facilities were estimated in the report to cost $36 million; the actual amount was $100 million. For Cincinnati the estimate in 1942 was $19 million; the cost of the works that were ultimately built represented an investment of almost $70 million.

not considered advisable for the federal government to take action toward
the enforcement of pollution control unless all state and interstate action
failed to secure desired results. The proposed Ohio River Valley Water
Sanitation Compact, if modified and vitalized, would provide an improved
means for uniform control of all pollution that was interstate in its effect.
Individual states co-operating with the compact commission should be
able to achieve effective control of intrastate pollution.

Because the principal obstacle to pollution abatement was the financing
of facilities, the committee felt that active support on the part of the states
and the federal government was needed. A comprehensive program of
research and education was also needed to discover new and more economical methods of waste treatment and recovery, and to inform the
public of the necessity for pollution abatement.

The tangible and intangible benefits that would accrue to the federal
government from the protection of health and general welfare and from
the reduction of damage to commerce and navigation were regarded as
justification for federal financial aid. And it was recommended that this
aid be provided in the form of grants (say, 35 per cent of the construction cost of abatement projects), and loans to states, their political subdivisions, or municipalities.

What was expected of the states in promoting such a program was set
forth in two categories. Individually, they were urged to advance local
procedures for administrative, political, and fiscal programs which would
facilitate the installation, maintenance, and operation of treatment plants.
It was considered a prerequisite that the states provide the legislation that
would promote the development of sewerage districts, sewer-rental programs, city-county integration, and other such local activities.

Collectively, the states were urged to ratify a compact that would
permit the proposed Ohio River Valley Water Sanitation Commission to
take control over pollution when waste discharge in one state affected the
normal use of water in another state. This would include control of acid
drainage from mines other than that specifically recommended for correction by the federal government. The interstate commission should
determine and designate usage of all streams in the basin including those
intrastate in character, advising the proper state agency of its findings
and decisions but issuing no orders on intrastate streams unless the pollution adversely affected another state.

Concerning the compact that had already been negotiated, the committee recommended that it be "modified and vitalized" by an amendment that would give the three commissioners representing the United
States Government voting power equal to that of the commissioners

representing the states; and by deleting the following clause in the first paragraph of Article IX, which stated ". . . no such order upon a municipality, corporation, person, or entity in any State shall go into effect unless and until it receives the assent of not less than a majority of the commissioners from such State," so that enforcement orders could be made effective by a two-thirds majority of the commissioners.

Concerning federal participation, the committee offered these recommendations. Subject to fulfillment of state co-operation in providing effective control procedures, the Public Health Service should be authorized and funded to make grants and loans to states, their political subdivisions, and municipalities to assist in financing abatement projects. Independent of state activities, the Bureau of Mines should be authorized to complete the present limited mine-sealing program at an estimated cost of $5,500,000. Also the Bureau of Mines should be charged with the inspection and maintenance of all mine seals and should conduct investigations into ways and means of further reducing the amount of acid reaching the streams, at a cost not to exceed $1 million annually for a period of 15 years. Finally it was concluded that Congress should provide an annual appropriation to the Public Health Service sufficient to cover the cost of supervising federal aid for conducting research on waste treatment methods, and for informing the public of the need for pollution abatement.

Destiny of Ohio River Committee Report

The report of the Ohio River Committee was submitted to the House of Representatives on July 21, 1943, by Robert P. Patterson, acting Secretary of War. In his letter of transmittal he said:[14] "The Undersecretary of War advises that the project as recommended is not essential to, nor of indicated value in the war effort and he points out that the mine-sealing program, if adopted, would require substantial amounts of critical materials, man power and construction equipment, without being a necessity to the prosecution of the war program."

Continued Mr. Patterson's letter: "The Bureau of the Budget has been consulted and advises that while there would be no objection to the presentation of the proposed report to the Congress, the submission during the present emergency of any estimate of appropriation for federal participation in the program therein recommended would not be in accord with the program of the President, in the absence of further evidence of the need of undertaking any part of that program in conjunction with

14. House Doc. No. 266, *op. cit.*, p. vii.

the war effort; and that no commitment is made at this time as to the relationship with the program of the President of the proposed degree of federal participation in the recommended pollution-abatement program."

Unlike many reports which are filed and forgotten, this was not to be the destiny of the *Survey of the Ohio River and its Tributaries for Pollution Control*. Circulated widely in the Ohio Valley when ratification of the compact by some states was still in doubt, it had a salutary effect in motivating favorable action. And in the *First Annual Report* of the Ohio River Valley Water Sanitation Commission, in 1949, this comment was made: "As a base line of reference and for orientation in reaching its goals, the Commission finds the Ohio River survey invaluable. It gratefully acknowledges the availability of this authoritative documentation of the basin's problems and needs."

Part II

From Dream to Reality

". . . it takes nerve, guts, persistence
and luck to realize any workable
regional scheme"—Robert Moses

8

Activating the Commission

On June 30, 1948, the Ohio River Valley Water Sanitation Compact was signed in the Hall of Mirrors of the Netherland Plaza Hotel in Cincinnati, in a ceremony that combined the pageantry and ritual of a solemn state occasion with the festivity of a victory celebration. "An Historic Event," is how the Cincinnati *Enquirer* described the signing in an editorial on July 1, 1948.

> When we consider that the territory west of the Alleghenies has been settled and has grown into the heart of a nation without any regional effort to keep its sources of drinking water pure . . . when we consider that countless generations of Americans have lived and died knowing none but polluted streams and rivers—some of them dying because of it . . . and when we consider that never since the formation of the republic have so many states, over so wide an area, moved collectively in so important an undertaking, it becomes obvious that the signing of the Ohio River Valley Water Sanitation Compact in Cincinnati Wednesday truly was an historic occasion.
>
> In a matter of several hours, amid pomp and ceremony extending to the nicest detail, the Governors or their representatives of the eight signatory states put into effect a document that took 13 years in the achievement. Tedium, frustration, delay, obstructionism, opposition by special interest, and worst of all, no interest at all in some quarters, lay back of the accomplishment hailed with such elegance in the ceremonies at the Netherland Plaza.

An editorial in the Cincinnati *Times Star* (June 30, 1948) reminded its readers that "Like another famous document signed in the Hall of Mirrors at Versailles in 1919 this is a treaty. It is an agreement, however, marking not the end of a war, but the beginning of one—a concerted fight by eight states backed by the federal government to end the disgusting pollution of the Ohio and its tributaries."

Decisions on Organization and Policy

The covenant to which the governors affixed their signatures pledged "faithful co-operation" in the control of future pollution and the abatement of existing pollution from the rivers, streams and waters of the Ohio valley. How simple and direct was this declaration; but how complex and challenging were its implications.

On the morning after the ceremonial signing—July 1, 1948—the Ohio River Valley Water Sanitation Commission held its first meeting. It had no officers, no headquarters or staff, and no funds. All it possessed at the moment was the will to do and the authority to exercise it. In swift order, this is what transpired.

By acclamation the twenty-seven commissioners elected Hudson Biery of Ohio as chairman, and Joseph L. Quinn, Jr., of Indiana as vice-chairman. And they accepted the offer of the State of Ohio to provide the services of its chief sanitary engineer, Fred H. Waring, as temporary secretary until a staff could be assembled. Mr. Biery and Mr. Waring, it will be recalled, had worked together for many years as chairman and secretary of the compact negotiating committee.

The commissioners next agreed to establish an executive committee composed of the officers and one commissioner from each state. Subcommittees were appointed to draft bylaws, policy, and budget statements. It was determined that an initial operating fund of $20,000 was required and that each state should contribute according to its pro rata share as set forth in the compact. The commissioners suggested that the governors expedite such an allocation by drawing on their emergency funds. Finally, the chairman was empowered to designate a treasurer, employ secretarial help, and secure office space and purchase supplies.

During the next four months three additional meetings were held, and not only were the basic questions of organization, policy, and budget resolved, but the Commission began to make decisions with regard to specific problems of pollution control. In the meantime, five of the states made remittances (totaling $13,830); office space was rented and furnished with equipment borrowed from the Ohio River Division of the Corps of Engineers; and the Cincinnati Chamber of Commerce made available the services of its treasurer to establish and maintain bookkeeping procedures.

Staff recruitment. The commissioners devoted considerable discussion to the qualifications of the man to be chosen as managing director. Should he have the specialist background of an engineer? Or should he be practiced in administrative and public relations activities? One group, composed of the engineers and medical doctors on the Commission, insisted that the bylaws should specify that the director be a registered professional engineer. Another group, led by Commissioner Henry Ward, majority leader of the Kentucky Senate and a former newspaperman, saw no virtue in the Commission restricting itself to an engineer candidate for the post. They visualized the director's job as one that commanded, first, the talents of an executive-type administrator combined with those of a good public-relations man, and argued that a chief engineer could be appointed to work under the director. The latter would then be free to devote his energies to the vital job of establishing good public relations with municipalities, industries, and state and federal agencies.

The personnel subcommittee of the Commission announced that it had already solicited applications from "some 30 top-flight engineers in the country, including a few members of the existing Commission." They were convinced, as were a majority of the commissioners, that the engineering aspects of the program would be dominant. Furthermore, since it was traditional in the states for pollution-control activities to be under the direction of an engineer, there was a built-in bias that the work of the interstate agency should be similarly guided. Consequently, the professional engineer stipulation was written into the bylaws. At the end of the year the post was offered to me, and I was designated both director and chief engineer.

Selection of legal counsel. The matter of legal counsel was resolved in a happy manner. The Commission felt that it needed expert legal advice, but not a full-time staff member. Accordingly, an agreement was reached with the firm of Taft, Stettinius, and Hollister, of Cincinnati, whereby one of its partners would serve ORSANCO on a part-time basis. Robert A. Taft had drafted the preliminary form of the compact in 1935. Later, as a U. S. Senator from Ohio, he sponsored the first federal water pollution control law, which became operative the very day on which the Ohio Valley Compact was signed. John B. Hollister, a former congressman, introduced in 1936 the legislation giving congressional approval to the compact, and he also sponsored the first bills developed by the Ohio Valley group looking toward federal participation in pollution control. Leonard A. Weakley, who had assisted Mr. Taft in early drafts of the compact, was selected by the firm to work with the Commission.

In brief, members of Taft, Stettinius, and Hollister possessed an unusual and intimate background for counseling the Commission. In accepting the assignment for the firm, Mr. Hollister said there were three reasons why he was interested: because of past participation in developing legislation; because he appreciated the importance of controlling pollution in the Ohio Valley, which he hoped ORSANCO would bring about; and because of the significance of eight states seeking to work together and the "interesting legal propositions" that might arise therefrom. Actually, a basic legal proposition did arise—perhaps sooner than he had expected. It involved the question of whether or not a signatory state could withhold its appropriation to the interstate body, and thus, in effect withdraw unilaterally from the compact. Mr. Hollister argued that a state could not, and this view was sustained by the Supreme Court of the United States, as detailed in Chapter 18.

Committee on engineering. Two other decisions by the Commission completed its initial organization chores. One provided that the federal commissioners should have one of their members represented on an executive committee, which was composed of one member from each state; it was designed as an instrument for interim decisions and used only rarely. The other decision concerned the establishment of an engineering committee, which was to include the chief sanitary engineers of the signatory states and a technically qualified representative of the federal government.

The engineering committee, conceived primarily as a technical board of review, was destined to wield considerable influence in the formulation and implementation of Commission directives. Its members were not only equipped to furnish technical guidance in the development of control measures, but, because of their individual responsibility for directing affairs in each of their states, they were in a strategic position for securing compliance with interstate directives.

Only a few of the chief engineers of the states were commissioners as well. By making all of the chief engineers members of a committee intimately allied with the decision-making functions of the interstate agency, the Commission actually created a clearinghouse to facilitate co-ordination of a host of administrative and technical matters.

From the perspective of time, it is clear that no activity contributed more effectively to the welding of state and interstate relationships than the operations of this committee. Each of its members was engaged in the day-by-day conduct of state programs, many aspects of which were involved with regional concerns. As a result, they maintained intimate contact with the staff, which in turn was encouraged to rely on guidance from the committee.

The engineering committee meets with the staff the day before each Commission meeting for a detailed review of all technical matters on the agenda and the development of recommendations. Discussions at these meetings were so illuminating that it soon became customary for commissioners not on the committee to arrive a day early to attend these sessions in order to become fully acquainted with the issues to be resolved.

Policy and objectives. For internal guidance as well as to promote external understanding of its proposed program the Commission promptly addressed itself to drafting a statement of policies. The need was evident because there was virtually no precedent for an operation of this kind. And among twenty-seven commissioners, there obviously was a variety of ideas on how the machinery provided by the compact should be assembled, geared, and operated.

The document that evolved is reproduced in Appendix 3. It amounts to a blueprint for action. It reasserted the broad objectives of the compact and then translated these into more specific terms. Of importance from an administrative standpoint was the declaration concerning relationships of the Commission with municipalities or industries. This read: "Except when it may not be conducive to the satisfactory accomplishment of any of its objectives, the Commission proposes to deal with individual communities and industries through appropriate state agencies, rather than to do so directly."

This statement was reassuring to the states because it dispelled any notions that ORSANCO sought to act in the role of a supergovernment. It prescribed the Commission's intention not to upset the traditional relationships of the state regulatory agencies with local communities and industries.

The question of state identification was a sensitive one, as was revealed in discussions of how the municipalities and industries in the valley were to be officially notified of the existence of the interstate compact. It was agreed that copies of the compact and the policy statement should be sent to all affected parties with a covering letter saying that this material was for information only and that any inquiries regarding compliance with the compact should be directed to the appropriate state pollution control agency. Virginia elected to make the identification itself among the 30 communities and 105 industries in that state. The other states decided to permit ORSANCO to make the mailings to a list of 1,129 communities and 1,317 industries they supplied.

Complexities to be faced in dealing with industrial-waste control were tacitly acknowledged in the policy declaration by a statement of intent to call upon industrial representatives to submit their views on the establishment of standards for treatment of waste. The policy paved the way for one of the most fruitful endeavors of the Commission based on the formation of industry-action committees.

It was recognized that some states would be handicapped in carrying out their obligations under the compact because of inadequate laws. A policy was therefore enunciated that ORSANCO would study such legislation, make recommendations to remedy deficiencies, and assist the states in enactment of appropriate changes. This provided additional evidence that the Commission did not intend to supplant state endeavors but would seek to strengthen them as the principal means for achieving its objectives.

Legislative changes were long overdue in several of the signatory states, particularly Ohio, Kentucky, and West Virginia. It will be recalled from prior comment that the State of Ohio had a law that not only restricted action in preventing pollution until a nuisance existed, but likewise exempted cities on interstate streams from the necessity of installing sewage-treatment works until all other communities upstream had done so. Aided by the commissioners from Ohio and the ORSANCO staff, the legislature reviewed the situation and in 1951 removed these restrictions. It also provided the state health department with additional powers to curb pollution.

Perhaps the unhappiest situation existed in Kentucky where a body of unrelated enactments against pollution had developed over a long period of time. It was said that, if all the laws were applied, a person spitting into a stream could be penalized with fines alone that totaled $35,000. Furthermore, authority for exercising pollution control measures had become diffused among a host of state agencies.

At the request of the Kentucky commissioners, the ORSANCO staff was instructed to prepare recommendations for legislative consideration. Based on these proposals, the 1950 Kentucky General Assembly developed and enacted a bill establishing a state pollution control board. Among other things, the new law consolidated all pollution-control duties and powers in a single agency and required everyone discharging effluents into streams to register with the board to permit determination of treatment requirements.

When West Virginia completed revision of its laws in 1955, every state signatory to the compact could report that it felt adequately prepared to discharge its obligations under the interstate agreement. New York, Illinois, and Virginia had adopted changes earlier. The significance of this achievement in the short period of five years was dwarfed only by the progress made by the states at the same time in securing compliance with pollution control measures. By then, almost 600 communities—representing 53 per cent of the population of the valley—had treatment plants in operation or under construction. And more than 800 of the 1,250 industries discharging effluents directly to the streams were operating control facilities.[1]

The Commission was convinced that, regardless of their number and stringency, prohibitions against pollution would be of limited effectiveness unless public opinion supported their enforcement. Vice-chairman Joseph Quinn put it in this fashion: "The work of this Commission should be distinguished by its ability to impel rather than compel." As a result the staff emphasized development of community-action programs, radio and television projects, and the production of documentary films and brochures.

The Commission decided that in the initial period of its program it would not undertake the establishment of a laboratory or engage in research activities. This did not signify any lack of appreciation of the desirability of scientific investigations. Rather it reflected recognition that the primary business of ORSANCO was to expedite application of what was already known about curbing pollution, and its meager resources hardly justified consideration of research activities.

Before long ORSANCO did have reason to concern itself with the assembly of analytical data and to sponsor some applied research. Basic needs for analytical work on river quality were satisfied initially through a co-operative arrangement with municipal and private water companies in the valley and with virtually no outlay of funds. Additional data was developed through a contract with the U. S. Geological Survey, which makes its capabilities available on a matching dollar basis. It has proven far more desirable and less costly to have work performed in this way than for ORSANCO to have a laboratory and a research staff of its own.

Budget determination. The Commission next had to decide how to budget for an entirely new enterprise, for a program whose magnitude was yet to be determined, and for a staff yet to be employed. This matter was assigned to a committee of commissioners headed by Blucher A. Poole of Indiana. Here is how he arrived at an estimate of $100,000. First, he analyzed the probable cost of conducting meetings, for which the major expense would be for travel and subsistence. Assuming four regular meetings annually, along with double this number of committee meetings, he calculated that $13,340 should be allotted for this purpose. Office expenses, including purchase of some furniture and equipment were estimated to total $18,700. Salaries and travel expenses for a staff of eight were established at $64,200.

1. ORSANCO, *Fifth Annual Report,* 1953.

Having made these projections, Commissioner Poole later reported to the Commission that they totalled $3,760 less than $100,000 "and that is the way the miscellaneous item was arrived at—it was what was left over."[2] He then added: "Two months ago, I was one of a group that felt we might get by very comfortably on $80,000 a year. I carried that figure around in my head for a good while. When I took my pencil and sat down and said, 'What would I want if I were executive director of this Commission,' the items totalled $130,000. After that I thought I might as well take $100,000 and work backward." The chairman remarked that this appeared to be reasonable because prior to adoption of the compact the state legislatures were informed that the annual cost might be in the range of $100,000 to $200,000.[3]

Operating experiences later proved that the original $130,000 appraisal would have been a more realistic sum to start with. Fortunately, federal grants-in-aid for administrative purposes became available in 1950, and for the next four years the Commission received grants averaging some $27,000 annually. However, the federal grants were eliminated in 1954. Thereafter the states made up the difference by approving a $130,000 budget for the compact agency. It would be fair to conclude that with such a modest allocation of funds the Commission would have no illusions about essaying the role of a supergovernment.

Immediate Regulatory Decisions

In retrospect, the demands made upon the commissioners in the first few months appear overwhelming. Not only did they have the tasks of organization, budgeting, and policy-making, but while these matters were still in the discussion stage they were called upon to render decisions on specific pollution-control problems. One commissioner said the situation was analogous to that of a new railroad company being asked to move freight before the tracks had been laid.

Abatement of existing pollution. Less than a month after the ceremonial signing of the compact, the executive committee of the Commission received a request to meet with the City of Cincinnati and representatives from northern Kentucky communities to discuss the type of treatment facilities they should provide. The municipalities said they

2. ORSANCO, minutes of meeting, October 29, 1948, p. 25.
3. This statement appeared in Appendix III of *Proceedings,* Fifth Conference of Delegates Appointed to Draft an Ohio River Valley Water Sanitation Compact, Cincinnati, Ohio, October 11, 1938.

were prepared to lead the Ohio Valley in support of the clean-up program, and they wanted to get started on design and construction.

While ORSANCO was delighted with this prompt display of community responsiveness, it had no ready answer. First, technical data must be assembled and evaluated. And, if the findings indicated the need for more than primary treatment, it would be necessary under the compact to conduct a public hearing. No one, of course, had as yet considered the matter of appropriate procedures for such a formal undertaking.

The petitioners were assured that everything possible would be done to expedite an answer, and six months later the commission was prepared to call a public hearing, based on an engineering committee study appraisal of river flow records, deoxygenation and re-aeration characteristics, bacterial conditions, population trends, and other factors relating to sewage-treatment requirements in the Cincinnati Pool, a 22-mile stretch of the Ohio River. The findings indicated that cities in this area should install facilities that would be capable of providing more than primary treatment during certain periods of low flow.

The technical investigation was expedited by enlisting the efforts of three veteran state sanitary engineers (B. A. Poole, Indiana; F. C. Dugan, Kentucky; and F. H. Waring, Ohio), a hydrologist from the Corps of Engineers (John W. Wiseman), and a river-sanitation specialist from the Public Health Service (Maurice LeBosquet). They analyzed the situation and also recommended a standard for this stretch of the river so far as dissolved oxygen was concerned. It was their conclusion that ORSANCO would be justified in requiring treatment facilities whose design and operation would assure maintenance of 4.0 parts per million of dissolved oxygen except under drought conditions that had a probability of occurrence once in twenty years. They ruled out until a future date the requirement for chlorination of effluent because it did not appear then that the benefits would justify an estimated annual cost of $100,000 for this purpose.

Meantime, the legal counselor drafted procedures to assure compliance with requirements for the conduct of public hearings. At the hearing, held on January 16, 1949, no exceptions to Commission findings were registered despite the fact that the proposals called for a greater outlay than had been anticipated by the municipalities. Construction of sewers and treatment facilities in the Cincinnati Pool began a few months later and ultimately resulted in an investment of over $70 million. When the facilities were completed, a burden of more than 90,000 pounds of organic pollution was removed daily in this area alone.

The Commission's first exercise of its regulatory function produced heartening evidence that in at least one stretch of the 981-mile Ohio River the citizens in two states were prepared to give more than lip service to the clean-streams crusade. And it served as notice throughout the valley that the new interstate agency was geared for action.

Control of new pollution. The promptness of the Commission in dealing with its first case of abating existing pollution was equaled by the manner in which it dealt with its first problem in preventing the occurrence of new sources of pollution.

On the very afternoon it was meeting with representatives of the Cincinnati metropolitan area, the State of Ohio formally requested consideration of a preliminary request from a new industry to discharge salt solutions in the upper Ohio River. The company proposed to tap an underground source of natural brine and to extract from this mother liquor the bromine-salt constituent, which represented less than 0.2 per cent of the total salt content. This would mean that some 3½ million gallons of spent brine liquor (which is five times as salty as sea water) would be discharged into the Ohio River each day.[4]

Obviously, this proposal to add such a large volume of salt to the river was of concern to more than one state. Had the compact not been in existence, there would have been no compulsion for Ohio to have concerned itself over this discharge. On the contrary, there was incentive for Ohio to give every encouragement to location of the industry because it promised to bring a $20 million capital investment to the state. Here, indeed, was a test of the effectiveness of the interstate agreement, which was not yet a month old.

In response to the state's request, the Commission instructed the Committee on Engineering to make a recommendation. In analyzing the situation, the committee determined that this operation would contribute hardness to the river water varying from 11 to 60 parts per million depending on variations in amount of flow, and that such a degradation of quality undoubtedly would inflict an economic penalty on users of water downstream.

The committee noted that present brine discharges in the Muskingum, a tributary of the Ohio, had already "ruined" the water supply of Coshocton and "injured" the supply further downstream at Marietta, and that this salty tributary was adversely influencing the quality of the Ohio River itself.[5] The committee concluded that if ORSANCO established a prece-

4. ORSANCO, minutes of meeting, October 29, 1948, p. 7.
5. ORSANCO, minutes of meeting of Executive Committee, July 28, 1948, p. 27.

dent of permitting one new industry to increase hardness by such a large increment, it would be in a difficult position to deny a similar privilege to other industries.

After weighing these considerations, the committee unanimously recommended that the State of Ohio should refuse permission for such a discharge. The state authorities thereupon informed the company it was not in a position to approve discharge of the waste as proposed. They suggested that an alternative scheme of disposal be considered, such as return of the unwanted brine solution to underground formations where it had originated. The company did not regard any alternatives as feasible, and informed the state that it would not press the matter further. As a result the Commission had no reason to schedule a public hearing and render a formal decision.[6]

Interests allied to promotion of industrial development in Ohio were not happy over this initial evidence of the influence of the interstate pollution-control agreement. When they learned some months later that the company had abandoned its plan to locate in Ohio, they sent a delegation to Cincinnati to air their dismay before the Commission staff. The attitude of this group was not shared by all. Governor Frank Lausche of Ohio told the secretary of the Commission (who was also chief sanitary engineer of Ohio) that when he placed his signature on the compact, he expected nothing less than that every one of its provisions would be diligently executed. And one of these provisions was that pollution originating in one state should not injuriously affect another state.

It might be added that Governor Lausche never missed an opportunity to give inspiration and support to the Ohio River Valley Water Sanitation Commission—before, as well as after, its negotiation. His appearance before the Virginia legislature in 1948, when ratification by that state was crucial to the establishment of the compact, was followed by numerous other evidences of personal interest in promoting regional pollution control, ranging from help in presenting a case to the U. S. Supreme Court to participation at groundbreaking ceremonies for sewage-treatment plants.

Accomplishments in the first six months of its existence indicated that the role of the Commission was to be one of action. It is a tribute to the dedication of the commissioners that the lack of funds, staff, and precedent did not hinder them from getting things done. All of this was a portent of the aggressive manner with which the Commission would pursue its mission in the years ahead.

6. ORSANCO, *First Annual Report,* 1949, p. 7.

9

Winning Public Support

Strategy of the ORSANCO crusade for clean streams was predicated on this premise: securing action in curbing pollution would depend on something more potent than research projects, technical investigations, promulgation of regulations, or even the exercise of legal compulsions. The primary need was for acceptance of social reform, which was dependent on securing public understanding and approval. Indeed, the Commission might have adopted as its slogan the words of Abraham Lincoln: "Public sentiment is everything. With public sentiment nothing can fail; without it nothing can succeed. Consequently, he who moulds public sentiment goes deeper than he who enacts statutes or pronounces decisions."[1]

Conditions in the Ohio Valley could hardly be attributed to the lack of laws or of technical know-how; there was an abundance of both. The unrestrained fouling of streams stemmed basically from public indifference. Few people were informed about the circumstances and their implications. And fewer still were inspired to bring about a change.

Thus it was no mere euphuism to identify this joint undertaking of the eight states as a crusade to generate support for clean streams—from millions of people and the managers of thousands of industries—and with it willingness to pay the price.

The situation prevailing on the Ohio River in 1948 validated the conviction that most people were apathetic to acceptance of responsibility for keeping streams clean. *Less than one per cent of the 2,800,000 people living in sewered communities along its banks had installed facilities for treatment of sewage.* This almost universal indifference of communities in safeguarding the quality of their water resources was matched by the disregard of the corporate citizens of the valley of the need to curb discharges of industrial wastes.

1. First Debate with Stephen A. Douglas at Ottawa, Ill., August 21, 1858. From Basler's *Abraham Lincoln—His Speeches and Writings* (New York: World Publishing Co., 1946), p. 458.

Accordingly, a major part of the ORSANCO effort was channeled into activities designed to activate some 3,000 communities and industries to accept an obligation to abate pollution. What was envisioned was a program to motivate the investment of local funds in municipal sewage-treatment facilities serving more than 8 million people—at a cost averaging $100 per capita! Perhaps somewhat smaller in magnitude, but nevertheless substantial, was the investment expected to be made by industries.

Dimensions of this task suggested that at least ten years would be required to achieve tangible results. Once public approval had been won for expenditure of funds, it would take substantial time to convert blueprints into structures of steel and concrete and to install trunk sewers to bring the wastewaters to a central site for treatment.

Components of the Public-Affairs Program

Taking its cue from the Commission's statement that it intended "to promote a program of public information and education pertaining to its functions and objectives," the staff began to develop a public-affairs program. Information and educational activities were devised that could be classified in two broad categories. One of these was termed the "buck-shot" routine because it embraced components designed to be delivered broadside so as to impinge on anyone who might be within range. The other category consisted of "rifle-shot" procedures wherein aim was directed toward, and ammunition selected for, a specific target.

Buck-shot campaign. To reach a wide audience this campaign used such devices as news releases, magazine articles, speeches, radio interviews, appearances on television programs, exhibits, and bulletins. These presentations were designed to make people aware of the nature of the pollution problem, to define what needed to be done about it, and to specify how it could be accomplished in terms of financial support and physical facilities.

But it was obvious that facts alone would not be adequate. Practitioners in the art of communication emphasize the importance of emotional appeal. With this in mind, ORSANCO sought to identify pollution control with individual welfare and developed the slogan, "Clean Waters Protect Your Health—Protect Your Job—Protect Your Happiness." Exhibits and motion pictures were used widely throughout the valley, notably at state and county fairs, to show people that they had a personal stake in pollution control.

At first, only two films were available. One of these was *Clean Waters,* produced by the General Electric Company. It was a pioneer in its field. Although it was rather general in its subject matter, it served ORSANCO so well that several copies were worn out. The other was *Waters of the Commonwealth,* produced by the Pennsylvania Sanitary Water Board. It focused on the efforts being made to protect stream quality in one of the states signatory to the compact.

As time went on, and it became increasingly clear that an informed citizenry would be ORSANCO's strongest ally, the staff was authorized to intensify public-affairs efforts. The broadened program consisted of two major components: (1) production of documentary films and (2) the periodic distribution of sets of transcribed messages to radio and television stations in the valley. For this purpose ORSANCO retained the services of Stuart Finley, who had produced several visual commentaries on water pollution for use on a television program he conducted in the Washington, D.C., area.

The documentary film library produced by Mr. Finley for ORSANCO now includes eight 25-minute motion pictures in color and with sound (see listing in Appendix 4). Some depict progress that has been made to abate pollution in the valley, and others deal with conditions yet to be remedied. Where possible the films are tailored so that the regional aspects of the interstate program can be followed by a segment dealing with situations in a specific state. Thus each of the eight states can be supplied with a version of the film in which local affairs can be highlighted with relation to activities in neighboring compact states.

To take advantage of the time made available by radio and television stations for the "airing" of public-service announcements, production of a series of one-minute spot transcriptions was sponsored. Every thirteen weeks, some sixty television stations and four hundred radio stations in the valley were sent sets of ten transcriptions on a current aspect of pollution control. During the boating season, for example, the messages were oriented to the theme, "Don't be a river litter lout."

The time on the air was made available at no direct cost, but the total would have been so substantial if measured by commercial rates that ORSANCO might have regarded this effort as its "million dollar project."

Rifle-shot targets. The targets for rifle-shot efforts were specific communities and industries. In every instance the aim was the same, namely, to promote action in solving a local pollution problem.

For use in communities, the staff developed a "Citizens Clean Waters Committee" campaign program. The object was to help community groups in the organization and detailed conduct of an intensive campaign to win support for sewage-treatment plant bond issues.

In the preparation of this program, ORSANCO received generous aid from the General Electric Company. As one of its national public-service functions, this company had been engaged for some time in promoting pollution abatement. When it was suggested to the General Electric management that ORSANCO would welcome help in developing its public education program, the services of H. Vance Crawford were made available. Mr. Crawford, a veteran employee of the company and producer of the GE film, *Clean Waters,* spent nearly a year in Cincinnati, where he worked with the ORSANCO staff in developing exhibits and other promotional aids. He also helped prepare the detailed program of the community-action campaign and some of the materials for it, as did H. Peter Converse, a specialist in community relations from the General Electric Company.

Community-Action Campaign

When a community requested help in promoting passage of a bond issue, ORSANCO would make available a staff member to meet with local leaders and officials. He carried with him a kit containing the following materials: an organization chart showing the suggested composition of a committee and duties of the various groups that should be represented in such an enterprise; a guide list detailing activities to be undertaken by the committee, by various subcommittees, and by individuals or agencies within the community; a timetable—generally covering a five-week period of activity prior to the bond voting date—outlining what should be accomplished each week and by whom in order to gain the greatest impact value from the effort expanded; and a list of services and materials that could be furnished by ORSANCO.

One of the services offered was the assistance of a staff member to serve as consultant, aide, and expeditor to the chairman and other members of the committee—a triune role that required considerable finesse.

Among the materials made available by ORSANCO were films, brochures, posters, television and radio spot annnouncements, suggested proclamations, resolutions, and petitions; also outlines and tip sheets for preparing speeches to be given by sportsmen, industrialists, or civic leaders on pollution control; and a set of news releases; each one designed for a specific purpose and time during the five-week campaign.

With this preplanned program and the materials needed for its execution, it was possible for ORSANCO to go to a community and help get things started with dispatch. Modifications to meet local conditions could easily be improvised. And the experience gained in each campaign provided ideas with which to improve a succeeding one.

Because water-pollution abatement is a subject that can claim universal support, it was possible for a well-organized citizens' committee to enlist the efforts of virtually everyone. For example, in one city the Junior Chamber of Commerce was assigned the chore of painting "Vote Yes" at every important street intersection. In another community, the Boy Scouts and Girl Scouts were offered prizes of bicycles, gloves, dolls, and other gifts donated by local merchants as special incentives to provoke interest in pollution abatement and get out the vote. The contest was sponsored by the Chamber of Commerce. "I Have Voted" tags were provided at every polling place, and the scouts were urged to solicit tags from those who had cast a vote. The tags could then be redeemed for prizes, each prize being worth a given number of tags. Publicity given to this contest fired interest among the scouts who generally exacted promises for tags long before the election.

Promotional activities included arrangements made with stores to use their windows for display of exhibits and posters. Managers of industries that provided parking lots for their employees were solicited to give permission to their attendants to pass out car stickers carrying the slogan "Vote Yes for Clean Waters." The libraries were enlisted to feature a display of books, pamphlets, and magazines relating to water resources and pollution control. School authorities were encouraged to conduct essay contests, to utilize assembly programs for showing films, and to emphasize in science classes the various aspects of safeguarding water supplies.

The community-action campaigns were credited with having turned the tide in several municipalities where sewage-treatment plant bond issues previously had been voted down.[2] However, this program was not as widely used as it might have been because some states had misgivings about the interstate commission being too intimately involved in local affairs. As an alternate arrangement, several of the states themselves undertook distribution of the kits containing the materials for organization and conduct of local campaigns, and they sought to provide from their agencies such staff aid as might be required.

2. ORSANCO, *Eighth Annual Report,* 1956, p. 25.

Action on the Industrial Front

The rifle-shot technique for motivating action was also used with industrial groups. The commission approved a program whereby management representatives of generic industry groups—steel, coal, metal-finishing, oil refining, chemical, and paper—were invited to form "action" committees. The purpose of these committees, broadly stated, was: (1) to assist in the assembly of facts on waste disposal and to make an appraisal of problems confronting their members in accommodating to the goals of the Ohio Valley clean-up program; and (2) to consult with and be available to the Commission for the review of proposed regulations.

This undertaking proved to be one of the most fruitful endeavors of the Commission. Among other things, there was a decided change in the general attitude of industry in the Ohio Valley toward the concept of a regional pollution-control program. It is common experience that one does not have much success in changing attitudes simply by presenting facts. Providing the opportunity to share in the development of a program is likely to be far more effective.

The industry advisory committees meet once every three months or oftener with members of the staff for the exchange of findings and the exploration of viewpoints. The committees are kept acquainted with developments and are encouraged to give attention to matters of mutual concern. Perhaps the greatest dividend from the relationship has been the illumination of why certain things should be undertaken and the alternatives available for their accomplishment.

A case in point is the problem of oil pollution. Observations revealed that much of the trouble originates from lack of safeguards in transferring the product at river terminals. The Petroleum Committee was requested to survey experiences among its member companies and draft a memorandum on recommended practices. This document served as a basis for the oil pollution control measures subsequently adopted by ORSANCO to be applied uniformly throughout the eight-state area. The measures advanced were made with the assurance that they would warrant support of the entire industry. Similar procedures have been employed in developing other industrial-waste control measures. But this does not imply that the formulation of these measures has been free from travail and controversy. The virtue of the approach lay in the fact that opportunity was provided for the resolution of issues before the rules were promulgated.

In its industry committees, ORSANCO created a liaison group of over two hundred people strategically located throughout the district to communicate to all industrial entities both the goals of the interstate program and the means sought for their accomplishment. Although the industry committees may not have enjoyed this exercise, nevertheless, they were conscientious in performing it.

Just how far the spirit of mutual responsibility has been nurtured is evidenced by the comment of the chairman of one industry action committee, who told his group: "Every one of the control measures adopted thus far has originated within the Commission. I feel that our committee has now learned enough about the problems of keeping streams clean that it might consider initiating some additional control measures for consideration by the Commission."

Reports and Manuals of Practice

The annual report to the governors is regarded as the most effective means of general communication available to ORSANCO. Some 7,000 copies of this report are distributed. The mailing list includes members of the state legislatures, as well as the U.S. Congress. In addition, copies are sent to all communities, industries, chambers of commerce, and civic organizations in the Ohio Valley, and to state and federal agencies, as well as to universities and libraries, both in this country and abroad.

One week in advance of transmittal to the governors, the annual report is mailed with a news release to all newspapers, radio and television stations, and wire services. Because every community in the valley is either operating, building, or planning facilities for water-pollution control, the ORSANCO report generally receives good coverage. Advance mailing of the report encourages such treatment because it gives the editor time to contact his state agency or Commission headquarters and obtain such additional information as may seem appropriate from a local-interest standpoint.

In each annual report an effort is made to provide a narrative account of goals achieved and aspirations not yet attained. This is supplemented with a statement on activities of the Commission and its committees, a summary on the status of pollution-control installations, comparative data on river-quality conditions, and, of course, a record of funds received and their disbursement. The function of these reports, which average twenty-eight pages, is to convey information. But they are also designed to invite attention, and for this reason special care is taken in layout and typography.

The usefulness and the reception given to the ORSANCO annual reports has encouraged some of the signatory states to publish similar accounts. This has further improved communication with the public on pollution-control problems and progress.

Staff investigations as well as reports and manuals prepared by the advisory committees are also published for general distribution. Industrial waste control manuals, most of which relate to methods of treatment, have enjoyed a lively demand from all over the world. Because of budget limitations, the practice has been to make a nominal charge for these, except to tax-supported institutions; the return from such sales is modest but it has compensated for expenses incurred in the mechanical costs of production. (ORSANCO publications are listed in Appendix 5.)

Clean Water Rallies

Not the least of initial public relations endeavors was the promotion of ceremonies to mark both the ground breaking and the completion of community sewage-treatment projects. These occasions provided opportunities to give recognition to local and state efforts, and to point out how they helped to achieve regional goals. Frequently it was possible to arrange for the governor of the state to attend and thus add further recognition to the significance of the undertaking.

One of the largest rallies was conducted at Cincinnati in October of 1953 to signalize the start of operation of one treatment plant, partial completion of another, and ground breaking for a third in the Greater Cincinnati area of Ohio and Kentucky. More than 400 civic and industrial leaders participated, including the governors of Ohio and Kentucky. The event invited the attention of President Eisenhower, who sent a congratulatory telegram to the chairman of the Commission, saying: "Stream sanitation in the Ohio Valley is a civic objective of tremendous importance to the whole nation. Your accomplishments are a dramatic evidence of what can and will be achieved by unselfish community cooperation."[3]

The Cincinnati rally was designed for more than local impact, however. The occasion was contrived to stimulate action in other communities along the Ohio River. To this end the Cincinnati Chamber of Commerce invited and subsidized the attendance of mayors from about 100 towns. All of them were presented with chrome-plated shovels to be used in the ground-breaking ceremony, and they were asked to carry these back home for early use in starting construction of treatment works in their communities. After the ceremonies the visitors were taken on a tour of Cincinnati's completed plant, where many of them saw for the first time

3. ORSANCO, *Sixth Annual Report,* 1954, p. 10.

what a sewage-treatment plant looked like and how it performed. A few years later many of the communities represented at this giant rally were engaged in building treatment works of their own.

Another rally, marking completion of the $100 million Allegheny County (Penna.) sewage-treatment works, was attended by the entire Commission. This facility, serving the City of Pittsburgh and sixty-eight adjacent communities as well as a number of industries, is the biggest in the valley. Its completion in April, 1956, was properly regarded as one of the most important events of the interstate crusade for clean streams. By this time some 800 communities throughout the Ohio Valley had treatment facilities in operation or under construction, and another 200 had submitted final plans for approval.

Measuring the Payoff

The cause-and-effect relationships associated with public information and educational efforts are often elusive. But on the basis of what happened in the Ohio Valley there can be no reason to doubt the wisdom of emphasizing the conduct of such efforts.

Among other things, the states could cite this fact: Within eight years after they had launched their regional campaign 3 million people along the Ohio River, representing 85 per cent of the population, had supported the crusade by financing with local funds the construction of treatment works. All of this occurred in the period before any federal grants became available. Obviously, public attitudes had changed.

How thoroughly the people of the valley are now indoctrinated with a personal sense of responsibility for keeping streams clean is illustrated by a letter received by ORSANCO in 1963, in which the writer stated that he had requested that his last remains be cremated and dispersed into the Ohio River, and that in view of the ORSANCO campaign to free the Ohio and its tributaries of stream pollution, he would like to know what liabilities would be incurred by his estate. "Frankly," he wrote, "I do not feel that this would be very harmful, but I do not want to cause any problems for my heirs. If there is a set fine for this type of pollution, I wonder if it could be paid before the event takes place. Please advise me of your decision as I have not felt too healthy recently."

In replying to this query the Commission could say only that it had not yet contemplated the promulgation of regulations suited to this situation, but it was gratified that its public-education program had evoked such a conscientious response.

10

Advancing Municipal Action

When the Commission began operation in 1948, records from the signatory states revealed that about a third of the 8.3 million "sewered population" in the compact district was provided with treatment facilities. "Sewered population" has been adopted as the most meaningful measure for evaluating pollution control in the Ohio Valley where almost half of the total population is distributed in rural areas. Household sewage from unsewered and often isolated dwellings is confined to the immediate area of the premises and disposed of through the use of septic tanks or cesspools. Therefore, the potentialities of stream pollution from these sources generally are not significant. It is the sewered communities discharging untreated wastewaters from a concentrated population that are of major concern.

Most of the treatment facilities were on tributaries where the local impact of stream pollution had provided incentives for citizens to support state action for instituting remedial measures. However, virtually no progress had been made in halting the discharge of raw sewage into the Ohio River. Less than one per cent of the 2.8 million sewered population along the river were provided with treatment facilities, and even these were of questionable effectiveness because they were outmoded.

By 1965 the sewered population of the entire district had climbed to 11,390,000. Meantime, substantial progress had been made in curbing pollution. Now wastewater from 94 per cent of the population is being treated, and that from another 1.5 per cent will be upon completion of works already started. Even more dramatic is the situation on the Ohio River, where sewage-treatment plants now serve more than 99 per cent of the population.

In 1948 the most sanguine projection with regard to securing compliance from communities was that it would take at least a decade for substantial completion of this task. Actually, this goal was not reached until some fifteen years later. The Korean war occurred during this period, and for about a year construction materials were not easily available for public-works projects.

Believing that municipalities who had stalled for years in building treatment works would now find a new excuse for delay, and disturbed to learn that some projects already under way might be shut down because of impending curtailment of materials, the Commission passed a resolution, addressed to the President of the United States, the Congress, and the federal agencies concerned with mobilization for defense, advancing reasons why pollution-control projects might qualify for a higher priority than other types of public-works endeavors.[1] There is no evidence to suggest, however, that this resolution did anything more than to call attention to the concerns of ORSANCO because at that time pollution control did not rate the national attention it is now receiving.

Main-Stem Pollution Commands Priority

In charting its regional program, the Commission concluded that primary consideration should be given to securing action by municipalities, notably along the Ohio River. There were several reasons for this decision: (1) municipal sewage discharges presented a potential health hazard to many water supply systems, as well as to recreational uses; (2) municipal compliance with regulations probably would require more time than that involving industrial-waste control because of the efforts necessary to overcome community inertia and the difficulties that generally beset public bodies in developing engineering studies and plans, arranging for financing, and letting contracts for construction; and (3) utilization of limited staff and budget for interstate problems of broadest concern.

These considerations dictated that ORSANCO should embark on investigations and public hearings for the 981-mile Ohio River, the condition of which involved the interests of six states in the compact. This undertaking culminated in the successive adoption of seven "standards" of performance setting forth treatment requirements for municipalities. Division of the river into seven zones, with a specific set of requirements for each, reflected an evaluation of variations of streamflow, quantities of sewage discharged, and such other factors as the proximity of downstream water-supply intakes to pollutional discharges and the natural purification characteristics of the river in each zone.

The order in which the investigations and hearings were conducted reflected both opportunism and the relative intensity of the pollution

1. ORSANCO, *Second Annual Report,* 1950, Appendix B, p. 42.

problem in various stretches of the river. Thus, first attention was given to a zone at the midpoint of the river where communities in the Greater Cincinnati area expressed readiness to build works as soon as treatment standards were promulgated. Because of the intensity of pollution upstream from Cincinnati, the next investigations were scheduled in zones that terminated at Pittsburgh, at the head of the river. Altogether, four different sets of requirements were specified for the 480 miles from Pittsburgh to Cincinnati, each tailored for conditions in a specific stretch of river. Following this, the studies were continued downstream, where three more sets of standards were developed for stretches of the river extending to its junction with the Mississippi River. (Standard No. 3 is reproduced in Appendix 6.)

Establishing treatment standards for the entire Ohio River represented a major undertaking in terms of data assembly and evaluation and the conduct of all formalities associated with public hearings. It was accomplished over a period of five years, during which many other components of the regional program were simultaneously being advanced.

During this period, the Commission also acted on requests from several states for studies of interstate tributaries of the Ohio. It recommended sewage-treatment requirements on the Wabash River between Terre Haute, Indiana, and Mt. Carmel, Illinois,[2] in response to a request from Indiana and Illinois, who sought to strengthen their position in advancing enforcement actions against polluters in this area.

A similar study with recommendations was completed in 1958 for the interstate Monongahela River with the co-operation of Pennsylvania and West Virginia.[3] Earlier, at the request of Virginia and West Virginia, a study was made on the New River relating to the effect of an industrial waste discharge in Virginia on water supply uses of the stream in West Virginia.

Hearing procedures. The Commission's legal counsel insisted upon meticulous observance of all formalities associated with public hearings. He pointed out that, if an occasion should arise for ORSANCO to issue an order for noncompliance, the simplest way for an offender to have such an order set aside or delayed without consideration of the merits of the case would be to find an irregularity in the initial hearings. Accord-

2. *Wabash River Pollution-Abatement Needs* (Ohio River Valley Water Sanitation Commission, August 1950).
3. *Monongahela River Sewage-Treatment Considerations* (Ohio River Valley Water Sanitation Commission, January 1959).

ingly, detailed procedures were drafted and formally adopted.[4] (See Appendix 7 for rules of procedure for public hearings.)

It should be mentioned also, in connection with public hearings, that ORSANCO punctiliously conformed with a provision in the 1948 Federal Water Pollution Control Act designed to promote co-ordination of state-federal relationships. This provision[5] placed a responsibility on the Surgeon General of the Public Health Service to prepare or adopt comprehensive drainage basin plans for pollution control or to pass judgment on programs that were to be activated by nonfederal agencies. Therefore, in all hearings conducted by ORSANCO the Surgeon General was invited to participate and to register his views on the adequacy of the proposals advanced. The record shows that the interstate requirements were accepted as compatible with the federal interest, a matter that was not given much consideration when a federal enforcement conference was called on the Mahoning River. (See page 263.)

Compliance notice formalities and follow-up. Under the procedure established by ORSANCO, every discharger of sewage (municipality, corporation, or individual) is issued a notice (signed by the chairman and director of the Commission and by the three commissioners of the state in which the discharge is taking place) which sets forth the specific requirements for treatment and calls upon the affected party to inform the state regulatory agency as to the extent to which the standard is now being met or when treatment facilities will be completed for that purpose. The state agency, in turn, makes reports to the interstate agency at regular intervals on the status of compliance.

At ORSANCO headquarters, a docket file is maintained for each municipality, corporation, or individual to whom a notice has been issued. This file contains a copy of the notice, registered receipts for all notices mailed (or when the notice is mailed by the state, a copy of the forwarding letter and answer), and copies of status reports received from the state agency. In this fashion a dossier is compiled for each discharger, and this serves as the official record should there be any necessity for legal enforcement under the terms of Article IX of the compact.

Bacterial quality criteria. Before sewage-treatment standards could be established it was necessary to secure agreement among the states on what should be regarded as an acceptable bacterial limit for interstate

4. ORSANCO, minutes of meeting, July 6, 1949, pp. 8–10.
5. Public Law 845, 80th Cong., 1st Sess., June 30, 1948. See Section 2, paragraph (a).

waters. There was a variety of viewpoints throughout the nation regarding appropriate criteria for waters used for potable supplies and recreational purposes. Obviously, a decision had to be reached in order to prescribe appropriate disinfection.

This important matter was brought to a prompt resolution through an arrangement that had been made some time earlier for the services of Harold W. Streeter, who had retired from his post as sanitary-engineer director of the Public Health Service Stream Investigations Station in Cincinnati. Not only was Mr. Streeter recognized internationally as an authority on the bacteriological aspects of water quality, but he had studied Ohio River conditions since 1914. He made an analysis of the application and current validity of bacterial quality standards, and from this he developed recommendations that were accepted by the eight states. The recommendations were adopted by ORSANCO on April 1, 1951, to be used "as a guide in the establishment of treatment requirements for sewage discharged into the Ohio River, and as a yardstick for evaluating sanitary conditions in waters used for potable supplies and recreational purposes. . . ." The criteria were set forth in this fashion:

Water supply uses—The monthly arithmetical average "most probable number"[6] of coliform organisms in waters of the river at water intakes should not exceed 5,000 per 100 milliliters in any month; nor exceed this number in more than 20 percent of the samples of such waters examined during any month; nor exceed 20,000 per 100 milliliters in more than 5 percent of such samples.

Recreational uses—For bathing or swimming waters, the monthly arithmetical average "most probable number" of coliform organisms should not exceed 1,000 per 100 milliliters during any month of the recreation season; nor exceed this number in more than 20 percent of the samples examined during any such month; nor exceed 2,400 per 100 milliliters on any day. For non-bathing or non-swimming waters, the monthly arithmetical average "most probable number" of coliform organisms should not exceed 5,000 per 100 milliliters during any month of the recreational season, nor should exceed this number in more than 20 per cent of the samples examined during any such month.

In justifying this judgment on the choice of numerical values, Mr. Streeter said: "The limits for potable supply sources are premised on the desirability of a return to normal water treatment methods (coagulation, sedimentation, rapid-sand filtration and pre- and/or post-chlorination) with a minimum of chlorine residuals in the finished water, in order to

6. The "most probable number," referred to in the bacterial criteria, is based on a statistical interpretation of a series of water samples planted in fermentation tubes where gas is produced if coliform bacteria are present.

insure palatability as well as bacterial safety of water supplies drawn from the river. Too many water-treatment plants must now resort to auxiliary processing as a regular practice because of excessive pollution loads.

"Recommendations for recreational waters are tentative, pending further knowledge of the epidemiology of bathing water sanitation, and are intended to provide reasonable safeguards to bathers along the river against more serious water-borne diseases. For recreational uses not involving bathing or swimming, a bacterial quality goal at the water-supply level is recommended."

The ORSANCO bacterial quality objectives have since been recommended for use or adopted in many places outside the Ohio Valley. The report[7] itself must be considered a classic among the many produced by Mr. Streeter during his half century of pollution investigations. It contains a wealth of background information on the significance of bacterial analyses of water and their interpretation, and the rationale employed in developing the recommendations.

Financing of Municipal Projects

When ORSANCO was established and for some years thereafter there were no state or federal grants to assist in the financing of municipal sewage-treatment projects. This situation has changed, notably with respect to the availability of federal aid.

In 1953 the Commonwealth of Pennsylvania pioneered a modest program of financial assistance under which an annual grant of about 2 per cent of the total cost of treatment works would be given to its facilities in operation. The federal government instituted a grant-in-aid program in 1956. In 1962 the State of New York authorized a program of aid for construction of treatment facilities but did not appropriate funds except for planning purposes; in 1965 a billion-dollar bond issue was approved by the voters in New York to promote construction of community projects.

During the first eight years of the interstate program, compliance by municipalities meant that local funds had to be raised for this purpose. Despite the large sums required and the traditional reluctance of taxpayers to support expenditures for sewage treatment, many municipalities did rally to the challenge. By 1956, ORSANCO could state in its eighth annual report to the governors of the signatory states that treatment

7. With a realization of the importance of this scientific appraisal, the Commission published the report in June, 1951, under the title *Bacterial-Quality Objectives for the Ohio River* and it was introduced as an exhibit at all public hearings.

facilities were in operation or under construction to service three-quarters of the sewered population. This represented a doubling of facilities that had been installed in the years preceding the start of the interstate crusade; and all of this work was financed with local funds.

Financing of public works had not become any easier. On the contrary, municipalities were more hard-pressed than ever to raise money to satisfy the increasing demands on them for a multitude of services. Obviously, something had happened to cause a change in public sentiment about the value of clean streams. And this great change in the Ohio Valley occurred during a period when municipalities in many other parts of the nation were awaiting federal subsidies.

How funds were raised. One of the means favored by municipalities for raising money to pay for all or part of the cost of treating sewage was the imposition of a service charge, generally based on a percentage of the water bill. Such financing involved the issuance of mortgage-revenue bonds, the repayments on which were guaranteed from income (service charges) and a mortgage on the physical assets of the facility. Thus, a community that was not in a position to issue general-obligation bonds because it had already reached constitutional debt limitations, or one that sought to avoid placing the additional tax burden solely on property owners, had an alternative means for borrowing money.

The City of Cincinnati not only employed revenue-bond financing but introduced a "pay-before-you-go" feature. Service charges were applied in 1948 when it was agreed that a sewage-treatment program would be undertaken. In this fashion, funds were accumulated for two years at the rate of $1,750,000 yearly.[8] The city was able to finance engineering costs, site purchase, and other preliminary expenses without floating bonds prior to actual start of construction, and thus minimized the interest charges on the debt.

The idea of using a service charge for sewage disposal was not new. Perhaps the earliest application in the United States was at Natick, Massachusetts, in 1894.[9] In 1923 the State of Ohio provided an incentive to impose user charges by enacting a "sewer rental" law whereby communities were authorized to collect a fee specifically for the purpose of assuring adequate funds for operating sewer systems and sewage plants.[10] In

8. ORSANCO, *Second Annual Report,* 1950, p. 19.

9. See *Sewer Rental Laws and Procedure,* Third Progress Report of a committee of the Sanitary Engineering Division, American Society of Civil Engineers, 1942.

10. See F. H. Waring, *Sewer Rental in Ohio,* Bulletin of the Ohio State Department of Health, Columbus, Ohio, April 1946.

the 1930's utility-type charges for financing municipal services became more common throughout the nation. During the depression years, municipalities had difficulty in selling general-obligation or special-assessment bonds. But revenue bonds found ready buyers.

In brief, there was adequate precedent for communities in the Ohio Valley to employ mortgage-revenue bond financing for sewage-treatment facilities. All that was needed was a willingness on the part of the citizens to utilize the means available.

Installation of the biggest project in the valley—the treatment works serving Pittsburgh and 68 adjacent communities—was accomplished by taking advantage of Pennsylvania legislation first enacted in 1935. This permitted the governing bodies of counties, cities, and towns to establish a separate agency (called an authority) for financing and operating sewage-disposal services. An Allegheny County Sanitary Authority was created under this act and its plan for serving the area required a bond issue of $100 million. The project was dedicated in 1956—half a century after recommendations for sewage treatment were first advanced for Pittsburgh in 1906.

The federal-aid program. In June of 1956, Congress passed an amendment to the Water Pollution Control Act,[11] which authorized the appropriation of $50 million annually for federal grants-in-aid to municipalities over a period of ten years. Until then, federal aid had been limited to interest-free loans from the U. S. Housing and Home Finance Agency for community planning including sewage-disposal systems.[12]

This new federal grant policy was disturbing to many commissioners of ORSANCO. They noted that three-quarters of the citizens in the Ohio Valley had already dug down in their pockets to pay for treatment works. Now these people were faced with the additional burden of helping to finance pollution control throughout the nation. In addition to questioning the propriety or the need of a national subsidy for financing local projects, some commissioners thought that the grants program might retard rather than stimulate progress in the compact district. If a community were eligible for a federal grant, it seemed likely that it would now stand by until it got its share.

11. Public Law 660, 84th Cong., 1st Sess., amending the Water Pollution Control Act, 33 U.S.C. 466–466j.
12. In 1950 such loans were advanced for 47 projects in the Ohio Valley, totaling about $2,000,000. The communities were required to repay these loans when the projects went into construction.

The reasoning went like this: distribution of $50 million annually among the states would mean that about $1 million could be earmarked for each state. Since the law required that this sum be allocated among communities on the basis of 30 per cent of the cost of a project (and not to exceed $250,000 for any single project) the federal grant in any state would only support about $3.5 million of total construction. In some states of the Ohio Valley, however, the municipal sewage-disposal program had been averaging three to four times that amount. If communities now refused to go ahead without a grant, state programs would be cut back to the amount of federal money made available.

The feeling of communities that had recently completed their projects and therefore were ineligible for federal aid was typified in the comments of Mayor Forester Farley of Marietta, Ohio, at the dedication of his community sewage-treatment plant on June 27, 1956:

> The cost to our city has been $1,900,000, or nearly $120 for every man, woman, and child in our corporate limits. . . . I have brought up this matter of cost for a specific reason . . . exactly two weeks ago today, the U. S. House of Representatives in Washington, passed a bill which was of the utmost importance to almost everyone here today. . . . As passed by our House of Representatives, this money will only be made available to those cities which have thus far not progressed beyond the planning stage. In other words, we are not to be considered eligible because there is no need for an incentive in our case. Our plant, you see, is already built.
>
> I am sure that you will all recognize the serious inequity of this bill. We are expected to bear the entire cost of construction here in Marietta and then contribute, in the form of federal taxes, to those communities which have dragged their feet.

Similar sentiments were expressed at Henderson, Kentucky, which dedicated its treatment works a month after the federal-aid bill had been signed. Said Mayor Hecht S. Lackey, in a letter of July 24, 1956, to the President of the Kentucky Municipal League:

> I have discovered the existence of this law [P.L. 660] and find it very interesting as well as disturbing. Interesting in that it provides for aid to communities in their efforts to correct and eliminate water pollution, and disturbing in that it provides no help to those communities like yours and mine that have acted promptly to comply with state edict.
>
> I find Henderson in the unhappy situation of having exhausted its credit in building the disposal plant and now we can neither improve nor enlarge our water pumping and storage facilities. Neither can we provide sewers in unsewered areas or correct flooding conditions in low areas.

Some consolation, however, could be offered to the municipalities who had gone ahead. Construction costs had been steadily moving upward at the rate of about 5 per cent annually since the end of the war. Therefore, those who had delayed—though now eligible for a grant—were faced with the prospect of paying more for what they got.

Although federal aid as envisioned in Public Law 660 was designed specifically to help those communities which were in financial straits—the determination of which was left to the states in order that appropriate priority might be assigned—the fact is that after the law was enacted not many projects in the Ohio Valley moved forward until a grant was made available. In 1961, the act was amended to raise the limitation on a single grant from $250,000 up to $600,000; and for a joint project serving several municipalities, the grant could go as high as $2.4 million. Total authorizations to the states were upped to $80 million in 1962, to $90 million in 1963, and then to $100 million for a period of four years. A new bill passed in October, 1966, authorizes grants of $450 million in 1968, $700 million in 1969, $1 billion in 1970, and $1.25 billion in 1971.

Federal funds allocated to projects in the Ohio Valley since the start of this pollution-control aid program have been (in each case for the year ending June 30) :[13]

1957	$3,616,200
1958	5,907,900
1959	6,564,300
1960	5,557,400
1961	4,787,500
1962	6,892,000
1963	9,010,300
1964	7,349,400
1965	6,273,900

In 1962 additional federal funds for sewage disposal projects became available to communities from the Public Works Acceleration Act,[14] which was designed to provide unemployment relief. For fiscal year 1963 the total allocated to communities in the compact district totaled $9,618,-600; in 1964 the amount was $17,209,000.

13. Data for this tabulation derived from the *Project Register* of the Division of Water Supply and Pollution Control, U.S. Department of Health, Education, and Welfare, June, 1965.

14. Purpose of the Public Works Acceleration Act (P.L. 87–658), which became effective in September, 1962, was to provide immediate useful work for the unemployed in economically depressed areas through construction of public works. From the $880 million appropriated by Congress in fiscal years 1963 and 1964, $112 million was allotted to sewage disposal projects. Public Health Service Publication No. 867 (Washington, D.C.: U.S. Government Printing Office, 1964).

Altogether, $82,786,500 of federal aid was allocated from 1957 to 1965 to 638 projects in the Ohio Valley, costing an estimated $282,-966,000. Thus, every federal dollar was matched by the communities with $2.50 of local funds.

Impact of federal grants. The situation that prevailed in the ORSANCO compact district does not lend itself for adequately weighing the influence of the federal-aid program. The fact that three-quarters of the job—as measured by population served—had already been locally financed before grants became available would suggest that a majority of the municipalities were able to meet their obligations. However, there is no way of predicting how well the remaining 25 per cent would have performed without aid. Some of these communities could have proceeded on their own; there were others, however, where self-financing of a major capital investment such as a sewage-treatment plant posed difficult problems.

For a small community a grant of almost one-third the cost of the project would be attractive, provided there were incentives for raising the other two-thirds locally. However, it was left to each state to decide to whom the grants were to be made, and generally there were more claimants than could be accommodated.

The states recognized that preference should be given to projects that would produce the most benefits in abating pollution, and, as a rule, it was more beneficial to favor a large community with a grant than to allocate the same amount among several smaller ones.[15]

A glance at the situation in 1956 bears out the conclusion that the task remaining in the Ohio Valley was to provide plants for the small communities. Seven hundred municipalities with a population of 7,600,000 had already provided treatment. Still without treatment was a population of 2,400,000 distributed among 780 communities, almost all of which had a population under 2,000, and half of which had under 1,000. In 1965, the average population of the 329 communities that lacked treatment facilities was 1,800.

The Pennsylvania grant program. When the federal-aid program was begun in 1956, Pennsylvania had already been embarked for almost three years on a program of state grants for its municipalities.[16] The principle

15. Distribution of grants by population groups for the period 1956–62 is tabulated in a report, *Intergovernmental Responsibilities for Water Supply and Sewage Disposal in Metropolitan Areas,* Advisory Commission on Intergovernmental Relations, Washington, D.C., October 1962.

16. This was authorized in an act passed August 20, 1953 (Pamphlet Law 1217 of the Commonwealth of Pennsylvania).

of allocation provided that every community upon completion of a sewage-treatment project was eligible for an annual payment of up to 2 per cent of the cost of the project (including interceptor sewers).

Unlike the federal grants, which are given only to new projects, the Pennsylvania program made provision for communities that had already met their obligation in preventing pollution as set forth in a 1937 clean-streams act, and the amount of the grant was proportioned to the original cost of the project. The amount made available for distribution each year is dependent upon legislative appropriations. Over a nine-year period (1953–62) this has totaled $18 million.

The actual percentage allocation varies each year, depending upon the amount appropriated and the number of claimants. In 1962, for example, when 252 communities registered a claim for their share of a total appropriation of $3 million, it was possible for the state to make a grant to each equivalent to 1.2 per cent of their investment in sewage disposal works.[17] The state requires that these funds be applied to annual costs of operation and maintenance of existing facilities. State funds are given in addition to federal grants.

The New York grant program. The only other state in the Ohio Valley compact district that thus far has sought to provide direct aid to municipalities is New York. In 1962, a law was passed to promote pollution abatement by providing funds to: (1) pay for comprehensive engineering studies and reports by municipalities; (2) subsidize one-third of the cost of operation of treatment works provided they met prescribed performance standards; (3) supplement federal grants when the allotment to the state for a given year falls short of claims made on such funds. The New York program contemplated a state commitment of aid over a ten-year period. However, money was appropriated at that time only for implementing the comprehensive planning element of the program, $1 million being made available in 1963 and $1½ million in 1964.

In December of 1964, Governor Nelson Rockefeller unfolded a proposal for state leadership in federal, state, and local sharing of costs for construction of treatment plants and interceptor sewers.[18] The essence of

17. In 1965 checks totaling $6,766,350 were mailed to 340 municipalities under this program. In addition to municipalities, 93 school districts were scheduled to receive a 2 per cent reimbursement for cost of sewage treatment facilities. (News Release: Pennsylvania State Department of Health, November 27, 1965.)

18. Press release of Dec. 27, 1964, issued from the State of New York Executive Chamber. See also the brochure titled *Pure Waters—A Program to Rescue New York State's Waters from Pollution,* issued by the State of New York at the same time.

his plan was that the state assume 30 per cent of the cost, the federal government another 30 per cent, and local communities the remainder. To finance the state share over a six-year period he urged the authorization of a billion-dollar bond issue. The bond issue was approved by the electorate in November 1965 by a vote of four to one.

Price Tag on Sewage Treatment

What has it cost municipalities to meet the obligation of preventing stream pollution? In the Ohio Valley a price tag of $100 per capita would represent a fair average of expenditure to cover the cost of treatment works, interceptor sewer installation, site purchase, and the associated engineering and legal fees.

Such generalization, however, deserves further scrutiny. The variability of local conditions, notably the size of the community, the degree of treatment required, and the topography and geology of the area greatly influence the per capita cost. With respect to size of treatment plants, the larger the population served the lower the unit cost. For the installation of facilities to provide secondary, or so-called "complete" treatment, which is required on smaller streams, the expenditures will be from one-third to one-half greater than those for primary treatment (sedimentation, sludge-digestion, and chlorination). Additional costs are incurred in hilly areas where pumping stations must be included, where a plant requires elaborate interceptor sewer connections, and where sewer installation involves rock excavation.

An analysis, using contractor's bid prices or final payments (thus excluding land costs and engineering and legal fees), revealed that the per capita costs of installations completed in the period 1950–58 (all converted to a common base using the *Engineering News–Record* Construction Cost Index for January 1966 and based on population served)[19] averaged as follows:

Population of community	Primary treatment	Secondary treatment
1,000	$88.00	$131.00
5,000	60.00	84.00
10,000	51.00	69.00
25,000	40.00	54.00
50,000	34.00	44.00

Actual per capita cost for a specific installation may be expected to vary from one-half to double the estimates shown. Most treatment plants

19. The construction cost index (1913＝100) measures the effect of changes in wage rates and materials prices. The index was developed by and is published weekly by *Engineering News–Record*, McGraw-Hill, Inc., New York, N.Y.

are built with capacity greater than immediate needs in order to service future increases in population. When per capita costs are computed on this basis the plant costs are slightly lower than those based on population served.

Interceptor sewers and pumping stations to convey sewage to a treatment plant site must be regarded as an integral part of the installation. The cost for these necessary appurtenances may vary from $20 to $200 per capita. This wide difference reflects the influence of topography and physical development of the area. Unit costs are generally higher in the smaller towns.

Average annual operating costs (including salaries of personnel, supplies, maintenance, and utility charges) will range from $1.75 to $6.00 per capita for primary treatment plants, and from $2.25 to $8.75 for installations providing complete treatment.

The total annual expense per capita for sewage-treatment installations, including amortization and interest charges on investment for interceptor sewers and treatment facilities, as well as operating costs, has averaged as follows:

Size of community	Primary treatment	Secondary treatment
Small towns (5,000 pop. or less)	$13 to $18	$18 to $22
Cities (25,000 pop. or over)	$ 9 to $13	$10 to $15

Per capita costs for some selected cities on the Ohio River (all prices adjusted to the January 1966 ENR Construction Cost Index) were as follows:[20]

Place	Population in 1950	Year contract let	Interceptor	Treatment plant	Total
Pittsburgh	1,366,000	1956	$ 68	$ 18	$ 86
Cincinnati	122,000	1950	55	74	129
Cincinnati	520,000	1956	55	82	137
Louisville, Ky.	369,000	1957	31	26	57
Wheeling, W. Va.	59,000	1958	55	121	176
Parkersburg, W. Va.	30,000	1955	144	39	183
Henderson, Ky.	17,000	1955	36	55	91
Jeffersonville, Ind.	15,000	1953	173	34	207
Wellsville, Ohio	7,900	1957	55	36	91
Tiltonsville, Ohio	2,200	1958	55	103	158
Rising Sun, Ind.	1,900	1954	170	68	238
Yorkville, Ohio	1,900	1957	211	161	372
Ravenswood, W. Va.	1,200	1957	21	139	154

20. It should be noted that construction costs in the period 1950–66 increased 4–5 per cent per year. Adjustment of contract costs to the January 1966 index brings these costs to a common base for comparison.

The average per capita cost for these projects is $161; cost for inter-ceptor sewers was $87 and for treatment-plant facilities $74.

Employment of Legal Compulsions

Not until nine years after its formation was the Commission confronted with a situation that prompted use of its enforcement powers. And up until the present writing there have been only six occasions of formal intervention. Meantime, the states have secured compliance from hun-dreds of municipalities and industries.

It will be recalled that Article IX of the compact empowered the Com-mission to issue orders on any municipality, corporation, person, or entity to abate pollution. However, such order could not go into effect without the assent of at least a majority of the commissioners from each of not less than a majority of the signatory states coupled with the assent of not less than a majority of the commissioners from the state in which the order is to be issued.

Critics of the compact had regarded the restraints set forth in this clause of the compact as greatly limiting its effectiveness for enforcement purposes. They not only foresaw reluctance on the part of the states to utilize this police power but pointed out the likelihood of action being blocked by "any municipality, corporation, person or entity . . . if it con-trolled a majority of the commissioners . . . from the state in which the municipality, corporation, person or entity resides or conducts its busi-ness."[21] In no instance were their misgivings borne out. And after the success of the first action—the Gallipolis case—a spokesman for the Ohio Valley Anti-Pollution Subcommittee of the Izaak Walton League appeared at an ORSANCO meeting to say that his group was no longer dubious of the efficacy of the enforcement provisions of the compact.[22]

The Gallipolis case. The first time ORSANCO was called upon to "unsheathe the velvet glove" was in January, 1957.[23] The City of Galli-polis, located on the upper Ohio River, instituted proceedings in the local common pleas court, challenging an order of the Ohio Water Pollu-tion Control Board. The board sought to invoke penalties against that city because of lack of progress toward compliance with interstate require-ments for sewage treatment. The city successfully secured a stay of action

21. Report of the Ohio River Committee, House Doc. No. 266, 78th Cong., 1st Sess., August 27, 1943, p. 51.
22. ORSANCO, *Ninth Annual Report*, 1957, p. 12.
23. *Ibid.*, p. 10.

in the lower court on the plea that the state board lacked appropriate jurisdiction. The state was thus hindered by one of its own communities in meeting interstate obligations, and the chairman of the Ohio board, who also was an ORSANCO commissioner, concluded that the state should avail itself of the enforcement powers in the compact. This view was shared by the other two commissioners from Ohio and all three joined in a formal request that ORSANCO institute proceedings to enforce compliance by the city of Gallipolis. Representatives of the other seven states unanimously supported this move.

When Gallipolis was formally notified of the intention of the eight states to bring suit for compliance, the city officials had a change of attitude. Three months later they informed the Commission that an emergency ordinance had been passed fixing rates for service charges in anticipation of floating a revenue bond issue of $900,000 to finance construction of treatment works. Thereupon the Commission voted to hold in abeyance the instigation of court action provided the city continued to advance installation of facilities. The city was also to keep the Commission informed by submitting regular progress reports. Some three years later the Gallipolis plant was in operation. In the meantime, the attack of the city upon the jurisdiction of the Ohio Water Pollution Control Board, which was successful in the trial court, was defeated upon appeal by the state.

The Huntington case. Not until 1959 was the Commission again called upon to intercede in bringing about compliance from a municipality. This time the request came from the commissioners of West Virginia, who concluded that their state agency had virtually exhausted both its patience and its legal remedies in seeking action from the City of Huntington. Ten years had elapsed since the state ordered Huntington to cease polluting the Ohio River, and the city still had no sewage-treatment works.

As a first step, after ORSANCO was requested to intervene, Huntington was requested to submit a report on September 16, 1959, outlining what it proposed to do about complying with interstate requirements. The city replied that it sought to complete a $5 million sewer program, following which it would endeavor to complete a treatment works by 1969. This proposal was regarded as unacceptable, and the Commission appointed a "fact-finding committee" to go to Huntington and consult with city officials.

Following this meeting the committee concluded that the city could complete treatment works by May, 1963, without undue financial difficulties. Huntington officials were then cited to appear before the Commission and show cause why, in the absence of an acceptable program, legal proceedings should not be initiated. At the "show cause" meeting the city countered with an offer to complete the work by 1965, an offer which the commission rejected. Further conferences finally led to an agreement whereby the city would complete the installation of treatment facilities by 1964. A schedule for financing and construction was established, and it was further stipulated that every three months a report on adherence to this schedule was to be submitted for review. This agreement was adopted on April 8, 1960, and under the able direction of City Manager Robert Hoisington, on whom the City Council placed the responsibility for executing the agreement, the schedule actually was speeded up.

One of the developments that helped to convince Huntington officials of the desirability of prompt compliance was a recommendation by ORSANCO to the State of West Virginia that it deny permits for the extension of sewers in that city until a satisfactory schedule for treatment was adopted. This procedure of placing an embargo on sewer extensions was shortly thereafter adopted as an ORSANCO policy to be followed by all the signatory states in dealing with delinquent communities.

The Terre Haute case. Shortly after the compact was signed, Illinois and Indiana requested ORSANCO to investigate pollution of the Wabash River (the boundary between the two states) and make such recommendations for its abatement as would satisfy interstate requirements. The report was accepted, and the two states undertook to promote remedial action.[24]

The Indiana Stream Pollution Control Board found it very difficult to deal with Terre Haute, a major source of pollution. In 1953, when city officials were finally about to issue revenue bonds to finance treatment works, a taxpayer's suit was filed to prevent the sale of bonds. The case was not settled until seven years later when the Supreme Court of Indiana decided in favor of the city. By this time, January 1960, the Indiana state highway department was considering a route for a new road, part of which would traverse the site chosen by the city for location of the treatment plant.

At an ORSANCO meeting in September, 1960, the Illinois commissioners asked for a report on the progress of the Terre Haute sewage-treatment works, and the Indiana commissioners conceded that they anticipated further delays. Not only was the city unwilling to accept the

24. ORSANCO, *Second Annual Report,* 1950. See Appendix A, p. 40.

offer made by the highway department for the site, but it had done little to expedite financing of the treatment works. Furthermore, a change in site would require revision of engineering plans. To break this impasse the Indiana Pollution Control Board requested the attorney-general of the state to enter a suit against Terre Haute seeking compliance. In view of past frustrations, the Indiana commissioners said they would not object if ORSANCO was asked to intervene.

On motion of the Illinois commissioners and with the concurrence of those from Indiana, the Commission unanimously agreed to employ its powers of enforcement. Accordingly, Terre Haute was notified that if it was not prepared to submit an outline of proposed action to ORSANCO along with a time schedule of performance, legal proceedings would be initiated under interstate authority. The reply from the city was nothing more than an account of its difficulties in dealing with the state highway department.

The Commission regarded this as an unsatisfactory response. But it extended one further opportunity for the city to comply, and at the same time appointed a fact-finding committee to stand by and go into action if the city did not reply promptly. Apparently convinced by now that ORSANCO was geared for legal action, the city supplied a proposed schedule calling for start of construction in December, 1961, and completion of the treatment works two years later. This was accepted with the understanding that progress reports were to be submitted quarterly by the city, and if these indicated that the schedule was being maintained the Commission would hold in abeyance any further action. Once started, Terre Haute applied itself so assiduously that the plant was completed six months ahead of schedule—on June 15, 1963.

Pomeroy and Middleport. On the Ohio River about 250 miles downstream from Pittsburgh the villages of Pomeroy and Middleport, Ohio, lie nestled together on the outer curve of what is called on the navigation charts "The Great Pomeroy Bend." Before and shortly after the turn of the century when the river and its fleet of packet boats were important means of transportation, Pomeroy and Middleport were bustling places. Today, they serve primarily as trading centers for farmers in the vicinity, and provide a pleasant, though somewhat isolated, home for some 7,000 people who are about equally divided among the two communities.

As was the custom for all communities up and down the Ohio River, these villages piped their sewage to the nearest outlet to the river. After the establishment of ORSANCO, Pomeroy and Middleport, along with every other community, big and little, along the Ohio, were notified that within a reasonable time they would be expected to provide facilities for the treatment of sewage prior to its discharge. Notice of specific requirements was served upon both villages in June, 1953, following a public hearing for this stretch of the river.

The Ohio Water Pollution Control Board, which requires every community in the state to obtain a permit for sewage disposal, thereupon conditioned its renewal of permits for these villages on a showing of progress to abate pollution. Finally, in March, 1960, the board concluded that Pomeroy had abused the privilege of reasonable time for compliance and denied renewal of a permit. Pomeroy then started suit in an appeal to the county court to have the permit issued.

A year later the Ohio board took similar action with respect to Middleport. Believing that this village would also attempt to delay compliance by legal action, the state board simultaneously instructed its interstate commissioners to initiate intervention by ORSANCO. The commissioners of the other seven states unanimously agreed to this request,[25] and then began the process of formal notice, conduct of fact finding, and citation to show cause why the Commission should not issue an order of compliance.

ORSANCO negotiations with Pomeroy reached a satisfactory settlement with respect to establishment of a time schedule. The village council sold a bond issue for $180,000, which had been authorized in 1956 but not acted upon, and thus secured funds to contract for preparation of engineering plans based on preliminary investigations made some years earlier. And it was aided by the Ohio board in applying for construction grants under the federal Public Works Acceleration Act. Both the Ohio board and ORSANCO thereupon agreed that Pomeroy had demonstrated its willingness to move forward toward compliance, and, at the request of the Ohio commissioners, ORSANCO withheld further action.

Middleport was not so co-operative. When it declined to submit a plan for intended financing and construction of facilities, the fact-finding committee went to Middleport to discuss the matter. The village officials were then given an opportunity to present their case before the entire Commission. The village insisted that it could not finance the required facilities and contended, further, that the sewage it contributed to the Ohio River was so small in volume that it was of no consequence from a pollution standpoint. Unimpressed by these arguments, the Commission ordered a formal hearing. Guided by the recommendations of its hearing board, the Commission, in May, 1964, ordered installation of facilities

25. ORSANCO, minutes of meeting, May 11, 1961, p. 212 in bound book.

to be completed not later than April 30, 1966. Middleport officials there-upon submitted financing and construction schedules that conformed to this deadline date. When delays resulted from legal action to obtain a suitable plant site, the village requested—and was granted—a time extension for completion to July 1, 1966. Other aspects of the program then began to fall behind schedule, and in September, 1965, the Commission adopted a resolution calling upon Middleport officials to show cause why enforcement proceedings should not be instituted in the United States District Court. At this point, the village submitted a program for starting construction by May 15, 1966.

The Youngstown case. It appeared for a time that ORSANCO might become involved with compliance proceedings at Youngstown, Ohio. Situated on the Mahoning River, a short distance above the point where this stream crosses the state line into Pennsylvania, Youngstown had been under pressure from the Ohio Water Pollution Control Board since 1952 to comply with pollution-abatement measures. Its progress over an eight-year period was limited to installation of trunk and intercepting sewers. Problems of financing and local litigation started by a taxpayer who questioned the validity of suggested financing contributed to delay in building treatment facilities. Finally, the Ohio board in February, 1960, refused to renew the city's permit to discharge untreated sewage. The city then instituted a suit in the county court to have this state action set aside.

Delay in having this suit processed led the Ohio board to adopt a resolution in July, 1961, requesting intervention by ORSANCO. Word of this reached Youngstown officials before action was taken, and when the matter appeared on the ORSANCO agenda in September the state reported it was on the verge of reaching an agreement with the city and asked that interstate action be postponed. Several months later a ground-breaking ceremony inaugurated construction of the treatment works, which went into operation late in 1964.

Embargo on Sewer Extensions

The denial of permits for sewer extensions proved to be one of the most potent administrative devices for inducing laggard municipalities to install treatment facilities. The Commission discovered in the Huntington case that what really disturbed the city officials was the ORSANCO recommendation that West Virginia refuse approval of further extensions to the Huntington sewer system if a satisfactory progress schedule could not be negotiated. The city was at that time already committed to a $5 million sewer-extension program seeking to bring service to real estate developments and industrial areas.

The embargo recommendation stemmed from the view that a community already causing stream pollution should not be permitted to create additional pollution by enlarging its sewage collection system. Most state laws contain a provision that municipalities must obtain state approval for extensions to a sewer system. However, such approvals were routinely granted provided the installation met required construction standards; they were not made contingent upon progress in providing sewage treatment.

As far back as 1949, shortly after ORSANCO was organized, Commissioner Clarence W. Klassen of Illinois advanced the view that this otherwise routine procedure might be effectively employed in dealing with recalcitrant communities. He cited an experience with a municipality in his state that had for years been dodging its obligation to provide sewage treatment. One day this city applied for a permit to extend its sewers to serve a proposed multimillion dollar federal hospital. Fortified by the knowledge that this extension would result in the discharge of more raw sewage into a stream already being polluted and thus make a bad situation worse, the Illinois Sanitary Water Board refused to sanction the extension until the city passed an ordinance formally establishing a financing and construction schedule for treatment facilities.

To add further emphasis to its position the Illinois board notified federal authorities that the city would not be in a position to render sewer service to the proposed hospital until it complied with state laws. Faced with the prospect that the hospital might be located elsewhere in the state, the city officials agreed to a stipulation that sewage-treatment facilities would be placed in operation before the hospital was completed.

The report of this experience made a strong impression on the commissioners from Kentucky, and, when Kentucky adopted its new water-pollution control law in 1950, provision was made for imposing a sewer-extension embargo: "It shall be unlawful for any person to construct or install a disposal system, or to make any change in, addition to or extension of any existing disposal system, or to operate any such new or existing system so changed, added to or extended, without first obtaining from the [Kentucky] Commission approval of the plans and specifications therefor and a written permit for its construction and operation." It should be added that the Kentucky law defined a disposal system as "a system for disposing of sewage, industrial waste or other waste, and includes sewer system and treatment works."

It might also be noted that in the "Suggested State Water Pollution

Control Act,"[26] first published in 1950 by the U. S. Public Health Service and endorsed by the Council of State Governments, it was recommended that state control agencies be empowered: "To issue, continue in effect, revoke, modify or deny, under such conditions as it may prescribe, to prevent, control or abate pollution, permits for the discharge of wastes into waters of the State and for the installation, modification or operation of disposal systems or any parts thereof." A disposal system was defined in the act as "A system for disposing of waste and includes sewerage systems and treatment works."

Recognition of the virtues of an embargo on sewer extensions to impress upon delinquent communities the necessity of meeting sewage-treatment requirements found expression in a resolution adopted by the Commission on April 8, 1960. The signatory states agreed to a policy of issuing permits for extension of sewers in a community "only when adequate treatment facilities exist or are definitely assured within a time satisfactory to the state."

One of the reasons why an embargo on sewer extensions can be so effective is that it creates a whole series of pressures on a city. Bonding attorneys, for example, are unlikely to give a favorable opinion on the salability of bonds for sewer construction, since they would be issued under a cloud of illegality, and municipal financial officers would not consider it prudent to release city monies for the unauthorized installation of sewers. Furthermore, a consulting engineer retained by a municipality could hardly afford to risk his license to practice in the state by working on a construction project unsanctioned by the state. And finally, every real estate developer or builder whose project depends on the installation of sewers makes his voice heard in the city council.

Thus, by the simple process of denying a sewer-extension permit, the burden of compliance with state anti-pollution regulations is placed exactly where it belongs—on those who are creating the pollution.

Summarizing Community Progress

What may be regarded as the fundamental measure of progress in the regional crusade to convert apathy into action—in winning support for the proposition that river cleanup is everybody's business—is the fact that the citizens of the Ohio Valley thus far have invested almost a billion dollars for the construction of pollution-abatement facilities.

26. A revised version of this document was issued in May 1965, by the Department of Health, Education, and Welfare, Washington, D.C.

By mid-1966, more than 99 per cent of the sewage emanating from communities along the 981-mile Ohio River was being piped into treatment plants. Eighteen years ago all of this effluvium poured into the river untreated. To visualize what these facilities are handling in terms of quantity, here is a comparison: if this sewage flow had to be carried away in railroad tank cars for disposal, it would require a train 350 miles in length every day to do the job.

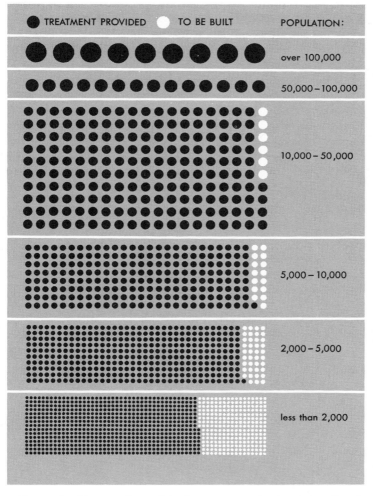

Figure 5. Status of municipal treatment plant construction in the Ohio Valley district by size of communities, 1966.

This advance in clean-up efforts on the main stem of the river has been matched by the installation of community treatment facilities on the tributaries to the Ohio. Throughout the entire drainage district, 1,399 communities—with a total population of 10,800,000—are now provided with sewage purification plants. What this means is that 94 out of every 100 persons connected to a sewer system in the Ohio Valley has made an investment in pollution abatement. How much? The expenditures, based on costs at time of installation, average $100 for every man, woman, and child! At current costs, the average would be $161 per capita.

Such is the story that unfolds from the united effort of eight states in promoting local support for clean streams. Figure 5 portrays the situation. Here, each circle represents a sewered community in the Ohio Valley; those in solid color had already made their investment in clean streams; those in white had not yet started construction. With the communities grouped according to size, this chart shows how much has been accomplished in relation to what remains to be done. The pattern reflects the outcome of the plan to secure compliance from the larger communities first because they contributed the greatest amount of pollution. The efforts of the states were thus tailored to secure maximum benefits from the efforts expended.

11

Industrial-Waste Control

Probably in no other region of the United States is there greater variety or more intensive concentrations of industrial activity than in the Ohio Valley. Many of these industrial operations are the largest of their type to be found anywhere in the world. Some had their origins in the valley a century ago and had long presumed a vested right—by tradition if not by law—to practice indiscriminate discharge of wastes. Even more of them had their beginning within recent decades when restraints on pollution received little support from a society that favored industrial activity more than it valued clean streams.

When ORSANCO started, some 1,700 industries spewed wastes directly into the streams of the compact district, and the wastes from thousands more were conveyed along with untreated sewage through municipal sewers into the rivers.[1]

As if this were not enough, industry was expanding at an unprecedented rate. The records of the Ohio Valley Improvement Association show that in the period 1950–64 new capital investment for industrial facilities in counties fringing only the Ohio River totaled $21.7 billion.[2]

Since industry obviously held one of the biggest stakes in the use and abuse of water in the valley, the Commission concluded it would be appropriate to devise means for enlisting the active participation of industrial management in the development and implementation of pollution-control measures. And since there was little uniformity of concepts or practice in the conduct of industrial-waste control among the states signatory to the compact, it was obvious that the viewpoints of the states must

1. A survey by the ORSANCO Chemical Industry Committee revealed that in eighteen of the largest cities of the district 4,200 industries were connected to municipal sewer systems. See "Report of Survey of Combined Industrial–Domestic Wastes Treatment Practices in the Ohio Valley Drainage District," May 23, 1963. Archives of the Ohio River Valley Water Sanitation Commission.

2. "Ohio Valley Industrial Expansion Survey 1950–64." Archives of Ohio Valley Improvement Association, Carew Tower, Cincinnati, Ohio 45202.

be reconciled to form a base for Commission policy and procedure. Accordingly, action was initiated simultaneously to find a way to secure industrial participation in the program and agreement on policy among the states.

Industry Action Committees

The ORSANCO suggestion that major industries assume leadership in promoting the control program through establishment of industry action committees met with considerable skepticism. The proposal was advanced in a series of exploratory meetings with management representatives of generic industry groups representing steel, metal-finishing, oil refining, chemical, coal, and paper and pulp interests.

As viewed by the Commission, the aims and purposes of these several industry action committees would be: to promote within the ranks of their specific industry an appreciation of the need to minimize pollution of wastes; to assemble facts and make an appraisal of the waste-disposal problems of their industry, with specific reference to conditions in the Ohio Valley; to consult with the Commission in the establishment of water-quality objectives and treatment requirements; to encourage joint research and development of more effective control of waste discharges through better housekeeping or by treatment measures; and to maintain liaison through the Commission with other industry committees for the pooling of knowledge and the dissemination of information.[3]

The Commission made it clear that it was not expecting an industry committee to define either in degree or method what any company should do. And it was emphasized that ORSANCO did not intend to interfere with any of the traditional relationships that existed between specific industries and the regulatory agency of the state in which they were located.

The organization, size of membership, and work program of each committee were matters to be determined solely by the industry groups themselves. The Commission did offer to furnish a staff liaison member to keep the committee posted on interstate plans and policies, to aid in the execution of the committee's program on matters of data assembly, research, and technical developments, and otherwise assist the group in its operations.

As a result of these proposals six committees were activated, each with its own "personality," reflecting industry characteristics and relation-

3. ORSANCO, *Third Annual Report,* 1951, p. 23.

ships, geographical and physical situations, and technical problems peculiar to certain processing or manufacturing methods. There was no uniform pattern of committee organization or activity.

Skepticism initially voiced by industry representatives as to the intent and value of their participation in the deliberations of a pollution-control agency began to disappear as they were faced with practical questions of mutual concern. For example, the metal-finishing group discovered through an exchange of experiences that there were a host of "good housekeeping" measures, which would not only minimize pollutional wastes but also permit the salvage of otherwise wasted materials. Indeed, it concluded that as much as 80 per cent of the pollution potential from some types of plating operations could be eliminated by the observance of certain precautions.[4] Since there were an estimated 2,000 plating shops in the Ohio Valley, the Commission urged the committee to incorporate its findings in a manual to be published and given wide distribution.

This venture stimulated the production of a series of manuals or handbooks on various aspects of industrial-waste treatment, analytical procedures, and the methodology of control. The educational value of the manuals was enhanced by the fact that they were compiled by practical experts in their field and written in a simple, terse style.

Eventually ORSANCO found itself acting as a publisher of a library of handbooks for which a lively demand soon developed both in the United States and abroad. Unable to keep up with requests for some of them, the Commission authorized their reproduction by others, either in whole or in part, and for those now out of print a loan service is provided. Among the most popular are such titles as: *Preventing Stream Pollution from Pipe-Line Breaks, Planning and Making Industrial-Waste Surveys, Disposal of Spent Sulfate Pickling Solutions, Reducing Phenol Wastes from Coke Plants,* and *Methods for Treating Wastes from Plating Plants.*

Because of professional interest in many of the ORSANCO committee technical reports, an arrangement was made with the Journal of the Water Pollution Control Federation for publication of those that were acceptable. Not only does this assure wide initial dissemination of the information, but it enables ORSANCO to acquire reprints at low cost to satisfy requests for copies.

---

4. "Plating-Room Controls for Pollution Abatement," ORSANCO Metal-Finishing Industry Action Committee. Published by the Ohio River Valley Water Sanitation Commission, Cincinnati, Ohio, 1951.

Developing control regulations. The manner in which the committees were encouraged to aid in development of regulatory measures is typified by the situation pertaining to control of oil pollution from boats and shore installations. It had become evident to ORSANCO that much of the oil pollution in the compact district could be attributed to carelessness or failure to employ adequate safeguards during the transfer and storage of oil cargoes along the river. It was not practical, of course, for ORSANCO to assign inspectors on these operations, for oil was being transported and transferred day and night on some 2,000 miles of navigable waterways in the district and at scores of installations. Furthermore, there were few established rules on specific safeguards that should be observed by those who were handling oil. Consequently there was no adequate basis for either the development or the enforcement of control measures.

The Petroleum Industry Committee, which represented the major oil companies in the valley, was requested to outline what might constitute appropriate safeguards. Their first step was to assemble advice and experience from among their marine and terminal-facilities managers. Working with the ORSANCO staff, who made a study of practices in other parts of the nation, the committee drafted "recommended practices for oil pollution control." This report described precautions to be observed by personnel and listed equipment and facilities to be employed on tank vessels, on river craft, at terminals and bulk plants, at marine service stations, and at other installations where oil products are handled. Also, it described emergency measures that might be taken to minimize damages caused by accidental spills.

ORSANCO invited the U. S. Coast Guard to participate in review of these practices because that agency has the duty of qualifying those members of a ship's crew who are to be put in charge of loading and unloading oil cargoes. Furthermore, the Coast Guard is charged with certification of vessels carrying oil and is empowered to order them out of service if leakage is discovered.

ORSANCO followed up its adoption of a regional oil-pollution control measure[5] with an administrative guide, setting forth the practices recommended by the petroleum committee. This document was widely circulated among all those engaged in using, transferring, transporting, or storing oil. It has served since not only as a handbook of good practices but also as a standard for judging compliance with the ORSANCO control requirements.

5. See "Recommended Practices for Oil Pollution Control." ORSANCO Resolution No. 2–59, adopted February 6, 1959.

As a further aid in promoting observance of these practices, the petroleum committee co-operated in the production of *Oil on the River,* an ORSANCO educational film that depicts the unfortunate consequences of carelessness in handling oil and illustrates the application of appropriate safeguards.

Industry committees also collaborated in the development of regulations for control of acid mine-drainage and for the notification of spills and accidental discharges. This collaboration in promulgating regulations improved their content and the practicality of their application. In addition, the exchange of viewpoints had an "educational" effect. Although it cannot be said that the restraints adopted by ORSANCO received universal endorsement from industry committee members, at least the aims were understood and in most cases sympathetically supported by industry representatives.

The detergent question. One of the special problems on which the Commission early sought help from industry was that relating to detergents. To what extent and at what rate were these synthetic compounds building up in Ohio Valley streams? Could orthodox sewage treatment processes be adjusted to remove them? What were the implications of detergent residues in relation to water supply and other uses of streams?

These and related questions were referred to the Chemical Industry Advisory Committee in 1957. A subcommittee on detergents was activated, consisting of companies engaged in their manufacture. As one of its first activities the subcommittee established two monitoring points on the Ohio River and thus supplemented the measurement of detergents undertaken by ORSANCO through a co-operative contract with the U.S. Geological Survey. Analyses furnished by the subcommittee of some 1,000 samples of river water taken at weekly intervals revealed that detergent concentrations averaged only 0.16 parts per million (ppm), the highest value being 0.59 ppm and the lowest 0.01. Findings of the Geological Survey from analyses in other sections of the river confirmed the fact the detergent levels were quite low; they showed a monthly average of 0.10 ppm, with the highest value at 0.30 ppm.

For comparative purposes, it can be noted that the detergent content in the Ohio River has averaged less than one-third of the limit (0.50 ppm) set forth in the 1960 Federal Drinking Water Standards.

Because the chairman of the subcommittee, Frank J. Coughlin of the Procter and Gamble Company, was also chairman of the research committee of the American Soap and Glycerine Producers Association, it was possible for ORSANCO to be fully informed on the results of research in the field. The activities of the subcommittee ultimately resulted in the production of a report, which was regarded as the most definitive assembly of information on detergents currently available.[6] Highlights of the report, which was released for publication in 1962, include the following:

—Household synthetic detergents have two ingredients[7] of primary concern: alkyl benzene sulfonate (ABS) derived from polypropylene, and complex phosphates, usually sodium tripolyphosphate (STP) and tetrasodium pyrophosphate (TSPP).

—Trace levels of ABS do not cause taste or odor in drinking water. The threshold level for each factor appears to be many times that encountered in water supplies. Only very sensitive individuals can detect taste levels of 16 ppm ABS.

—ABS has been shown to have no physiological effects on animals at concentrations many times higher than those in drinking waters.

—Laboratory studies have shown that as much as 75 per cent of the ABS can be degraded in river water over about 30 days, although the remaining fraction is degraded at a much slower rate.

—Laboratory studies suggest that the median toxicity limit (TL_m) of commercial ABS to fish is 3.5–6 ppm. Additional evidence suggests that the residual ABS after secondary sewage treatment is much less toxic than the original ABS. These ABS levels are many times higher than those normally occurring in surface waters.

—The complex phosphates used in household synthetic detergents are toxicologically safe, as indicated by their acceptance by the Food and Drug Administration as food additives. Related phosphates are also used in water treatment.

The effort of the Chemical Industry Committee on the detergent question is illustrative of the response received by ORSANCO from its industry committees in assembling information that otherwise would have been costly and in most cases quite difficult to obtain. A similar project involving the assembly of data on pollution from phenolic compounds was undertaken by the Steel Industry Action Committee. And both the

6. ORSANCO Detergent Subcommittee, Frank J. Coughlin, et al., "Components of Household Synthetic Detergents in Water and Sewage," Journal of American Water Works Association, Vol. 55, No. 3 (March 1963), pp. 369–402. Incidentally, this report was awarded a prize by the AWWA as an outstanding contribution to the advancement of knowledge.

7. The detergent industry in the United States has now replaced the nonbiodegradable ABS in household synthetic detergents with the biodegradable linear alkyl sulfonate (LAS). This changeover in composition, which was completed in 1965, was made in response to a growing public concern with foaming in sewage treatment plants and in waters receiving municipal sewage discharges.

steel and metal-finishing committees were major collaborators in the conduct of a pioneering venture on toxicity evaluation, which will be described later.

Summary. A unique and mutually productive relationship emanated from the decision of ORSANCO to enlist the intimate participation of industry representatives in its program. The effectiveness of the committees may be attributed, in part, to their composition. The membership was restricted to industries with operations in the Ohio Valley on the principle that only those who had a definite concern and responsibility should have a voice. Some industries suggested that they might be represented by their national trade associations, but ORSANCO felt it would be best to work with those who had common geographic and economic interests, who were informed on local situations and personalities, and who were organized for the sole purpose of pollution control.

Principles and Procedure for Control

There was little uniformity among the eight states in the practice of industrial-waste control. It was apparent, therefore, that agreement must be reached on the principles and procedures that should govern the conduct of the regional program. One of the earliest experiences of the Commission supported this view. Shortly after the compact was signed two states requested decisions in the case of several new industries that sought answers on permissible waste discharges into the Ohio River.

In the absence of any established interstate policies or standards the best that could be done was to ask the Engineering Committee for ad hoc recommendations applicable to the specific situations under consideration. In no sense, however, could this procedure be regarded as an appropriate basis on which to execute a co-ordinated program for the control of wastes from some 1,700 industries that discharged directly to streams in the region.

Existing practices. In some states the regulation of industrial wastes was administered through use of an effluent-standards system. Others preferred a stream standards-and-zoning approach. These differences reflected administrative adjustment to the varied legislative and institutional arrangements that prevailed in different states. The differences also reflected budget appropriations; where funds and staff resources were limited, reliance had to be placed on simplified types of regulation.

For example, the use of an effluent-standards system is suited to simpler administration. Limits are prescribed, in terms of a permitted concentration, to how much of a specific constituent can be discharged. These restrictions generally are applied to discharges from all plants, regardless of the size or characteristics of the stream into which the discharge is made. This procedure offers administrative convenience, but it furnishes no assurance that the controls will be equitable or rational. An extraordinary example is a requirement in one state where plants discharging acid to a stream were restricted to 25 per cent of the amount of acid purchased. Obviously the quantity of acid purchased by a plant bears no relationship to the capability of different streams to assimilate it. The best that may be said for such a regulation is that it does provide a crude form of restraint. The establishment of effluent standards without reference to stream uses and capability of assimilation has many shortcomings, not the least of which is that it may permit undertreatment of wastes in some cases and require unnecessary overtreatment in others.

Regulation by stream standards and zoning overcomes these shortcomings but requires much more data assembly and evaluation. First, a stream is zoned according to the existing or desired uses for particular stretches as revealed through studies and public preferences expressed in hearings. Quality standards are then prescribed for each zone, and restrictions on wastes are keyed to these standards. Zoning or classification of a stream calls for the appraisal of considerable data relating to stream uses as well as to the characteristics and volumes of individual waste discharges. The system lends itself quite readily to the control of sewage discharges, which are generally uniform in composition or volume. However, the procedure is somewhat more complex for industrial wastes.

A prerequisite for such practice, however, is detailed knowledge of stream-quality characteristics and hydrologic variability as well as data on waste loadings. From an engineering standpoint the techniques for such an analysis are fairly well developed. Ideally, the determination of treatment requirements should reflect economic evaluation as well as engineering feasibility, specifically in the realm of costs and benefits associated with the maintenance of various levels of stream quality. However, the paucity of data suitable for economic analysis is such that it places limitations on how far one may apply such refinement. Furthermore, the methodology for economic optimization in the field of water resources planning is only now becoming available.[8] Even so, use of the stream

8. See Allen V. Kneese, *The Economics of Regional Water-Quality Management* (Baltimore: The Johns Hopkins Press for Resources for the Future, Inc., 1964).

standards-and-zoning procedure for the establishment of treatment requirements—in contrast to the rough-and-ready application of effluent standards—does offer some opportunity for consideration of economic aspects
of decision making.

Formulating a plan. The problem that faced the Commission was one
of devising a program that would satisfy obligations prescribed by the
compact and which could be made compatible with variations of practice in the eight states.

The compact obligations were stated in these broad terms in Article VI
of the compact: "All industrial wastes discharged or permitted to flow
into [interstate waters] shall be modified or treated . . . to such degree as
may be determined . . . by the Commission after investigation, due notice
and hearing." From an operational standpoint this could be interpreted
to mean that no industry—regardless of how obviously it polluted a river
with oil, solids, or scums—would be subject to compliance with interstate
restraints until the Commission had completed time-consuming studies
and hearings. With its small staff the Commission could only conclude
that many years might elapse before industries in some stretches would
be legally accountable to interstate waste-treatment requirements.

In probing possibilities of overcoming this difficulty the Commission
noted that Article I of the compact pledged the states to "maintain the
waters of [the] basin . . . free from unsightly or malodorous nuisances due
to floating solids or sludge deposits." Taken together, these two provisions of the compact suggested a two-step procedure. The first step was
to impose minimum standards that would be universally applicable and
thus eliminate the need for studies or surveys. These standards represented the minimum conditions that must be met at all places and at all
times regardless of any other circumstances, and they could be justified
solely on the basis of preventing gross and obvious pollution. The second
step involved promulgation of supplementary requirements, the determination of which would require time for data assembly and evaluation.
By proceeding on a step-by-step basis, the urgent necessity for halting
obvious pollution need not be paced to the more deliberate and sophisticated process of promulgating detailed specifications.

There was no precedent either in concept or application for such a
procedure. Accordingly, the matter was referred to the Engineering Committee. Since the members of this committee were the administrators of
state pollution control programs it appeared logical that they should determine what course of action might best be harmonized with existing practice.

For a period of two years this proposal and various modifications were discussed, each in turn being referred to the industry committees for comment. This exchange of views provoked an intensive examination of the rationale of pollution-control practice, which proved to be as useful to the administrators as it was enlightening to the industry representatives.

Finally, there was sufficient reconciliation among the state administrators and industry representatives to permit agreement on a proposal to submit to the commissioners. The Commission made some minor refinements and then invited all parties involved to a joint meeting for final determination of the practicality and acceptability of the procedure.

Shortly thereafter, the Commission formally adopted a statement of principles and procedures by which it would be guided in establishing industrial-waste requirements. The principles outlined were these:

—Interstate requirements modifying or restricting industrial-waste discharges would be designed to safeguard and maintain those water uses that would serve the public interest in the most beneficial and reasonable manner. However, certain minimum requirements for blanket application to every industrial-waste discharge would be stipulated in accord with the basic directive in the compact that all waters are to be "free from unsightly or malodorous nuisances due to floating solids or sludge deposits."

—In reaching conclusions on water uses to be safeguarded, the Commission would be guided by its findings with respect to present uses and such future uses as could be reasonably foreseen. However, decisions on water uses could not be regarded as fixed and therefore would be subject to review in accord with changing conditions and on the request of any interested parties.

—Quality criteria would be employed in the appraisal of water suitability for various uses. These criteria would define within the boundaries of current knowledge the physical, chemical, biological, and bacteriological characteristics associated with various uses. Criteria would not be regarded as effluent standards but as a guide to decisions on maintaining quality conditions appropriate to the optimum use of a stream or a portion of it.

—The standard for water quality would be referenced to optimum use. Before a standard is established, there should be an evaluation of both tangible and intangible values, identification of penalties and benefits associated with alternative standards, and public hearings to ascertain public preferences and the practicality of their attainment.

—In designing control measures, the factors to be taken into account would include: (a) variations in the size, flow, location, character, assimilative characteristics, and uses of the receiving stream; (b) the variability of industrial operations and the influence of changes in location, volume, type, and combinations of waste discharge; and (c) economic considerations.

The policy statement concluded that implementation of control measures would be executed on a two-step basis: (1) the enunciation of basic or minimum requirements applicable to all industrial wastes discharged into interstate waters, and (2) a determination of supplementary, "tailored" control requirements developed in collaboration with appropriate state agencies for specific industrial plants. It was acknowledged that circumstances would determine where and how quickly supplementary requirements would be stipulated. Meantime, each state should aggressively seek to obtain compliance with minimum requirements from each discharger of industrial wastes.

Basic requirements. The concept of establishing minimum requirements was unanimously favored. But views varied on what should be included. What ORSANCO hoped to prescribe was a set of requirements that would apply universally to *any* industry discharging into *any* stream at *any* time. The draft finally submitted to the commissioners by the Engineering Committee, which by now was referred to as the "four freedoms" document, read as follows:

Industrial wastes shall be treated or otherwise modified prior to discharge so as to maintain the following conditions in the receiving waters:

(1) Freedom from anything that will settle to form putrescent or otherwise objectionable sludge deposits which interfere with reasonable water uses.

(2) Freedom from floating debris, scum, and other floating materials in amounts sufficient to be unsightly or deleterious.

(3) Freedom from materials producing color or odor in such degree as to create a nuisance.

(4) Freedom from substances in concentrations that alone or in combination with other substances in the receiving water may be toxic to aquatic-life organisms or may create toxic hazards to waters used by humans or animals. The burden of proof that questioned concentrations and combinations thereof are nontoxic is the responsibility of a corporation, person, or other entity making the discharge, and suitable evidence to support this must be provided to the Commission.

With respect to the first two requirements it was explained that no elaborate argument was needed to justify their inclusion as basic to the conduct of a pollution-control program. The third requirement, it was admitted, might be open to varying interpretation because there could be differing judgments as to what might constitute a nuisance or what was aesthetically offensive. The intent, however, was to rule out the indiscriminate discharge of dyestuffs, blood from abattoirs, odoriferous compounds, and similar materials which vitiated use and enjoyment of streams by the public.

The committee stated further that compliance with the first three requirements would satisfy pollution-abatement requisites to be set forth ultimately in whatever tailored requirements were promulgated. This conclusion rested on experience, which had shown that control facilities designed for the removal of solids, the capture of scums, and the prevention of color often provided substantial reduction in other pollutional characteristics of a waste discharge. For example, a sedimentation and skimming tank that removes organic solids and oily materials also minimizes the taste-producing potentials associated with such wastes.

The committee admitted that the fourth requirement—freedom from concentrations of substances toxic to aquatic organisms, humans, and animals—might be regarded as falling in the category of requirements tailored to each individual industry. However, the committee said it could not ignore a number of practical considerations. The discharge of materials that might be toxic to human and animal life, to say nothing of their effect on the chain of aquatic organisms essential to maintaining the self-purification capabilities of a stream, could not be permitted under any circumstance. Secondly, there was an admitted paucity of information on the potential toxicity of many materials discharged into streams; even with increases in financial resources and personnel, regulatory agencies would find it virtually impossible to keep abreast of the problem of establishing permissible concentration limits for every constituent or combination.

Finally, it was entirely in order to insist that industry not discharge wastes until it could provide assurance that the discharge would not constitute a hazard to public health or cause the stream to become sterile with respect to aquatic life. As a practical necessity, therefore, the committee recommended that the Commission promulgate a basic stipulation with regard to the discharge of toxic substances and in so doing place the burden of proof of nontoxicity upon the industry.

In the debate over adoption of these recommendations, the toxicity requirement was a principal target of attack. Industry representatives objected to the "burden of proof" stipulation as unreasonable. Objection was also voiced by some commissioners who believed that it would be unwise for the Commission to imply that it would accept industry's findings on so vital a matter as the toxicity of a substance. To the staff of ORSANCO this seemed to be an unrealistic viewpoint considering that the public water pollution agencies had so little information on the toxicity potential of industrial wastes. Furthermore, the staff argued that the Commission was not bound by this declaration of policy to accept findings offered by an industry. The recommendation simply asserted that the industry was to provide information on the toxicity of its wastes, from which point the Commission could then decide how far it should go in checking these findings.

To the staff at least, the position of the Commission was analogous to that of the U.S. Food and Drug Administration, which had long since pointed out the handicaps it faced in seeking to establish the toxicity implications of new products that were coming on the market. In fact, at that time the Food and Drug Administration was supporting federal legislation to place the burden of proof of nontoxicity on manufacturers.

To bolster its position the staff arranged for Dr. Robert A. Kehoe, director of The Kettering Laboratory, Graduate School of Medicine, University of Cincinnati, to address a joint meeting of the members of the engineering and industry committees of ORSANCO. An international authority in the field of industrial medicine, notably in matters relating to toxicity hazards, Dr. Kehoe and his assistant, the late Dr. Frank Princi, had already been at work for several years on an ORSANCO-sponsored project at The Kettering Laboratory concerned with the physiological aspects of substances in water.

Dr. Kehoe prefaced his remarks by acknowledging that the concept of "burden of proof" might be regarded as a relatively new responsibility to be thrust upon industry.[9] Nevertheless, he pointed out, the impact of industrial activities upon environmental health was such that public safety would depend upon more information than was currently available. The big question at issue was: who is to supply the evidence regarding the toxicity of a substance? In his opinion this was a responsibility that industry could not afford to dodge. And ORSANCO, despite its laudable effort to support toxicity studies, simply did not command the financial resources to deal with the host of toxicity determinations that should be made.

At this point, the staff requested Dr. Kehoe's opinion on the use of an adaptation of a statement of responsibility proposed by the National Com-

9. ORSANCO, minutes of the Engineering Committee, January 11, 1955.

mittee on Radiation Protection. The statement read as follows: "A written statement made by a qualified expert based upon his analysis of the situation shall be acceptable as evidence of the absence of a toxicity hazard in a given area. A qualified expert is a person fitted by training and experience to perform dependable toxicity surveys and to estimate the degree of toxicity hazard. If the ability of a qualified expert is questioned, the [Atomic Energy] Commission shall be the judge of his qualifications, in regard to which it may consider the testimony of other persons whom it deems expert."

Dr. Kehoe was doubtful that a single expert qualified in matters of water-pollution toxicology would be found. He recommended the substitution of a board or committee in place of a "qualified expert." He also took issue with the phrase, "evidence of the absence of a toxicity hazard in a given area." Noting that there would often be situations where no one knew the answer, he suggested that the objectionable phrase be replaced by "presence or absence of a toxicity hazard or lack of such hazard."

Unfortunately, the toxicity item recommended by the Engineering Committee was not accepted by the commissioners as a basic requirement. The requirement was adopted three years later, but no provision was made to place the burden of proof on the discharger of wastes. This omission was unfortunate, as such a provision is fundamental and should be included in any legislation relating to water-pollution control.

One other type of industrial waste was initially exempted from the basic requirements. Mine drainage was excluded "until such time as practical means became available for control." This was a concession to the notion prevalent in 1955 that there were no methods for control of acid mine drainage. In 1960, however, after the ORSANCO staff had compiled evidence to the contrary, this exemption was removed.

Summary. Following some two years of study and exchange of experience among the eight states, coupled with industry committee consultations, the Commission adopted on April 6, 1955, a statement on policy and procedure for expediting industrial-waste control. This statement enunciated the principles that would govern conduct of the regional program and set forth a two-step procedure for their application.

Recognizing the need for flexibility in dealing with a wide variety of local situations, the Commission asserted that it would promulgate tailored requirements as promptly as circumstances permitted. However, regardless of what these tailored requirements might be, it was also agreed that certain minimum requirements could be specified as immediately applicable to all industries. Compliance with these requirements was regarded as the foundation for the industrial-waste control program.

Accordingly, so-called *Basic Industrial-Waste Requirements* (designated as IW–1) were stipulated. This 1955 document was amended September 12, 1958, and again on January 14, 1960. The current version is shown in Appendix 8. By 1965 somewhat more than 90 per cent of the 1,705 industrial establishments in the Ohio Valley had complied at least with these minimum requirements.

Thus the stage was set to proceed toward accomplishment of the second step—determination of tailored requirements.

12

Tailored Requirements
for Salt Discharges

After the Commission had agreed on a general policy and procedure for control of industrial wastes, the staff began an exploration of how "tailored" requirements might be prescribed and applied. The specific problem addressed was how to control the discharges from brine-processing industries, which contribute salinity to streams, and in some cases add hardness-causing constituents such as calcium. This particular form of wastewater was chosen because salt pollution can be mitigated by dilution. And once the principle of scheduling waste discharges had been demonstrated for the control of salt, it could be adapted to substances with similar characteristics. The staff proposal that emanated from this exploration was later described as representing "the first effort in the United States to view a waste disposal problem on a fully basin-wide basis and to articulate waste discharge at all points with a regional objective."[1]

A bit of background. Underground accumulations of brine, along with coal and oil resources, are among the great buried treasures in the Ohio Valley. Origin of the brines is traced to the remote past when sea water covered this area. Saturated salt solutions, rich in chloride compounds of sodium, calcium, and magnesium, seeped into subterranean crevices. These reservoirs of brine are now a rich source of basic materials for an ever-expanding chemical industry. But, after the brine solutions are pumped to the surface for extraction of desired constituents, large volumes of saline liquid must be disposed of. Indiscriminate discharge of these unwanted liquids into the nearest stream has long been common practice. Where these releases are large in relation to streamflow, the quality of the water suffers.

An extreme example of such impairment is to be found in the Muskingum River in Ohio. Brine-waste discharges (containing primarily cal-

1. Allen V. Kneese, *The Economics of Regional Water Quality Management* (Baltimore: The Johns Hopkins Press for Resources for the Future, Inc., 1964), p. 99. Dr. Kneese analyzes the proposal and outlines an alternative approach employing a system of effluent charges based on damage costs.

cium chloride) from chemical plants near the headwaters of the river contribute so much salinity, corrosiveness, and hardness to the river that it is no longer considered suitable as a source of potable water supply. When the Muskingum empties into the upper Ohio River the tributary stream has on occasions doubled the salt content of the Ohio.

Downstream states had reason to be concerned about larger salt loads reaching the Ohio River, not only from the Muskingum but from other tributaries as well. Although the situation was not critical, a review of records dating back to 1914 revealed that over a period of 40 years the chloride-ion concentrations had doubled. Added to this was the knowledge that in the two upstream states of West Virginia and Ohio an increasing number of industries were tapping brine resources. Indeed, the very first case on industrial-waste control placed before ORSANCO— just a few days after signing of the compact in 1948—was related to disposal of spent brine. At that time the State of Ohio sought a recommendation from the new interstate agency on what it should do about the application of an industry for approval of the discharge of a daily load of 3,000 tons of salt.

As was outlined in an earlier chapter, the best the Commission could do was to render an ad hoc decision. Available data indicated that this single new source of brine waste could result in a 10 per cent increase of hardness in the river during periods of low flow. In the judgment of the engineers this was "too much," and since the company did not find it feasible to adopt another method of waste disposal it abandoned its plans for locating in Ohio.

This experience furnished no clues on how to deal on a regional basis with the regulation of brine waste. It left unanswered such questions as: if a 10 per cent increase were "too much," what percentage below this would be acceptable? And if a concentration limit was specified for the river, how might the assimilative capacity of the river be allocated among present claimants?

Not until the eight states had established ground rules, was it possible for the staff to suggest how these and related questions might be answered. Thus, when the Commission did agree on policy for control of industrial waste, as described in the preceding chapter, the staff began to develop a method for applying the principle of tailored requirements to a specific substance.

The Concept of Quality Management

In seeking ways to control brine discharges, the staff considered the possibilities for introducing a management or "systems" concept of water-quality control.[2] This study called attention to the sequential aspects of pollutional discharges. It described why application of control measures in a single stretch of a river or one of its tributaries could not be viewed as an isolated decision but should be evaluated with respect to the characteristics of the entire river system and the variability of its impact.

ORSANCO had already taken steps to provide certain management tools. It had inaugurated a network of monitor stations to provide continuous data on river-quality changes, and negotiations with the U.S. Weather Bureau gave promise of a daily river-flow forecast service.

With the availability of continuous information on both quality and quantity of flow, it would be possible to inaugurate a centrally-managed system of control wherein the releases of waste from various contributors would be adjusted to the availability of stream flow. River quality could be regulated by taking advantage of variations in the assimilative capacity of the streams.

The chloride study pointed out that unregulated discharges of salt entering the Ohio River resulted in chloride concentrations reaching a peak of 188 parts per million during low-flow periods in 1952–55. However, by programming these discharges in accord with river-flow variations, it was possible to "smooth-out" peaks and valleys of chloride concentration to average out over the year at something less than 50 ppm.

In addition to outlining a method for quality management, the study compiled information on how the suitability of water for various uses was related to chloride concentrations.

The programmed-discharge schedule was premised on the fact that concentrations of chloride wastes can be diminished only by dilution. Unlike organic materials, chloride salts do not "die-away" as a result of the natural purification forces that operate in a stream. Consequently, a system of chloride control in the Ohio River district could be viewed as being responsive to variations in hydrologic conditions, and the effect of waste inputs on downstream users could be modified by the addition of dilution water.

Five objectives were cited for realization in the regulation of chloride discharges: establish safeguards to water quality for those uses that will serve the public interest in the most beneficial and reasonable manner; provide for optimum utilization of the dilution capacity of the river at varying levels of flows, consistent with maintaining chloride concentrations within desired limits; distribute the burden of compliance with con-

2. "Chloride Control Considerations for the Ohio River," a report submitted on March 25, 1957.

trol measures among the states and their industries in harmony with the guiding principle of the compact as stated in Article VI, namely, that pollution by industrial wastes originating within a signatory state shall not injuriously affect the various uses of interstate waters; establish a basis for equitable allocation of assimilative capacity among those who discharge chloride wastes; and make provision for flexibility in the application of control measures to accommodate industrial expansion and yet maintain desired river-quality conditions.

So far as could be determined, no experience existed for a control program of similar objectives or scope. Neither was there any practice that attempted to provide for the equitable allocation of the assimilative capacity in a stream. Accordingly, the staff addressed the following principles.

For a given chloride concentration, as delineated by water-use considerations, the assimilative capability of the river could be established as a function of flow. When flow provided greater dilution than that required to maintain a desired concentration, additional chloride waste could be discharged. However, when the river flow was deficient for adequate dilution, cutbacks in waste discharges—proportioned to the flow deficiency—would be invoked. Application of this fundamental principle to an entire drainage basin in a manner that would satisfy the several objectives obviously called for a systems-type of approach.

Effects on quality in a river system are variously influenced by the location and magnitude of chloride discharges. And consideration must be given to tributary streams and their influence on the main stem in terms of both quantity and quality of contributed flow. In addition, the system should give cognizance to the preservation of equity relationships among the states and their industries. And finally, provision should be made for flexible accommodation to future industrial expansion.

A Suggested Procedure

To achieve the desired objectives the staff proposed a control procedure that would call for a uniform percentage cutback of both main-stem and the combined tributary chloride-waste loads above a main-stem point of use at times when desired quality limits might be exceeded; this action to be coupled with an adjustment of cutbacks in each tributary dependent upon the relative amount of dilution water furnished by the tributary. (See Appendix 9 for illustrative examples.)

For this purpose it was recommended that programmed discharge be practiced in accordance with the following procedures:

Quality conditions desired at a point-of-use on the main stem would serve as the basis for regulating upstream releases of chloride waste. As a practical matter the control point would be in that section of the river where the highest concentration of chloride manifested itself.

Variations in chloride concentrations in the Ohio River represent the cumulative effect of wastes discharged into tributaries and those released directly into the main stem. Because ORSANCO jurisdiction with respect to conditions on an intrastate stream is limited to quality of the tributary at its confluence with the main stem, the load from each tributary would be recognized as representing a single source of load input. Thus, the total chloride load at any interstate point of water use could then be considered as the sum of the upstream tributary loads and the individual upstream discharges directly to the main stem.

Availability of dilution water at the control point on the Ohio River was computed as the sum total of the individual increments of flow contributed from each upstream tributary drainage basin.

Because the chloride assimilation capacity of a stream is a linear function of flow, it is possible under any given set of circumstances to establish for each tributary drainage basin a chloride allotment related to the flow contributed by the tributary and the concentration existing at the control point. Establishment of a chloride allotment based on contributed flow—and related to the cumulative loading from main-stream sources and the tributaries—thus offered a rational method for allocation of total available capacity. By employing this procedure, each tributary drainage basin in the compact district would be entitled to utilize that share of assimilative capacity as determined by permissible chloride conditions at the affected downstream point-of-use, and for which the tributary provided its proportionate amount of dilution water.

Under this system, the quota for any drainage basin represents a proportionate share of capacity; it is not a quantity fixed for all time. As new or expanded industries in the district seek accommodation for their waste loads (either on a tributary or on the main stem), the allotments for the various drainage basins can be adjusted, along with the permitted discharge from main-stem sources of chloride. How often such revisions may be required is dependent on the location and size of new loads. As a practical matter, it is probable that the schedule of adjustments would need to be changed only at periodic intervals, say every three or five years.

Application of the uniform percentage-reduction rule to chloride releases from upstream tributaries would be conditioned on seeking a balance between contributed load and allotment. For example, there is at present one tributary drainage basin in the district—the Muskingum—

which contributes a chloride load far in excess of its proportionate allotment as determined by the dilution water it provides. However, there are
other tributaries whose contribution of chloride is far less than their calculated allotments based on the dilution water they supply. It was concluded, therefore, that when cutbacks were required the interests of equity
could be served only by first imposing cutbacks on the tributaries that
exceeded their allotments, and then on other drainage basins to bring
them into balance.

After the initial proportionate allotment for a drainage basin had been
established, a load-discharge schedule based on flow variations would be
computed for each main-stem industry and for each tributary. These
schedules would be prepared by the ORSANCO staff and then submitted
to the signatory states for consideration. After a schedule was formally
adopted for each industry, it would be referred to the appropriate state to
secure compliance. The discharge schedule for a specific industry would
be referenced to the flow of the stream into which the discharge was made.

In summary, the staff stressed the following reasons for adoption of the
proposal. The proposal permitted control to be tailored to fit quality
conditions as revealed at a point of use. Further, the control would be
exercised in a manner that reflected the capability of the stream for
assimilating the wastes. In addition, a method was provided for promoting
equitable allocation of available assimilative capacity, and releases of
waste were regulated in accordance with variations in river flow—as,
when, and where that flow occurred. Finally, individual producers of
wastes could be provided with an operating schedule that would govern
their releases to conform with a regional pattern of control.

The staff also offered an alternative procedure. It did not include all
the refinements or niceties with reference to co-ordination of tributary
loadings embodied in the longer proposal outlined. Instead, it permitted
all tributaries to reach a chloride concentration equal to the limit established for the main stem at a downstream interstate point of use. Only
releases of main-stem chloride loads would be proportioned to achieve
desired quality conditions; tributary-load limits could not exceed a fixed
quota. In effect this proposal allotted to main-stem industries the excess
assimilative capacity from tributaries where the chloride load was less
than the quota.

Reaction to the Proposal

Initially, the systems-approach proposal was not embraced with much
enthusiasm by either the state regulatory agencies or the industry com-

mittees. There was no precedent, of course, for programming control of individual waste discharges within a state in terms of their regional influence and as part of an integrated management system. Not only was the method regarded as complex, but there was reluctance to concede the practicality—or even the desirability—of ORSANCO's prescribing discharge schedules for individual industries. Thus the proposal was challenged on both philosophical and administrative grounds.

Among the industry committees, representatives of the chemical group had decided reservations. First, they saw no need at this time for any control of chloride. Furthermore, they were troubled by staff viewpoints on proposed river-quality criteria, calling them "unduly restrictive." Opposition centered on the recommendation defining a chloride concentration of 125–250 parts per million as of "doubtful" quality for municipal supplies, and a concentration of 50–175 ppm as of a "doubtful" quality for industrial supplies. It was argued that if any numerical limits were established they should be much higher, preferably 250 parts per million, the figure cited as a permissible maximum concentration in the federal drinking water standards.[3]

However, the staff position was that the federal drinking water standards should be regarded as an upper limit only insofar as potability was concerned. It did not take into account the economic aspects of quality impairment and gave no consideration to the suitability of water for industrial use. The staff estimated—on the basis of information it had extracted from industry records on the cost of lagoons and on penalties resulting from use of water containing chlorides—that for every dollar spent to "even out" brine releases the aggregate benefits downstream might go as high as $150. Admitting that information was scanty and the evaluation crude, the staff nevertheless was convinced that benefits from the application of its chloride control proposal offered promise of far outweighing the costs.

Ultimately all these viewpoints were aired before the entire Commission. The Engineering Committee, representing the state administrators, agreed that ad hoc decisions had been unsatisfactory, and recommended that a program patterned on the staff proposal be given a trial.

Many industry representatives hammered away on eliminating consideration of numerical criteria. In one effort to demonstrate that the proposed values were too restrictive, the Chemical Industry Committee prepared bottles of water containing various concentrations of salt and at

3. These views were set forth in a detailed analysis of the staff proposal presented on June 17, 1957, by the ORSANCO Chemical Industry Committee.

a meeting with the commissioners invited them to participate in a taste-sensitivity test. Conditions for the test were not propitious because it was conducted during a recess of a regular meeting at which many of the participants had been smoking. Consequently the results were not convincing about the taste-producing potentials of various concentrations of salt. Furthermore, such a test could reveal nothing about chloride-quality impairment with respect to industrial uses, which was much more critical than that associated with potability.

Meantime, the staff was having its share of difficulties in communicating to the commissioners both the logic and the application of its proposal. Accordingly, a simple "model" was devised to demonstrate the concept and application of a basin-wide system of programmed discharge. In this model the chloride loads were depicted as spoonfuls of salt, and the river flow was portrayed as buckets of water. By varying the amounts of each on tributary streams, it was possible to illustrate changing consequences on the system in terms of spoon-bucket ratios representing concentrations of salt.

A counter-proposition. Over the course of many meetings during the period 1956 to 1958, the commissioners were exposed to further examination of the merits of a systems concept of quality management and constraints upon its application. When the group neared the point of decision, a provocative critique was offered by representatives of the company that discharged the largest amount of salt into a tributary to the Ohio River.[4]

It was said that the staff proposal ignored the unequal distribution of natural resources throughout the Ohio Valley, as well as the investments that had been made for utilizing these resources. Therefore, the proposal was unrealistic. Furthermore, the staff proposal had far-reaching implications. It suggested that the Commission could use its powers to bring about a cutback in production by an existing industry in order to permit a new industry to discharge wastes, even though this would result in exactly the same quantity of wastes being discharged into the Ohio River.

As an alternate proposal, the company saw merit in having ORSANCO promulgate a regulation that would require all existing and future generators of salt wastes throughout the valley to "impound or adopt other control measures deemed reasonable." It was said that this procedure would extend the capacity of the Ohio River to assimilate chloride wastes

4. Statement of the Columbia-Southern Chemical Corp., June 14, 1957. Archives of the Ohio River Valley Water Sanitation Commission.

for many years to come. And when the condition was reached at which salt releases equalled the maximum capacity as determined from quality records at a control point, the Commission would declare that the assimilative capacity had been pre-empted, and no new plants would be permitted to discharge salt wastes into the river system.

The company pointed out that the principal difference between the two proposals was that the latter recognized an existing situation with respect to distribution of natural resources and plant investments for their use. As a practical approach to specifying requirements for impoundment control, it was suggested ORSANCO should stipulate that each industry provide lagoons capable of storing from two to three months' production of their salt wastes for programmed discharge.

Declaring that its alternate proposal was "not as neat and orderly" as that recommended by the staff, but that it was much more practical, the company concluded: "It is our view that the least practical and least constructive approach which could be taken would be one which cut back one industry in order to allow a new industry to discharge equivalent wastes into the river system before all reasonable control measures had been applied to both the existing and new industries. . . . This would be regulation run riot, regulation for the sake of regulation rather than for any constructive purpose in reducing stream pollution."

Reconciliation of viewpoints. The task of reconciling divergent viewpoints was assigned to a three-man subcommittee of commissioners. Following meetings with representatives of various committees and the staff over a period of a year, this committee made recommendations that led to adoption of a chloride-control measure on September 12, 1958.

The measure incorporated the principle of proportioning all "significant" discharges in accordance with streamflow variations, leaving it to the discretion of each industry to determine if this was to be done with storage lagoons or by the adjustment of production schedules.

Where lagoons were to be used, the "preferred minimum storage capacity" was stipulated to be equivalent to three months' production of waste, with deviations permitted only after consultation with the Commission. Schedules for release of wastes were to be provided by the states in which the discharge originated, but they were to be developed and co-ordinated with regional requirements through consultation with the ORSANCO staff.

Adoption of quality criteria was deferred. Having been informed that, on the basis of existing loads and the availability of dilution water, the proportioning of waste discharges to variations in flow could be expected to maintain concentrations at less than 50 parts per million at the most critical point on the Ohio River, the Commission decided not to commit itself at this time to a statement on quality criteria. This decision was influenced by the uncertainties expressed by the engineering and industry committees as to how the criteria would be employed. It recognized that currently the states did not possess enough information on local situations to permit them to adopt regional criteria that might limit freedom of decision on some intrastate tributaries. State administrators felt that if they were made party to a criterion that provided, for example, that a 250-ppm concentration of salt was undesirable on the Ohio River, it might compound difficulties in justifying acceptance of a higher concentration in some local stretch of a tributary stream.

This reasoning failed to recognize the distinction between criteria and standards, a failure that to this day continues to invite confusion and debate.[5] As viewed by the ORSANCO staff the criteria values were not intended as immutable standards; they were offered as yardsticks to facilitate judgment on the relative suitability of water quality as related to use. In brief, the criteria did not stipulate requirements, but they did provide a basis for appraisal. Whether or not certain quality conditions should be stipulated for a given zone or stretch of stream would depend on an assessment of additional factors, not the least of which would be some knowledge of the penalties imposed and the costs of preventing them. The reluctance of the states to become involved with the enunciation of quality criteria was second only to the opposition of the industry representatives to such efforts. The latter pointed out the ORSANCO criteria might be used as standards by regulating agencies outside the valley without reference to the understanding that criteria represented only one basis for decision making.

The rejection of quality criteria introduced an additional complication in administering the chloride-control measure. The absence of criteria made it necessary for the Commission to define what constituted a "significant" discharge of chloride waste. This became apparent only after the interstate control measure was adopted and both the states and the industries were faced with determining who was subject to compliance.

The definition of what constituted a "significant" discharge ultimately was formulated by the Engineering Committee in this fashion: any existing chloride discharge equal to or greater than 25 tons per day; or any discharge from a new or expanded operation greater than 5 tons per day;

5. For a discussion on this distinction, see J. E. McKee and H. W. Wolf (ed.), *Water Quality Criteria* (Publication No. 34, 2d ed.; Sacramento: California State Water Quality Board, 1963), pp. 3–5.

or any discharge less than these values which, in the opinion of the state agency, would cause local impairment of water quality although it might not otherwise affect interstate quality.

What Was Achieved

As a first attempt in prescribing tailored requirements it could be said that much was gained as a result of the chloride-control exploration. A method was devised for executing a program of industrial-waste control within a systems-operation context wherein the separate and cumulative effects of component discharges under varying conditions of river flow could be integrated with respect to their regional impact.

Whatever modifications were made to what had been termed the "neat and orderly" procedure proposed by the staff could be accepted as concessions to practicality. These modifications reflected the view that the ends sought could in large measure be realized without certain refinements in procedural detail. This was inherent in the recommendations that all lagoons should have a capacity for three-months storage of wastes. Staff studies had indicated that in many cases this volume of impoundment capacity was more than adequate; since it was an approximation that favored maintenance of higher quality and because the cost of lagoons is not excessive, the matter of precise sizing was not too important.

What became obvious from this exercise in devising tailored requirements was that the practice of programming wastewater releases—scheduled in relation to streamflow variations—deserves more attention than it has received as a tool for the management of river quality. Application of this relatively low-cost practice at individual sources of waste discharge has merits for satisfying both local and regional requirements for chloride-waste control.

Furthermore, it was demonstrated that systematic adjustment of waste loads to the availability of dilution water magnifies many times the potential capacity of a stream to accommodate such loadings. Some idea of this may be gained from the fact that streams in the Ohio Valley generally exhibit a seasonal range in flow volume of 20 to 1. Thus, a wastewater discharge that produces a salt concentration of 100 ppm at the lowest flow would result in a concentration of only 5 ppm at the highest flow. Consequently, by holding back waste discharges at low flows and by scheduling releases to conform with changes in the hydrologic pattern, these large variations in concentration can be evened out.

The economic implications of practicing proportionate discharge are significant. The ORSANCO chloride-control measure sought to recognize them. But the concept of programmed releases is not limited in its application to chloride control. It claims consideration as an integral part of quality management practice with respect to other types of industrial wastes. In fact, it was advanced by the staff in 1958 for taste-and-odor control. This proposal has been under scrutiny by the ORSANCO advisory committees, but it has been sidetracked because of priority given to other matters. The proposal is designed to inaugurate some degree of control on the release of taste-and-odor producing constituents by application of the threshold-odor test on industrial effluents. Discharges would then be adjusted to the availability of dilution water in the stream.

It cannot be said that the signatory states have as yet been responsive in implementing the chloride-control measure. Several reasons account for this. An attitude prevails among the commissioners that while there is merit in developing and adopting the measure to provide an example of how tailored requirements could be applied, the current situation concerning chloride concentrations in the Ohio River is not one to create any urgency for action. Furthermore, following adoption of the measure the largest producer of salt wastes installed a huge lagoon on one of the tributaries and is endeavoring to practice proportionate discharge insofar as conditions on that tributary permit. Because of the novelty of this operation and the desire of the state agency to satisfy itself on the outcome in the tributary, no effort has been made to involve ORSANCO in the scheduling of releases with quality variations at a control point on the Ohio River.

In another state, which has seventeen small producers of salt wastes subject to compliance with the measure, programming of discharges has not yet been undertaken. This has not elicited particular concern among the commissioners presumably because ORSANCO monitor records do not reveal that chloride concentrations in the Ohio River have been worsening in recent years.[6] In fact, there is evidence that conditions are static, or even slightly better as compared with past records in the stretch where the highest levels have been consistently noted (between Parkersburg, West Virginia, and Portsmouth, Ohio). At Portsmouth, for example, the maximum monthly-average chloride concentrations in 1963 and 1964 were 106 ppm and 71 ppm. During a period of similar hydrologic pattern in 1952 and 1953, the values were 116 ppm and 107 ppm, respectively. However, in this stretch of the river the record continues to show a wide

6. See ORSANCO, *Seventeenth Annual Report,* 1965. On p. 16 there is a pictograph on chloride concentration values showing maximum, minimum, and average values for 1964–65 at various places along the Ohio River contrasted with similar values ten years earlier.

spread between maximum and minimum values, the ratio being about 8 to 1. The practice of programmed discharge provides opportunity for smoothing out this variation in concentration.

Apparently the incentive for the states to implement chloride control will not be asserted until quality conditions manifest further degradation or until a large new producer of wastes seeks a permit for waste discharge. Should the latter occur, ORSANCO will at least be in a better position than it was in 1949 for reaching a decision on how such an accommodation might be made.

13

Dealing with
Accidental Pollution

As long as the Ohio River could be made the recipient of anything that one might choose to dump into it routinely or accidently with no questions asked, there was virtually little that affected parties could do but grin and bear it. After the interstate commission was established in 1948, this situation was changed. With the opening of an office in Cincinnati, there was at least a place to register complaints. And as time went on, the Commission had referred to it numerous cases of indiscriminate pollution of a kind that could be remedied without waiting for the installation of waste-treatment facilities.

What these incidents demonstrated was that no program of pollution control would be adequate unless it included means for dealing with the extraordinary results of accidental spills and carelessness. With thousands of industries in the drainage basin, with community sewers draining the wastes from millions of people, and with some 90 million tons of cargo being transported on the rivers, it is inevitable that the unexpected will occur. And these accidental discharges can, and sometimes did, involve the release of potentially toxic materials.

One of the earliest problems presented to ORSANCO was oil contamination resulting from breaks in transcontinental pipelines. Many of these lines had only recently been installed across the Ohio Valley. The experience of the state control agencies indicated that the operators of the pipelines were not placing sufficient emphasis on the practice of emergency procedures to minimize pollution once a break had occurred. The Commission solicited the aid of fifteen pipeline companies in developing a compendium of practice.[1] This handbook contributed to development of uniformity of practice and organization by the companies, and oil pollution from pipelines breaks has been greatly curtailed.

1. Published by ORSANCO under the title "Preventing Stream Pollution from Oil Pipeline Breaks—A Guidebook of Recommended Practice." September, 1950.

Until ORSANCO came into existence, there was no single agency prepared to trace the origin of an unusual pollution condition on the Ohio River, alert downstream users, and otherwise assume responsibility for minimizing hazards and preventing a recurrence. Although such matters could logically qualify for interstate attention, they were not covered in the compact or in the policy statement of the Commission.

Presumably this omission could be traced to the lack of precedent in state administrative practice for organized endeavors related to the handling of accidental pollution. Furthermore, the signatory states were reluctant to embrace any proposals that could lead to ORSANCO's becoming involved in custodial functions. Therefore, recommendations for development of an interstate "hazard and alert" procedure had to be paced to the accumulation of experiences that clearly justified it and, once developed, had to be implemented in such a manner that would not intrude upon state responsibilities.

It was contrary to a policy directive, for example, for the Commission staff to deal directly with any industry or municipality except by invitation of the state in which that entity was located. This suggested that in matters relating to unusual pollution occurrences the appropriate role for ORSANCO would be to act solely as the clearinghouse. In this capacity the Cincinnati headquarters could relay information and provide those services that might aid the states in determining the cause, expedite the issuance of an alert to downstream water users, and otherwise promote organized remedial action.

Staff efforts were directed, therefore, to development of clearinghouse and service functions. Establishment of the Water Users Committee, which instituted surveillance of river-quality conditions through a network of monitor stations manned by members of the committee, was a first step in securing strategic observation posts. Later, when circumstances demonstrated how prompt notification of accidental spills would facilitate operation of the hazard-alert system, a regulation was adopted by the Commission calling upon industries to notify state authorities by telephone when a spill or accidental discharge occurred.

Meantime, the ORSANCO staff encouraged fishermen, boat owners, personnel at navigation locks, and operators of waterfront facilities to notify state agencies of unusual conditions or to telephone reports to the Commission offices collect. Boat patrol and airplane surveillance operations were instituted. And by 1960 a unique electronic sentinel system, called the ORSANCO Robot Monitor, was placed in operation. Establishment of a river-warden program has been advocated since 1955, but the Commission has not yet shared staff enthusiasm for this proposal.

The Impact of Spills

The effect of spills and accidental discharges on river conditions is illustrated by the following incidents, which by no means exhaust the catalog of ORSANCO experiences. During the past three years (1963–65), for example, a total of 550 incidents involving fish kills, spills, and visible violations received attention of the staff.

One of the most dramatic and mystifying events was the wholesale destruction of fish life in the upper Ohio River in May 1955.[2] The first intimation of an abnormality in river conditions was a telephone message from the monitor station at Wheeling, West Virginia, reporting that the acidity of the river was increasing and that fish were showing distress. State pollution-control personnel were immediately alerted in West Virginia, Ohio, and Pennsylvania. From their reports it was concluded that an acid discharge originating somewhere above the Pennsylvania-Ohio state boundary was the cause, but the source could not be pinpointed. None of a score of industries in the area was found accountable. And, when it was determined that some 70 miles of the river had become acidified, it seemed highly improbable that any one industry was responsible.

Several days later—after the river conditions had returned to normal and there seemed little likelihood of locating the cause—a Pennsylvania investigator spotted an item in a Beaver Valley newspaper telling how local authorities had successfully dewatered an abandoned clay mine, which was to be used for a civil-defense storage depot. This was the clue that solved the mystery. When the site was visited, it was learned that "millions of gallons of water" had been pumped from the old mine workings into the Beaver River, a tributary of the Ohio. Chemical analysis of drainage still trickling from the mine showed that it was highly acid.

The devastation produced by this carelessness—resulting from a state mine inspector's having neglected to make a test for acidity before giving permission to pump—created a new respect for the potency of water in abandoned mines. The incident also created a new respect for the usefulness of the ORSANCO monitor system and the opportunity it afforded for interstate collaboration in tracing sources of pollution.

The phenol spill. One of the incidents that helped to convince the commissioners as well as the industry committees of the merit in prompt reporting of spills occurred in December, 1955. Again it was the monitor station at Wheeling that provided the alert. The treatment plant operator

2. ORSANCO, *Seventh Annual Report,* 1955, p. 17.

reported that he was unable to cope with "something in the river that was causing extremely offensive odors and noxious tastes" in the city supply.

Only after several weeks of sleuthing, however, which required the combined efforts of the West Virginia State Water Commission and counterpart agencies in Ohio and Pennsylvania and the ORSANCO staff, was the cause determined. Inquiry among industrial plants upstream from Wheeling led to this discovery: during repairs on a phenol-recovery unit at a chemical plant no provision was made to prevent hundreds of pounds of this odorous compound from escaping into the river. The irony of the situation was that a few years earlier the company had invested half a million dollars in building this unit to eliminate the discharge of phenolic wastes. A new manager at the plant who had authorized the repairs had not yet been indoctrinated in the importance of pollution control.

Virtues of mandatory notification. In reporting on the phenol spill, the staff director of ORSANCO noted that the Wheeling episode pointed to the necessity for some formal procedure whereby the states and the Commission would be immediately notified of any accidental spills, leaks, or other discharges of an unusual nature from industrial plants, municipalities, or transportation facilities. Such notification, he explained, would provide an opportunity to warn downstream users and would relieve the pollution-control agencies of considerable unnecessary expense in fixing responsibility. The time-consuming Wheeling investigation could have been avoided if the plant involved had made an immediate report of its difficulties.

The notion of mandatory notification of spills was enough of a novelty that the commissioners wanted time to consider it. Members of the industry committees, however, did recognize some virtue in promoting this aspect of the hazard-alert program. They had noted that when ORSANCO received an alert of an unusual river condition and passed on this information, the downstream municipalities and industries generally were able to initiate precautionary measures to minimize difficulties. It was the unexpected changes in river quality that caused trouble.

Abnormalities in river quality created by spills could be dealt with either by adjustments in treatment procedures at downstream waterworks (adding carbon, stepping-up chlorination, or in extreme cases, simply by halting the intake of river water until the "slug" of bad water had flowed by). At Cincinnati, for example, provisions for raw water storage were sufficiently large to permit a halt in river pumping for as much as two days. Many other municipalities along the Ohio River were similarly equipped with such storage facilities, the engineers who designed these plants having had the foresight to provide a practical means to deal with unusual quality changes in the river.

An alert served a most useful purpose, therefore, because it gave water purveyors an opportunity to institute preventive measures before "bad water" could enter a distribution system. These considerations, coupled with the fact that industry committee members were beginning voluntarily to notify ORSANCO headquarters on spills, finally led to adoption of a mandatory notification procedure in September, 1959. This was subsequently amended to include responsibility for providing data concerning the toxic potentials of spilled material as well as information on analytical determination of unfamiliar chemical products.

Opening the wrong valve. What occasioned the latter revisions was a spill of aniline on the Kanawha River, one of the heavily industrialized tributaries of the Ohio. A plant technician opened the wrong valve on a piping system, and, before the error was discovered, some 6,000 gallons of this product had drained into the stream.[3]

Aniline is a poisonous compound. When plant officials notified the state agency and ORSANCO of the spill, these agencies were handicapped in assessing the potential hazard because of unfamiliarity with both the toxicity of the material and the analytical procedures for measuring the concentration in the stream. The company, although it had a score of competent chemists on its staff, lacked the requisite information, and several hours elapsed while it was being assembled. Meantime, the control agencies considered it prudent to halt pumpage of water from the river at the next town downstream. Since this was a small community with no alternate water supply facilities, the industry arranged to maintain limited water service by delivery from another source using a fleet of its tank trucks.

Fortunately, the next water intake was far enough downstream for appropriate tests to be initiated before the water reached this location. These tests revealed that dilution and natural purification forces had dissipated virtually all traces of the aniline and the crisis was passed.

Mandatory Notification Procedures

Such was the background that led to Commission action in requiring notification of spills and accidental discharges. This unique and eminently practical step to protect river quality was set forth in ORSANCO Reso-

3. ORSANCO, *Twelfth Annual Report*, 1960, p. 3.

lution No. 14–59, adopted September 30, 1959, and amended January 12, 1961. Its salient features are as follows:

(1) Each and every municipality, corporation, person or other entity which or who may cause or be responsible for any spill or accidental discharge into any of the waters of the Ohio River Valley Water Sanitation District of sewage, industrial waste or other substance of such character and in such quantity as to be unsightly or deleterious to the quality of such waters shall give immediate notification thereof by telephone to the water pollution control agency of the state in which such spill or discharge may occur;

(2) Such notification shall set forth the time and place of such spill or discharge, the type or types and quantity or quantities of the material or materials included therein, action or actions taken to stop such spill or discharge and to minimize the polluting effect thereof, the measure or measures taken or to be taken in order to prevent a recurrence of any such spill or discharge and such additional information as may be requested by the state agency;

(3) It shall be the responsibility of each industrial establishment or other entity discharging directly to a stream to have available insofar as practicable and reasonable the following information pertaining to those substances that are employed or handled in its operations in sufficiently large amounts as to constitute a hazard in case of an accidental spill and discharge into a public stream:

(a) Potential toxicity in water to man, animals and aquatic life,
(b) Details on analytical procedures for the quantitative estimation of such substances in water,
(c) Suggestions on safeguards or other precautionary measures to nullify the toxic effects of a substance once it has gotten into a stream;

(4) A written verification of such report shall be submitted upon request of the state agency;

(5) Whenever any such spill or discharge may affect interstate waters which are within the jurisdiction of the Ohio River Valley Water Sanitation Commission, the state agency receiving the notification to be given as above provided shall promptly relay the information contained therein to the Ohio River Sanitation Commission by telephone in order to permit it to alert downstream state agencies and water users which are or who may be adversely affected by such spill or discharge;

(6) Nothing herein shall relieve any municipality, corporation, person or other entity from responsibility for complying with the terms, provisions and conditions of the Ohio River Valley Water Sanitation Compact or with treatment standards and other regulations promulgated under authority thereof or from responsibility for complying with any federal, regional, state or local statutes, ordinances or regulations which may be applicable.

The resolution appeared to satisfy necessities so far as land-based installations were concerned. However, there was still uncertainty about its applicability to cargo barges in transit on the river because of U.S. Coast Guard jurisdiction over navigation affairs. The potential contamination hazards associated with loss of cargo and the sinking of barges is discussed later.

Public relations aspects. Some industries privately expressed concern over the possible adverse aspects of the requirement to report spills. They pointed out that such an admission could invite the filing of questionable damage claims. Whatever validity this view may have had from a legal standpoint, the fact was that the states and ORSANCO had improved capability for tracing spills and for fixing responsibilities for their origin.

From a public relations standpoint there were advantages to the control authorities when facts on spills could be promptly assembled and assessed. A regulatory agency was hardly in a position to inspire confidence unless it could do more than speculate about pollution happenings of which the public might already be aware.

Virtue of readiness. Usefulness of the hazard-alert preparation was illustrated almost at once in a case involving the spillage of 50,000 gallons of liquid asphalt, which occurred as an aftermath of a storage tank failure following a fire at a refinery located near the mouth of a tributary of the Ohio River. This material got into the river during the spring and congealed in the cold water to form floating lumps of sticky tar that traveled several hundred miles downstream.

Alerted to this happening shortly after the tanks collapsed, ORSANCO headquarters computed, on the basis of river-velocity data, an estimated time of arrival of this floating material at various locations. This information was passed on to downstream state agencies and in turn to lock masters at navigation dams, to power plants, and to municipal and industrial water plants. Newspapers were informed of the accident and were told what steps had been taken. As a result, arrangements were made at some places to stop pumping river water when the tar floated by. At other places, such as power houses, emergency crews were readied to keep intake screens cleaned. The precautionary measures minimized the difficulties.

Nevertheless, substantial costs were incurred. One power company asked the refinery to reimburse it for expenses of $3,621 for cleaning water-intake screens. Another plant reported an expense of $2,321 in cleaning its river intake, and a third $600. The Cincinnati waterworks estimated the cost of cleaning pumps and screens at $1,000. The Louis-ville Water Company, some 300 miles downstream, reported extra costs of $634. The refinery did not reveal the extent to which it honored claims for damages, but it may be presumed that the amount was sizable, as the costs at five water intakes amounted to over $8,000. The obvious way to have avoided these damages, as well as the loss of an expensive product, would have been the installation of earthen dikes around the storage tanks.

The oil problem. Spillage of oil products is particularly obnoxious to boat owners. The tar incident, for example, occurred at a time when marinas were being readied for the season and many newly-painted boats were already at their moorings.

Some idea of the cost of removing tar from boat hulls and dock struc-tures is provided by experience with a relatively small spill of Bunker C (heavy fuel oil) that occurred in the Cincinnati Pool in the summer of 1962, when a damaged barge moored at an unloading dock. After being informed about what had happened, the company that owned the barge sent a representative to the area. He visited marinas and offered to arrange for cleaning the boats. The cost for larger boats (those over 30 ft. in length), which had to be hauled out of the river for cleaning, was reported to average about $50.

One of the remedial measures taken with respect to oil leakage from damaged barges is for ORSANCO to notify the U.S. Coast Guard. This agency has authority to order removal of damaged barges from service until appropriate repairs have been made, and the Coast Guard stations in the Ohio Valley have been most co-operative in acting on ORSANCO reports.

How deeply ingrained is the habit of using the river as a convenient depository for things unwanted is revealed by the action of a municipal fire department in flushing 3,000 gallons of diesel-fuel oil into a sewer. An accident at a railroad yard resulted in filling an engine turntable pit with the oil. To prevent a conflagration the fire department undertook removal of the oil. However, no consideration was given to possibilities of salvage or disposal at a dump. The oil was simply pumped into a nearby storm sewer. Complaints of pleasure boaters on the Ohio River led to this unhappy discovery. Two aspects of this case deserve mention: the chief of the fire department was an ardent boater and might have been expected to appreciate the consequences of adding oil to the river; and the municipality was engaged in a multimillion dollar sewage-treatment plant program. If ever circumstances should have caused some thinking about responsibilities for keeping the river clean, this should have been one of the occasions. Unfortunately, it is common practice to flush gasoline and oil into sewers.

Hazards Associated with Barge Transport

The hazard to water supplies associated with the barge transport of chemicals has received scant attention. Certainly it had not occasioned concern in the Ohio Valley, despite the fact that the region is interlaced with navigable streams used by barges, and these same streams serve as the source of water supply for hundreds of communities.

On January 13, 1959, an incident occurred on the Ohio River that not only revealed the potentialities of hazard from barges, but inspired an inquiry whose findings and recommendations offered promise of providing safeguards in case of accident. Several hours after the beaching of a leaking barge a few miles above a municipal water intake, a "benzene-type odor" appeared in the city water supply as well as in the atmosphere.

When this situation was reported to ORSANCO headquarters, an investigation was directed toward the probability of an accidental spill from an industry. At the same time, ORSANCO requested the U.S. Corps of Engineers to query their lock-tenders, who are on 24-hour duty, concerning any unusual happenings. One of them provided the vital clue: he reported that during the night he had observed leakage from a barge after it had been passed through his lock going upstream. Believing the cargo to be inflammable, he had radioed the towboat master that passage through the next lock would be denied because of possible fire hazards associated with the leakage. This is why the barge was grounded.

ORSANCO contacted the master of the tow by radio telephone to obtain details. He reported an underwater hole in the barge, which was carrying a liquid chemical identified only as "Polymer D" on the manifest papers. By beaching the barge he had managed to elevate one end and thus slow down the loss of cargo while waiting the arrival of another barge for transfer of what remained. Because the manifest declaration provided no meaningful information as to the nature of the chemical product (which represented, incidentally, a violation of Coast Guard regulations relative to the use of true descriptive names) the next move by ORSANCO was to call the traffic department of the company to whom it was being delivered. Here the product was identified as ethyl benzene.

Reporting on this unhappy event to the Commission,[4] the staff posed these questions for consideration: what responsibilities, if any, does ORSANCO believe it should assert with regard to the interstate transport of river cargoes whose accidental spillage or submergence could cause pollution of the waters? Would it not be prudent to undertake an inquiry to determine the nature and volumes of cargoes transported on the river, to appraise the potential hazards involved, and to suggest ways of coping with such emergencies? And, finally, had the time come to consider who should be charged with the burden of developing information on the potential toxicity of substances transported on the Ohio River?

The Commission authorized a staff inquiry, from which the following findings and recommendations were developed.[5]

Findings. Materials shipped by barge on the Ohio River and its tributaries include many chemical products, some of which may be classified as toxic. During 1958 shipments of chemical products, some of them in bulk lots, constituted 3 per cent of the 73 million tons of river cargo transported. Shipment of these products is increasing both in tonnage and variety.[6] Loss of cargo from damage to barges, as well as accidental sinking of barges, is not an infrequent occurrence on the heavily-traveled Ohio River. Such incidents must be regarded as one of the risks associated with navigation.

Present practices and responsibilities related to the transport and handling of chemical cargoes should be re-examined by navigation authorities and shipping interests from the standpoint of safeguarding water supplies. The incident that prompted this inquiry reveals the following deficiencies: (1) unawareness on the part of navigation authorities, shippers, and their agents that accidents involving loss of chemical cargoes may jeopardize the welfare of an entire community; (2) lack of a system of notification whereby navigation interests might promptly alert state and local authorities regarding accidents affecting the quality of water supplies; and (3) laxity in providing the true name of chemicals and compounds on bills of lading and manifests, thus causing delay in obtaining essential information about the nature of a cargo when accidents occur.

4. ORSANCO, minutes of meeting, February 6, 1959, pp. 3–4.
5. ORSANCO, *Twelfth Annual Report,* 1960, pp. 5–6.
6. ORSANCO obtained from Dr. George A. Hale, president of the Marine Chemists Association, the following list of "hazardous" chemicals carried in bulk on river barges: Acids of various kinds; ammonia and ammonium compounds of chloride, chlorate, and nitrate; alcohols (butyl as well as isopropyl and methyl); carbon tetrachloride and other solvents; caustic, soda, creosote and acid tars; diethylene glycol. Dr. Hale predicted that within the next decade cyanides will be shipped in bulk from Memphis to Pittsburgh by barge, with off-loading stops at Cincinnati.

Recommendations. It was concluded that there are ways to establish more adequate safeguards to protect water consumers from the potential hazards of accidental loss, discharge, or submergence of chemical cargoes carried on the Ohio River inland navigation system, and the report outlined these possibilities:

—Invite the U.S. Coast Guard to take official cognizance of the potential hazards to municipal and industrial water supplies resulting from the transport of dangerous and toxic chemicals on inland waterways. Land-transit regulations of the Interstate Commerce Commission with regard to leaking or spilled cargoes offer a precedent for similar action by the Coast Guard, whose jurisdictional responsibility parallels the ICC on matters relating to water transit.

—Request the U.S. Coast Guard to alert state water pollution control agencies (or ORSANCO headquarters, if this be considered more expeditious) concerning barge-transport accidents that could result in the contamination of water supplies in the Ohio River district.

—Invite the Ohio River Division, U.S. Corps of Engineers, to designate municipal and industrial water intakes on all of its navigation charts when these charts come up for revision so that towboat pilots will know the location of these intakes, should accidents occur that may affect water supplies.

—Extend the relationship between ORSANCO and the U.S. Corps of Engineers, whereby lock masters have been encouraged to report unusual conditions observed in the river, to promote prompt reporting of observations related to leaking, stranded, or sunken barges.

—Invite the American Waterways Operators, Inc., to review this report and to communicate to its membership the vital responsibilities of those entrusted with the transport of chemical cargoes on rivers that are also used as a source of water supply. In particular, it was suggested that the association consider means to impress upon towboat masters and others the necessity for giving immediate notification to the Coast Guard of any leakage or loss of cargo on the "dangerous" list, and to make masters aware of the hazards of beaching damaged barges containing chemicals in the vicinity of municipal water intakes. The association might also emphasize the importance of shippers complying to the letter with Coast Guard regulations relative to the use of true descriptive names on bills of lading and manifests, so that time would not have to be taken to determine the precise character of chemical cargoes when a spill or leakage occurs. For the same reason, attention should be directed to the Coast Guard regulation (146.06–12) requiring that the manifest covering dangerous cargoes accompany the shipment until final delivery.

—Bring this report to the attention of marine-insurance underwriters, who may employ their influence in lessening liabilities and otherwise furthering safe practices in the handling and transport of toxic chemicals.

—Request the signatory states to consider the merits of advising municipalities and industries to erect identification signs or markings on water intakes to aid navigators in spotting the location of intakes.

—Invite the Water Users Committee of ORSANCO to undertake the preparation of a manual of emergency procedures to be followed by water purveyors in the event of accidental contamination of the river.

—Utilize the ORSANCO interstate alert system and monitoring facilities for prompt relay of information pertaining to the loss of chemical-barge cargoes.

Implementation of recommendations. Progress in implementing the recommendations is reflected in the following developments.

The U.S. Coast Guard has promulgated new regulations dealing with the identification, shipping, handling, and notification procedures for vessels or barges transporting hazardous materials. In addition, the Coast Guard has issued a Chemical Data Guide[7] for use by personnel whose duties may require decisions in situations involving chemical shipments. Meantime, the National Research Council of the National Academy of Sciences and the Coast Guard have established a joint advisory committee to make continuing recommendations regarding the transport of hazardous materials.[8]

As the Ohio River navigation charts come up for revision, the U.S. Corps of Engineers has been amplifying the designation of the location of municipal and industrial water intakes so that pilots will be aware of the proximity of such intakes if accidents occur.

The American Waterways Operators, Inc., has requested its members to impress upon navigation officers and crew the necessity for prompt reporting of accidental discharges, and for strict compliance with Coast Guard regulation No. 146.06–12, which requires that shipping manifest papers carry the true name of the cargo and remain with the shipment until final delivery.

7. *Chemical Data Guide for Bulk Shipment by Water,* Bulletin CG–388, June 1, 1965, U.S. Coast Guard, Treasury Department, Washington, D.C.

8. *Proceedings of National Academy of Sciences—U.S. Coast Guard Advisory Committee on Hazardous Materials Conference on Barge Transportation of Chemicals, July 28–29, 1965, Charleston, W. Va.* [Washington, D.C.: National Academy of Sciences (National Research Council–Division of Chemistry and Chemical Technology), August 17, 1965].

14

An Old Problem — Acid Mine Drainage

Circumstances having dictated that abatement of sewage pollution be given primary emphasis, followed in turn by control of industrial wastes, it was only when these programs were under way that attention could be directed to the mine-drainage problem. This allocation of priorities represented a realistic appraisal of obstacles to be overcome. The problem was a complex one, shrouded with the most baffling technical, legal, financial, and administrative questions. And it was almost universally conceded that practical means for curbing acid drainage were nonexistent.

Despite these handicaps, which will become apparent in what follows, ORSANCO finally made progress in dispelling defeatism and then with the help of its coal industry committee developed some practical measures for mitigating the problem.

The origin of the problem of acid production from mines goes back some 200 years to the time when coal was first extracted from an Appalachian mountain ridge in Virginia. However, the pollutional aspects of the problem did not become acute until several decades ago when drainage from mines had vastly increased, roughly in proportion to the cumulative tonnage of coal mined.

The situation that developed might be said to stem from an unanticipated conspiracy of man and nature. Coal deposits contain sulfuric minerals, which in the presence of air and water are conducive to the formation of sulfuric acid and acid salts. Extraction of coal from the earth resulted not only in exposing sulfur-bearing materials to oxidation from air but likewise encouraged seepage into mine workings and contact with water. In brief, man aided nature in speeding up the leaching of minerals with consequent production of acid.

Interestingly enough, it was acid drainage into streams that offered the first clues of coal deposits in the Ohio Valley. Early explorers of the region observed springs and creeks that were yellow or reddish in color,

167

and noted that this condition was similar to that found in the vicinity of coal mines in England and Europe. For example, in 1698, Gabriel Thomas stated in his account of the land, climate, and products of the province of "Pensilvania" that "I have reason to believe that there are good Coals also, for I have observed, the Runs of Water have the same Colour as that which proceeds from the Coal-Mines in Wales."[1]

In 1803 another traveler in the Pittsburgh area, T. M. Harris, revealed in his journal that: "The whole region abounds in coal, which lies almost on the surface. . . . This is of great advantage to the flourishing town, for it supplies all their fires, and enables them to reserve their timber and wood for ship-building, and the use of mechanicks." However, in commenting on the water supply for Pittsburgh he reported: "But the spring water, issuing through fissures in the hills, which are only masses of coal, is so impregnated with bituminous and sulphurous particles as to be frequently nauseous to the taste and prejudicial to the health."[2]

Another adventurer into the Allegheny Mountains of West Virginia, Frederick Pursh, told of a spring in Greenbrier County, which he visited in 1806, saying: "The water is very strongly sulphurous and used to flow which is very remarkable, at different times of different colors, from quite clear to muddy, and of all shades of red, yellow and blue."[3]

Like many other industrial activities in the Ohio Valley coal mining is carried forward on a grand scale. Three-quarters of the coal produced in the United States comes from this region. The annual value of coal produced in five of the Ohio Valley states is reported to exceed the value of the entire yearly national output of gold, silver, copper, lead, zinc, and aluminum.[4]

The production of coal has been accompanied by the degradation of the water resources. An estimate made by the U. S. Public Health Service in the 1940's[5] indicated that active and abandoned mining operations were discharging the equivalent of some 2.5 million tons of sulfuric acid annually into streams of the region; today there is reason to believe the amount may be even greater. This acid drainage not only has been ruinous to numerous headwater streams but has impaired the quality of major

1. See Howard N. Eavenson, "The First Century and a Quarter of American Coal Industry," p. 17. Privately printed, 1942. Available Library of Congress, Catalog No. TN 805 A5 E2.

2. *Ibid.,* p. 166.

3. *Ibid.,* p. 246.

4. Report of the Ohio River Committee, House Doc. No. 266, 78th Cong., 1st Sess., August 27, 1943, p. 988.

5. *Ibid.,* p. 24.

tributaries, notably the Monongahela and the Allegheny rivers. And this, in turn, has had an impact on conditions in the Ohio River.

In 1943, the federal Ohio River Committee described mine drainage, containing sulfuric acid and the acid salts (sulfates of iron and aluminum), as one of the most damaging industrial wastes in the Ohio River Basin, with pollution from this source being greatest in Pennsylvania and West Virginia, the two largest bituminous coal-producing states. "The immediate effect . . . is to change the chemical character of the water. More specifically, acid mine drainage will: Destroy or materially reduce the natural alkalinity resulting in conversion of carbonate to noncarbonate hardness; lower the pH; increase the total hardness; and add objectionable amounts of iron, manganese, aluminum and sulfate to the water."[6]

The committee pointed out that these changes in water quality produce both tangible and intangible damages. The former included additional expense and difficulty in conditioning river water for municipal and industrial uses, as well as the costs resulting from accelerated corrosion of steel structures and equipment such as culverts, bridges, locks, boat hulls, barges, pumps, and condensers. Cited as intangible damages were creation of conditions unsatisfactory for recreation; retardation of biological processes that promote natural purification in streams; and precipitation of sewage solids by chemical action of iron and aluminum salts, which might produce health hazards when they are flushed out during periods of high water.

Some measure of the economic penalty of mine drainage in 1943 is revealed in the following inventory[7] of damages reported by the committee for the upper portion of the Ohio basin above the state boundaries of Pennsylvania, West Virginia, and Ohio:

Domestic water supplies	$ 364,000
Industrial water supplies	407,000
Steamboats and barges	1,143,000
Power plants	76,000
River and harbor structures	76,000
Floating equipment (U.S. Engineers)	5,000
Total annual damages	$2,071,000

Adjusted to present-day costs, this estimate might be doubled. However, even after such a revision upward, the estimate could be regarded as conservative since it did not encompass all areas of the Ohio Valley affected by mine drainage. And it makes no allowance for aesthetic and

6. *Ibid.,* p. 1010.
7. *Ibid.,* p. 1011.

recreational-use damages resulting from severe discoloration in some streams.

Coal producers did not deny the damaging aspects of mine drainage. But they also credited it with some virtue, as revealed from this statement in 1936 by Howard N. Eavenson, a mining engineer and coal operator. Said Mr. Eavenson:[8] "There is no doubt that this (mine acid) is detrimental to the fish life, and the coal industry recognizes the fact that such drainage not only impairs the appearance of streams but also renders them unfit for human or animal use. It should be remembered, however, that the presence of such acid mine water in streams helps to neutralize the sewage which is discharged into so many of our streams, which would be a greater nuisance than it now is if it were not for this acid water."

A more recent appraisal by a coal-industry representative concerning damages and the cost of preventing them is contained in testimony presented at a 1963 conference on pollution control in the Monongahela River basin. The witness was Ernst P. Hall, research consultant of the Consolidation Coal Company, who said:[9]

> In its presentation, HEW [the U. S. Department of Health, Education, and Welfare] estimates that acid mine drainage in the Monongahela River causes damages in the amount of $2,251,000 per year, primarily to water treatment plants, boats and barges using the river and dam installations. While we do not desire to argue the amount of these alleged damages, we suggest that these claims should be viewed in their proper economic perspective.

Mr. Hall then pointed out that a survey of coal company operations in this valley indicated steps were being taken at every mine to "control, reduce and/or ameliorate the undesirable effects of mine drainage." Expenditures for this purpose were said to average more than 5 cents per ton of coal produced or a total of $3 million annually. This expense was cited as representing "one million dollars a year more than the alleged damages." Mr. Hall also reminded the conferees that: ". . . acid mine drainage can and does inhibit and destroy many pathogenic organisms which may find their way into surface waters. The high degrees of bacterial pollution which are theoretically possible have not developed in the Monongahela basin primarily due to the sterilizing effect of acid mine drainage present in these rivers."

---

8. *Hearings* before a subcommittee of the Committee of Commerce, U.S. Senate, 74th Cong., 2nd Sess., February–May, 1936, p. 189.

9. Statement presented at a conference called by the Secretary of the U.S. Department of Health, Education, and Welfare in Pittsburgh, Pa., December 17–18, 1963. On file in the office of ORSANCO.

Attempts at Corrective Action

Legal and technical efforts to promote the application of remedial measures, with only a few exceptions, reflect a dismal record of frustration and ineffectiveness. In regions whose livelihood depended on coal mining there were many influences that denied any hindrance to such activity. Thus when proposals were introduced in state legislatures to strengthen anti-pollution measures an exemption would inevitably be granted concerning mine drainage until such times as "practical means" were available to deal with it.[10] This situation was hardly calculated to create incentives for the industry to attack the problem aggressively.

How ingrained was the notion that the pollution problems of the coal industry occupied a privileged position was evidenced when ORSANCO adopted its minimum industrial-waste control requirements in 1955 (see Chapter 11). All industrial discharges were placed under restraints "exclusive of mine drainage until such time as practical means are available for control." It was not until 1960—after the engineering committee of ORSANCO asserted that the possibilities for control were not as hopeless as had been portrayed—that the commissioners found justification for removing the exemption given to mine drainage. This paved the way for removal of exemptions in some of the signatory states. How this came about will be detailed further on.

Meanwhile, it should be noted that the Commonwealth of Pennsylvania endeavored to deal with some basic aspects of mine-drainage control in 1945. At that time the Sanitary Water Board was given power to prevent drainage of mine acid into "clean waters of the Commonwealth which are being devoted or put to public use at the time of such discharge." Furthermore, it was made mandatory that mine operators apply for a permit before starting a new operation. Conditions set forth in each permit were designed to minimize discharge of acid waters. Violation of these conditions constituted grounds for rescinding a permit and halting an operation.

10. Typical of the provisos was that in the Pennsylvania Clean Streams Law (Act of June 22, 1937, P.L. 1987) wherein it is asserted in Section 310: "The provisions of this article shall not apply until such time, as in the opinion of the Sanitary Water Board, practical means for the removal of the polluting properties of such drainage shall become known." Amendments to this act in 1945 (P.L. 435–35 P.S. aa 691.1 to 691.801), although specifically intended to effectuate pollution control at mines, contained the same limiting language with respect to acid drainage. However, in 1965 the law was again amended (Act 194) and this time "industrial wastes" were redefined to include mine drainage, thus removing previous exemptions.

In essence, this legislation incorporated principles that had been espoused a decade earlier by Kenneth E. Reid, then a member of the Board of Fish Commissioners of Pennsylvania and later executive director of the Izaak Walton League. In 1936, in testimony before a subcommittee of Congress,[11] Mr. Reid argued that some degree of prevention could be exercised by imposing conditions prior to the opening of new mines. He said:

> The opening of a coal mine is more than an exclusive concern of private capital on private land. It is distinctly social and public in its aspect when it causes acidulous water to be formed and flow down over the lands of others, adversely affecting much land and many people below.
>
> In view of these considerations, it seems not only highly desirable, but entirely proper that some agency of the government function as a licensing board for proposed new mines. If the applicant could put up adequate guarantees that his water would not pollute an unpolluted stream and that he would properly seal the mine on completion of operations, he would qualify for a permit; otherwise he would not.

What the courts concluded. Pollution caused by mine drainage resulted in legal proceedings that provide some insight on how the courts viewed the matter. Details of five cases are shown in the tabulation on page 174.

In the Sanderson case the court ruled in effect that the Pennsylvania coal industry was more important than the preservation of a private fish pond, and consequently the inconvenience of the individual was secondary to the necessities of an enterprise that benefited the community. In the Indian Creek case the court concluded that since mine drainage was destroying both a public and an industry water supply it must be curbed in the interests of equity. The Pennsylvania court was upheld in the latter case by the Supreme Court of the United States.

In the third case, strip and underground mine drainage destroyed the water supply of Shinnston, W. Va. When faced with court action, the mining companies reached a settlement with the city by making a payment of $70,500. The money was used to develop a new source of supply.

In the Black and Goebel case the Pennsylvania Supreme Court upheld the right of the commonwealth to seek assurance, before issuing a permit, that new mining operations would not cause degradation of streams.

In the West Penn case where a water supply was polluted by the strip-mining activities of three companies, these companies elected to settle the matter when faced with court action. A sum of $500,000 was paid to the water company for development of a new water supply.

11. *Hearings, op. cit.,* p. 23.

Technological considerations. In addition to legal complications, the mine-acid problem was beset with frustrations associated with the employment of technological solutions. For example, neutralization of mine acid by treatment with lime or limestone was one of the earliest proposals advanced as a remedial measure. But the coal industry ruled this out as impractical on two counts: first, it was claimed that the cost of the enormous quantities of lime required for treatment could exceed the value of the coal produced; and second, it would be as expensive and difficult to dispose of the sludge as to deal with the acid itself. A 1933 report[12] of the Engineering Experiment Station of the University of West Virginia supported these views.

Andrew B. Crichton, an engineer and mine operator who represented the National Coal Association at a Congressional hearing in 1936,[13] offered these pessimistic conclusions:

> In the light of present knowledge there is no known satisfactory method of treating mine drainage. Under these circumstances, any legislation would be unwise, would result in confusion, unnecessary expense, and would do no good. The cost of neutralizing mine water has been variously estimated by different chemists at from 15 to 25¢ per thousand gallons. . . . the cost of lime treatment plants for the enormous quantity of mine drainage now flowing into the streams in the bituminous fields of Pennsylvania would be $75 million. The annual cost of treatment at 15¢ per thousand gallons would be over $41 million; and at 25¢ per thousand gallons, over $68 million.

Testimony from Howard N. Eavenson before the same committee included these comments:[14]

> It has been mentioned before this committee . . . that methods were devised years ago and put into practice by which valuable by-products could be recovered from this acid mine water, and the water be purified, but that the coal companies have purposely kept such knowledge from becoming public. The facts are these:
> About 1916 the H. C. Frick Coke Company, which is a subsidiary of United States Steel Corporation, was short of water for quenching coke at its Calumet Plant in Westmoreland County, Pennsylvania. This plant was on Sewickley Creek, which was intensely acid from mine drainage. As a result of years of study of this problem, a plant was built to purify this water and to recover the hydrated oxide of iron it

12. See *Acid Mine Drainage from Bituminous Coal Mines*, Research Bulletin No. 10, Engineering Experiment Station, University of West Virginia, September 1933.
13. *Hearings, op. cit.*, pp. 192–97.
14. *Ibid.*, p. 191.

Significant Court Cases Relating to Stream Pollution and the Coal Mining Industry[a]

Case and State	Type of Pollution	Action of Court	Remarks
Sanderson vs. The Pa. Coal Co., Penna. (1) (1878) 86 Pa. 401 102 Pa. 370	Destruction of private fish pond by mine acid.	Damage suit tried in Lackawanna County Court and twice in Supreme Court, Pa. Court finally ruled that trifling inconvenience to an individual must sometimes give way to necessities of a great community.	Court affirmed the fact that Pennsylvania coal industry was more important than this private fish pond.
Pennsylvania Railroad et al vs. Sagmore Coal Co. 281 Pa. 233 126 A. 386 Sagmore Coal Co. vs. Mountain Water Supply Co. 267 U. S. 592	Mine drainage destroyed Indian Creek, Penna., as source of water supply for several communities and the Pennsylvania Railroad (1).	Fayette County Court refused to grant an injunction against coal company and was reversed by state supreme court. Supreme Court of United States upheld state supreme court in that mining company must cease to discharge mine water into creek after certain date.	Court affirmed the principle that this discharge destroyed the public water supply of a large number of people and an important industry and thus must be discontinued.
Shinnston Water Supply West Virginia (16), (17), 1948. (Common law trespass action in Harrison County Circuit Court.)	Acid mine drainage destroyed Robinson Run as source of water supply for Shinnston and environs. City reservoir was seriously silted by strip mining.	Three mining companies involved. One company settled before suit was instituted. Two other companies settled after cases were instituted in the circuit court.	Damages were recovered as follows: Company A—$17,000 Company B— 50,000 Company C— 3,500 Total —$70,500

Black and Goebel, Westmoreland Co., Pennsylvania, 1949 (18) (Comm. of Pa. ex rel Chidsey, Attorney General, Appellant vs. Black et al) 363 Pa. 229	Strip mine drainage into Powder Mill Run and Loyalhanna Creek, both clean streams.	Sanitary Water Board sought an injunction against mining company in Dauphin County Court since mining was started without permit. Court ruled that mining could continue if stream were not polluted and brushed aside the contention that permit was necessary. When appealed to State Supreme Court, the lower court was reversed on permit question.	As a result of court action it is understood that the Black and Goebel lease has been cancelled. Supreme Court ruled that Commonwealth was justified in seeking assurance that new mining operations will not destroy purity of stream before issuing permit.
McDonald Water Supply Case (19) (21) Pennsylvania, 1945 (Turberville vs. West Penn Water Co. et al) 60 D & C 557	Strip mining destroyed stream as a source of water supply for the West Penn Water Company which supplied the town of McDonald and environs as well as several large industries.	Water Company brought suit in equity before Court of Common Pleas of Allegheny County to enjoin pollution. The suit was pressed to trial and a compromise settlement reached representing the valuation of the supply destroyed.	As a result of strip-mine drainage destroying the water supply and the imminence of a court injunction, the mining companies paid to the water company $500,000 damages.

a ORSANCO, *Second Annual Report*, 1950, p. 32.

contained.[15] It was operated until 1923, when the coke plant was shut down, and the water treating plant has since been dismantled. The treated water was used only for quenching coke and was suitable for no other purpose without additional treatment.

During the operation of this plant the best it ever did was to break even at war prices for the materials produced, which were much higher than they now are, and under existing costs of labor and materials, and of sales prices, it would be impossible to even approximately break even.

Some ten years after this testimony—the Pennsylvania pollution law having been amended in 1945 to prohibit the discharge of acid drainage to certain waters designated as "clean streams"—operators seeking permits for new mines found it feasible to accept a restriction requiring neutralization of acid. And a 1965 amendment to the law establishes discharge limitations for all mine drainage that, in many cases, can only be satisfied with acid neutralization. While it is too early to assess the impact of this requirement, some observations can be made. Treatment facilities are being installed; sludge problems do not appear as formidable as once pictured because plans are being made to dispose of this material in the workings from which the coal was extracted; and, finally, the compulsion of having to treat mine drainage has provided incentives to minimize its formation, largely by controlling entry of water in the mines.

Mine-Sealing Theory and Practice

What appeared to offer promise for control of mine acid drainage was a proposal by the U. S. Bureau of Mines in the early twenties to test the feasibility of applying nature's own remedy for preventing acid formation, namely, by excluding air or water or both from mine workings. Laboratory and field work started by the bureau in 1924 suggested possibilities of sealing abandoned mines to minimize exposure to air. But no funds were available to undertake a demonstration of mine-sealing procedures until 1933.

At that time the national government was embarked on a program of financing local unemployment-relief projects. Mine sealing was adaptable to use of local labor, and $1.5 million was initially allocated for such work in the eastern coal-producing states, including Pennsylvania, Ohio, West Virginia, Kentucky, and Indiana.

15. A detailed description was given by L. D. Tracy at a meeting of the American Institute of Mining and Metallurgical Engineers in 1926. See "Mine Water Neutralizing Plant at Calumet Mine" published in *Proceedings* of the Institute, Vol. 66, pp. 609–23.

Sealing operations involved the closure of mine entries with a masonry wall. A water trap or siphon-type opening built into the base of the wall permitted accumulated drainage to escape from the mine without letting air into the workings. At the same time, surface water was diverted from places where it could enter the mine, and attempts were made to close earth fissures through which water. might seep. In effect, therefore, two types of sealing were performed—air and water—but the results, unfortunately were not separately evaluated.

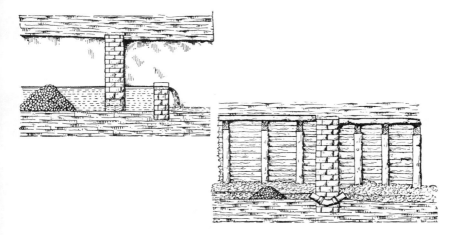

Figure 6. Two methods first given trial 30 years ago to exclude air from mines and thus check the formation of sulphuric acid. In both, a masonry wall just within the shaft entrance is sealed tightly on all sides save for an opening at the bottom. The water trap formed at this point, either by a small dam or a curved pipe, prevents the entrance of air but permits water to flow out freely. (From *Engineering News-Record,* Jan. 9, 1936, p. 42).

What was accomplished. The work was carried on with additional unemployment relief funds over a period of five years. During this period thousands of abandoned mines were sealed under a program administered jointly by the U. S. Public Health Service and federal relief agencies through a co-operative arrangement with state pollution-control agencies. Substantial reductions in acid discharge were reported. In West Virginia, for example, during the period 1934 to 1936 when 400 abandoned mines had been sealed, the total acid load in the affected streams was reduced by 40,000 tons annually, which represented a 50 per cent reduction.[16]

16. *Civil Engineering* magazine, January 1937, p. 56.

When the federal government concluded its work-relief activities with the outbreak of World War II, the states did not carry on with the sealing program. In fact they even failed to appropriate funds for inspection and maintenance service on existing seals. As a result there was a gradual disintegration of walls and drainage facilities with consequent dissipation of whatever benefits had been achieved.

An assessment of the mine-sealing program during its early stages from the viewpoint of a conservation leader was provided by Kenneth A. Reid, who said: [17]

> . . . the initiative that was responsible for the eventual allotment of funds after a long fight in overcoming fancied objections of federal officials, came not from governmental agencies entrusted with the protection of our streams, but from sportsmen . . . and other conservation and wildlife organizations that had no official recognition in the conduct of the work.
>
> From that time [December, 1933, when funds were first allotted] until the fall of 1934, the project ran the gauntlet of successive alphabetical agencies with frequent stops and changes in regulations and set-up that did not make for efficient conduct of the work. Nevertheless, in spite of these many handicaps, much real good was accomplished. . . . Farmers were able to water their stock in streams that were formerly highly acid, and sometimes they used springs that had long been dry or acid, fish returned to the streams that had been sterile for years, and public water companies began to see an improvement in their source of supply.
>
> After a lapse of nearly a year, a second project for sealing abandoned coal mines has been approved, carrying a total allocation of $3,500,000 to the Public Health Service for the conduct of work in eight states of Pennsylvania, West Virginia, Ohio, Indiana, Maryland, Kentucky, Tennessee, and Alabama under their respective health departments.

Opposing viewpoints. The coal industry saw little merit in the sealing program, the prevailing view among mine operators being that it was an overrated panacea. Research investigators at The Mellon Institute found reason to support this position.[18] Among other things they concluded that air-sealing efforts were nullified because of a natural "breathing" that occurs in mines due to changes in barometric pressure. And they pointed out that the accumulation of seepage in mines resulted in longer contact

17. See *Hearings, op. cit.,* p. 22.
18. Summary Report of Commonwealth of Pennsylvania Industrial Fellowship (No. 1 to 7). Prepared by S. A. Braley, The Mellon Institute, Pittsburgh, Pa., February 1954.

of water with sulfurous materials. In turn this was said to produce higher concentrations of acid, all of which would be flushed into streams eventually during heavy rains of spring and autumn.

The Ohio River Committee, appointed by President Roosevelt to evaluate pollution-abatement remedies, was more sanguine about the efficacy of mine seals. In its final report in 1943, it concluded that:[19] "Unless a mine-sealing program is vigorously prosecuted, mine acid loads will become increasingly heavy in the future, with the result that acid waste concentrations in streams not benefited by low-flow control will increase over present levels, and more severe damage to water users will result than that now experienced."

The committee recommended "that the director of the Bureau of Mines be authorized: To complete the present limited mine-sealing program at an estimated cost of approximately $5,500,000; and to inspect and maintain all existing and newly constructed mine seals and to conduct investigations into ways and means for further reducing the amount of acid reaching the streams from mines at a cost not to exceed $1 million annually for a period of 15 years and that additional funds be appropriated as required to extend the scope of the mine-sealing program."

When this report was submitted to the Congress in 1943 the nation was involved in World War II. In his letter of transmittal[20] the Acting Secretary of War pointed out that the mine-sealing program was not essential to, nor of indicated value in, the war effort.

No further cognizance was taken of the recommendations of the Ohio River Committee until ORSANCO queried the Bureau of Mines in the early fifties about the possibilities of their implementation. By now it seemed that interest in the subject of mine drainage had disappeared. Not only had the passage of time dimmed whatever enthusiasm may have originally existed, but the Bureau of Mines had neither sufficient staff nor budget resources to initiate any endeavors on mine-drainage control.

Where we stand today. Conflicting opinions on the efficacy of mine sealing have not yet been subjected to rigorous review. The less-than-sanguine views of the coal operators, coupled with a general attitude of defeatism, hardly provided a climate favorable to further trials. But it had been documented that in some places, at least, the mine seals installed under work-relief auspices had been effective in reducing acid

19. House Doc. No. 266, *op. cit.,* pp. 45 and 68.
20. House Doc. No. 266, *op. cit.,* Letter of transmittal signed by Robert P. Patterson, July 21, 1943.

in the streams. And these results led the Ohio River Committee in 1943 to recommend the work be continued.

It would appear, therefore, that mine-sealing procedures—especially those involving the flooding of pyritic materials and those related to reducing the flow of water into mine workings—deserve renewed consideration. At least, such measures ought to be investigated further under more carefully controlled conditions than were possible during the improvisations of the work-relief programs. Such demonstration projects should not be confined to abandoned mines; worked-out sections of active mines would also lend themselves to some form of sealing.

Prospects have brightened since 1965 for renewed effort in testing the potentialities of sealing as well as other techniques for control of mine-acid pollution. Substantial sums of money are being made available by the federal government for such research, and the Commonwealth of Pennsylvania is embarked on several projects. A comprehensive study in the Monongahela River Basin started under direction of the Public Health Service is concerned with inventorying the location, type, and amount of acid drainage from some 10,000 sources, and with developing recommendations and costs for abatement. Meantime, the Department of Health, Education, and Welfare and the Department of the Interior, in co-operation with the states involved, have embarked on a series of demonstration projects to determine what remedial measures might be feasible at locations in West Virginia and Pennsylvania. Additional sites are under consideration in Kentucky and Maryland. Ultimately, six projects will be under way, each costing about $1,250,000.

The Pennsylvania Coal Research Board is sponsoring a series of research projects. In one of them—"Operation Yellowboy"—a mobile treatment facility is being used for acid neutralization and sludge dewatering. Tests are being made at various mine drainage sites. Preliminary findings[21] indicate that treatment costs for water with about 4,000 ppm of total acidity (to pH 8.3) may range between $1.09 and $1.28 per thousand gallons of drainage-water treated; this includes haulage of dewatered sludge to a location 1½ miles from the treatment unit. Another project has focused on the application of a flash-distillation process to the treatment of acid mine drainage. There are three phases to this project—feasibility investigations, laboratory studies, and a field

21. "Mine Drainage Plan for Bethlehem Mines Corporation Marianna Mine No. 58," submitted to Pennsylvania Coal Research Board by Dorr-Oliver, Inc., Stamford, Conn., the principal investigator, January, 1966.

demonstration. The first phase has been completed[22] and it indicates that treatment costs for a 5 million-gallon-a-day, dual-purpose distillation unit and by-product power plant would range from 33 to 50 cents per 1,000 gallons of mine drainage, not including costs for sludge disposal. One suggested method of sludge disposal is transport to the sea. This would involve railroad shipment for 400 miles and a 100-mile movement by barge, the cost of which adds 9 to 16 cents per 1,000 gallons treated. Consideration is now being given to pilot-plant trial of this technique.

Other Techniques for Mitigating Acidity

Regulation of flow in streams containing acid, and the submergence of sulfurous materials in strip-mine pits are two methods that have been independently tested in recent years for mitigating the adverse effects of mine drainage. Still untried on a practical basis is the use of chemical inhibitors in mines suggested by laboratory findings at The Johns Hopkins University a decade ago.

Low-flow regulation. Reservoirs built in the upper Ohio Valley primarily for flood control have provided opportunities to supplement flow on a number of streams that are afflicted with a high concentration of mine acid. The additional flow serves in a dual role: it dilutes and thus reduces the concentration of acid with its associated hardness constituents, and it also adds water whose natural alkalinity helps to neutralize acid conditions. The construction of storage reservoirs for the single purpose of mitigating the influence of mine drainage has not been economically justified. But reservoirs already built or planned are being modified in operation and design to satisfy multipurpose functions, one of which is low-flow regulation.

Unlike mine sealing, which seeks to curb acid formation at its source, flow control makes it possible to dilute acid concentration of streams, and thus alleviate unsatisfactory conditions during periods of drought.[23] It would be unrealistic to assume that all acid discharges could be halted

22. "Summary Report of Phase 1 of the Feasibility Study of Application of the Flash Distillation Process for Treatment of Acid Mine Drainage Water," submitted to the Commonwealth of Pennsylvania Department of Mines and Mineral Industries, by the Westinghouse Electric Corp., Water Province Department, Lester, Pa., 1965.

23. C. Scott Clark, "Some Factors Involved in the Oxidation of Coal Mine Pyrite and Water Quality Trends in the Monongahela River Basin," *Proceedings, Symposium on Acid Mine Drainage Research,* The Mellon Institute, Pittsburgh, May 1965. Portrayed in this paper is the effect of the Youghiogheny flood-control

through mine sealing.[24] And the most that can be expected from reservoir releases is a reduction in peak concentrations of acid in a stream. Therefore, a combination of the two methods of control commends itself for application.

Strip-mine submergence. One of the most heartening demonstrations of a pragmatic approach to the control of acid in strip-mine operations was made by the Indiana Coal Producers Association in co-operation with the Indiana Stream Pollution Control Board. Coal deposits in the relatively flat terrain of Indiana are generally found covered by layers of limestone. The limestone cap is stripped off in order to reach the coal, whose removal results in the excavation of extensive areas. When water seeps into these pits, it turns acid.

The idea was advanced that by building small dams at outlets to these excavations after the coal was removed, it would be possible to submerge sulfurous materials and thus deny access of air and the formation of acid. Furthermore, whatever acid did develop would be neutralized by contact of the water with the surrounding limestone, thus rendering unobjectionable the overflow from these man-made lakes.

Under the direction of L. E. Sawyer, conservation director of the Midwest Coal Producers Institute, this procedure was first given a trial some fifteen years ago. The results have been rewarding. Not only have acid drainage problems been alleviated, but the small lakes created in the process are providing highly prized recreational opportunities. Fish abound in the neutralized waters. Where the lake shores have been planted with shrubs and trees, this has enhanced the attractiveness of the area and created a demand for sites for summer cottages. The Indiana practice is not adaptable to all areas where coal is mined. But it is an example of practical measures imaginatively applied in coping with a local problem of acid drainage.

---

reservoir, which was placed in operation in 1948, in reducing peak concentrations of acid at downstream locations. During low-flow periods before the reservoir went into operation the acid concentrations reached peaks that were 130 per cent above peaks in other months. Since then these monthly variations in peak concentrations have virtually disappeared.

24. In a memorandum prepared for a January 29, 1942, meeting of the Upper Ohio-Beaver Basin Committee of the National Resources Planning Board at Pittsburgh, Pa., E. W. Lyon, a mining engineer serving as regional consultant to the Public Health Service noted: "It is probable that today the efficiency of the process [mine-sealing] throughout the region is not over 25 per cent; whereas 80 per cent is a fair minimum to expect."

Chemical inhibitor theory. In 1953 the Interstate Commission on the Potomac River Basin sponsored research at The Johns Hopkins University on the fundamental reactions leading to acid formation in coal mines. Laboratory experiments centered on the possibility that traces of hydrogen-sulfide gas "triggered" the oxidation of pyrites. The findings gave rise to a corrosion theory of pyrite oxidation in which the reaction was started by hydrogen ions associating with hydrogen sulfide. This suggested the possibility of using electrochemical inhibitors for interrupting the oxidation process.

Laboratory trials with more than a dozen inhibitors appeared to confirm the theory. In further tests, conducted in small areas of an unused mine, phosphate and chromate solutions were sprayed on the exposed surfaces of the mine. The project was abandoned when the Potomac commission was unsuccessful in raising a fund of $40,000 to undertake field tests.[25] What data are available is outlined in a thesis submitted to The Johns Hopkins University ten years later by a graduate student who reviewed the previous work.[26]

ORSANCO Promotion of Mine-Acid Control

When ORSANCO began its anti-pollution crusade an aura of defeatism surrounded the mine-drainage control problem, and the odds for promoting action were not auspicious. Neither the attitude of the coal industry nor the findings from scientific research could be regarded as favorable. And most of the states signatory to the compact exempted mine drainage from regulatory control.

In 1950[27] a substantial part of the Commission's annual report was devoted to an appraisal of the mine acid situation and some comments on the legal position with respect to control efforts.

The quest for action. In 1951 the Commission invited leaders of the coal industry to participate in the regional clean-streams program, as it had other generic industry groups. This led to establishment of the

25. There are only a few accounts in the technical press relating to the project. See "4-Way Boon in River Plans," *Chemical Week,* September 26, 1953, p. 30; also "Solution for Acid Mine Wastes Seen Near," *Engineering News–Record,* September 17, 1953; and "Acid Drainage," *Business Week,* October 22, 1955, p. 123.

26. See C. Scott Clark, "A Basic Study of Acid Mine Drainage Formation." This thesis was submitted in 1963 to The Johns Hopkins University in partial fulfillment for a master of science degree and is on file with the university.

27. ORSANCO, *Second Annual Report,* 1950, pp. 29–34.

Figure 7. Open-cut or strip coal-mining operations, such as shown above, can lead to the creation of acid-drainage conditions with resultant degradation of water quality in streams. The photo below shows a remedial measure developed by the Indiana Coal Producers Association in co-operation with the Indiana Stream Pollution Control Board. Dams are built across excavated areas to form lakes; the acid-retained drainage waters eventually become neutralized, and the lakes provide opportunities for recreation. (*Photos courtesy Indiana Coal Producers Association.*)

ORSANCO Coal Industry Advisory Committee with representatives from both the commercial producers and the "captive" companies controlled by the steel industry. Activities of this committee during its early years appeared to be largely defensive. Its minutes reflect an obsession with the complexities of mine drainage and the hopelessness of instituting remedial measures.

It is not surprising, therefore, that when the Commission took steps to establish policy with respect to industrial-waste discharges, the only suggestion it received from the coal committee was that mine drainage be exempted "until such time as practical means are available for control." However, as time went on and members of the committee were drawn into discussions with the engineering and other advisory committees of the Commission, a more optimistic attitude began to prevail. This change prepared the way for effective collaboration in drafting an interstate control measure.

In the interim ORSANCO tried to stimulate federal sponsorship of some work. In 1956 it petitioned the Surgeon General of the Public Health Service to inaugurate investigations looking toward the prevention and reduction of acid mine drainage.[28] At that time the Congress had appropriated funds to permit the Service to expand its pollution-control research activities. Circumstances appeared propitious for the eight states to jointly appeal for allocation of some funds to the mine-drainage problem. Meantime, the possibilities of renewed activity by the Bureau of Mines were also being explored.

Nothing fruitful emerged from either of these efforts. In retrospect, it appears that while the Public Health Service had the funds, its research interests were oriented to other endeavors. And although the Bureau of Mines displayed much interest, it had no funds for mine-drainage research. Bureau representatives expressed the hope that the Commission might be able to subsidize their research.

What ORSANCO expected from the federal agencies was a thorough appraisal of findings from previous research, and notably from past experiences on field projects, on the basis of which it might find justification to institute some form of remedial action. Failing in this, it appointed a task group of staff and state regulatory personnel to explore the situation. Under the chairmanship of L. S. Morgan, mine-drainage specialist of the Pennsylvania State Health Department, the group reviewed histories of situations where it appeared some success had been achieved in alleviating adverse affects of acid drainage.

28. See ORSANCO, minutes of meeting, July 12, 1956, pp. 22–23.

Development of controls. The evidence compiled by this group led the Commission's engineering committee to endorse a report in which it was asserted that pollution from active mining could be mitigated by conscientious application of the following principles and practices:

—Reducing entry of water into mines through diversion of surface streams and by sealing crevices;
—Minimizing contact time of water in the mine with acid-forming materials;
—Exercising greater care in disposal of gob (slate and rock) and other refuse materials;
—Regulating drainage discharges from the mines to provide a continuous flow that was equalized so far as practicable over a 24-hour period, as opposed to the common practice of intermittent pumping of "slugs" of acid water;
—Employing adequate mine-closure procedures immediately following termination of mining activities;
—Treating acid drainage by chemical or other means to reduce its pollutional properties.

These concepts were finally endorsed by the ORSANCO Coal Industry Advisory Committee and subsequently incorporated by the Commission in a control measure that was adopted by the eight states in 1960.[29]

Agreement by the regulatory authorities and the coal industry that practical means were available to ameliorate the problem signalized a new era in thinking. No longer was acid mine drainage recognized as warranting exemption from interstate pollution-abatement requirements, and the Commission authorized the staff to conduct a series of "curbstone clinics" for state agency personnel to develop practical knowledge in applying corrective measures under varying conditions in the field.

In a message to coal industry executives, R. L. Ireland, chairman of the executive committee of the Consolidation Coal Company, vicechairman of the National Coal Association, and a member of the ORSANCO Coal Industry Committee, made this comment:

The Ohio River Valley Water Sanitation Commission has the obligation under law to ameliorate and, where practical, to abate stream pollution. Its attitude toward the coal industry is one of accomplishing this mandate through cooperation, rather than compulsion. Let's not force ORSANCO to change its attitude.

The Coal Industry Advisory Committee volunteered to promote demonstration projects in the field and otherwise aid mine operators in

29. ORSANCO Resolution No. 5–60, titled "Acid Mine Drainage Control Measure," adopted January 14, 1960.

complying with the measures. It also compiled a manual for publication by the Commission, which described the principles underlying control procedures, and how they might be applied. Included with the manual are case histories of how various situations had been handled.[30]

In collaboration with the coal committee ORSANCO produced an educational film *Coal and Water,* which portrays the pollution problem caused by acid drainage and illustrates what can be done to deal with it.

While this was being done, the coal committee was instrumental in stimulating a renewal of mine-drainage investigations by the U. S. Bureau of Mines. Studies now under way include one on the effect of water impoundment in an abandoned mine, several that relate to oxidation of pyritic conglomerates, and a feasibility study of direct neutralization of acid and disposal of resultant sludge.

All of this represents a good start in mitigating the adverse effects of drainage from active mines, strip-mine workings, and gob piles. Not yet answered is the question of what might be done about acid drainage from so-called abandoned mines. Despite conflicting opinions, there is some basis for belief that a program for sealing these abandoned workings, where possible, may offer at least a partial remedy.

30. The manual titled "Principles and Guide to Practices in the Control of Acid Mine-Drainage, Supplemented by Case Histories," was published in March 1964. New case histories are periodically compiled, and these are circulated to coal companies in the valley, as well as pollution control agencies.

15

A New Problem —
Radioactivity

Shortly after the formation of ORSANCO in 1948 the atomic energy industry came to the Ohio Valley, and with it came new problems. Two characteristics of the industry were of particular concern to ORSANCO. First, the industry produced radioactive wastes, which fitted no pattern of experience among state water pollution control agencies; and, second, the industry was a federal government monopoly managed through the United States Atomic Energy Commission, in which Congress had vested sole responsibility for controls relating to health and safety.

The ORSANCO commissioners were perplexed about what role the interstate agency could or should be expected to assume in carrying out its responsibilities for pollution control, if responsibility for radioactivity resided with and was wholly retained by the Atomic Energy Commission.

When ORSANCO learned that AEC gaseous-diffusion plants were to be constructed at Paducah, Kentucky, on the Ohio River, and above Portsmouth, Ohio, on the Scioto River, meetings were arranged with the sanitary engineering staff of AEC, during which assurance was given to the ORSANCO commissioners that all possible safeguards would be taken to prevent contamination of water sources. But these discussions did nothing to delineate areas of state or interstate-agency responsibility.

Shortly thereafter, the Ohio State Health Department queried the AEC area manager about operations of the Portsmouth plant, not only with respect to radioactivity releases but in connection with the discharge of chemical-waste pollutants and sewage. This resulted in a statement from the AEC that, ". . . even though we [the AEC] are not in a position to recognize an unlimited right of authority in the State to determine how federally-owned facilities are to be constructed or operated, we are, nevertheless, as a matter of comity desirous of cooperating with you to the fullest extent consistent with our responsibilities as a Federal agency, particularly in this matter of stream pollution."[1]

1. Letter of January 2, 1953, to F. H. Waring, chief engineer of the Ohio State Health Department from Kenneth Dunbar, manager of the AEC operations in the Portsmouth area.

The commissioners of ORSANCO were not entirely satisfied that civility and courtesy were an appropriate basis for exercising responsibilities relating to atomic-energy developments. It was a sense of frustration about the over-all situation and not the posture of the Atomic Energy Commission that troubled ORSANCO. Representatives of the AEC associated with waste-disposal problems were endeavoring as far as they were able to keep ORSANCO and its signatory states informed on the nature of various undertakings in the Ohio Valley.

The incompatibilities that presented themselves could be regarded as inevitable considering that the development of atomic energy had been created and nurtured almost exclusively by the federal government and without any participation by state governments. Senator Clinton P. Anderson, chairman of the Joint Congressional Committee on Atomic Energy in 1956, explained the situation in this fashion:

> Almost all important [atomic-energy] facilities were owned by the national government, means of finance were provided by the national tax power, major policy decisions were made by national officials and were hidden by a cloak of high secrecy. Private organizations, to the extent they participated in the development of the industry—which they did to a very great extent—functioned primarily as agents of the national government. State governments accordingly could reasonably remain unconcerned. This is prior to 1954—prior to 1956. But is this the case today? Has state unconcern now become state concern? In my opinion it has.[2]

The changed situation to which Senator Anderson referred came about with passage of the Atomic Energy Act of 1954.[3] This act was designed to widen civilian activity in the nuclear reactor program, and through its enactment the federal government partially relinquished its monopoly on the atomic-energy industry. Provision was made for private enterprise to become licensees to build facilities and possess nuclear materials for the development of peacetime uses of atomic energy. Heretofore, private persons and organizations had participated in atomic-energy activities only as employees, agents, or contractors of the national government, and, as such, they were in a position to claim federal immunity from state laws and regulations. As licensees, they no longer retained this privileged position.

Passage of the 1954 act paved the way for state governments to assume an active role in atomic-energy affairs and control of hazards. As a prac-

2. Clinton P. Anderson, "The Atom—Everybody's Business or Nobody's Business," *State Government,* December 1956, p. 243, published by the Council of State Governments, Chicago, Ill.
3. 68 Stat. 919, 42 U.S.C. 2011 (1957).

tical matter, however, the states were not adequately prepared to enter this new and vastly different arena of regulation. First, there was the necessity of securing competent personnel. Because of the limited number of radiation specialists and the modest salaries associated with state work it was no simple matter to acquire adequate manpower; training programs had to be relied upon to remedy the situation, and this took time. In addition, there was the question of appropriate organizational arrangements for radiation protection. More than one agency within a state administrative structure had reason to be involved with such matters. For example, the labor department was concerned with industrial hazards and the health department with water pollution.

As a consequence, state participation proceeded slowly and on a limited basis.[4] During the early transition period, many states did not go beyond establishing radioactivity monitoring programs. However, one of the ORSANCO signatory states—Pennsylvania—aggressively injected itself into the regulation of radioactive wastes when the AEC announced that the world's first commercial-scale nuclear power plant was to be located at Shippingport. The site was on the Ohio River a few miles above the Pennsylvania-Ohio border, and for this reason ORSANCO had reason to become involved.

Shippingport Reactor under State Purview

It was early in 1954 that the Pennsylvania Sanitary Water Board first learned about the power reactor proposed for Shippingport. The project was being planned as a joint undertaking of the Duquesne Light Company (a Pittsburgh-based utility) and the U.S. Atomic Energy Commission.

Despite the indecision at that time concerning the relative jurisdiction of the Atomic Energy Commission and state agencies, Pennsylvania informed the AEC and other interested parties that it intended to employ its authority under the general powers of its state health department to promulgate radiation protection regulations.[5] In addition, the Pennsyl-

4. For an assessment of the role of state governments see William H. Berman and Lee M. Hydeman, "State Responsibilities in the Atomic Energy Field," *State Government,* Spring, 1959. Among other things they concluded that the states must begin some realistic self-appraisal of their activities in the radiation protection field. If they did not begin to show a willingness and ability to cope with the problems, they would find themselves precluded from so doing.

5. Documentation of these events is contained in the statement of Karl M. Mason, director of the Bureau of Environmental Health, Pennsylvania Department of Health, in "Industrial Radioactive Waste Disposal," *Hearings* of the Special Committee on Radiation, Joint Committee on Atomic Energy, 86th Cong., 1st Sess., January 28–February 3, 1959.

vania Sanitary Water Board formally declared that it would consider radioactive liquid wastes to be in the same category as any other industrial waste, and that a producer of such wastes must apply for a discharge permit, which would specify the conditions under which the waste could be released.

Shortly thereafter, in September, 1955, the area manager of the Atomic Energy Commission invited representatives of the Pennsylvania Department of Health, ORSANCO, and the U.S. Public Health Service to a conference. Its purpose was to provide background on the construction and operating aspects of the proposed Shippingport installation, with specific reference to the safeguards that would be provided to prevent water pollution. The AEC stated[6] that treatment facilities would be designed to limit the discharge of radioactive substances to 6/100 of the permissible values set forth in the National Bureau of Standards *Handbook 52,* which listed provisional levels of maximum permissible concentrations of radioactive contaminants in air and water.

Further evidence of the promotion of co-operative relationships came a few months later when the AEC supplied copies of its program of "pre-operational" site monitoring to those who attended the conference. The purpose of this program was to determine the types and amounts of radioactive materials occurring in the environment around the Shippingport area some 1½ years prior to the start of operations. This monitoring would be continued after the plant was in operation and was designed to reveal any significant changes that might be attributed to operations. The memo also noted that the AEC data would be exchanged with the Public Health Service, which was then embarked on a valley-wide investigation of "background radioactivity."

Pennsylvania issues a permit. In April, 1957, the Duquesne Light Company made formal application for a permit to discharge liquid radioactive wastes into the Ohio River, stating that its discharge from the operation was designed to prevent radioactivity concentration in the river from exceeding the limits set forth in *Handbook 52.* The Pennsylvania Sanitary Water Board requested additional safeguards, and these were accepted. For example, the sampling point was established in the plant effluent, rather than in the river, thus providing an extra safety factor of about 100, inasmuch as the discharge was to be less than 1/100 of the mean flow of the Ohio River. A further factor of safety was introduced by

6. From report of the conference by H. E. Moses, director of the Bureau of Sanitary Engineering, Pennsylvania State Department of Health, to the commissioners of ORSANCO. See ORSANCO, minutes of meeting November 2, 1955.

requiring that the limits apply at any time rather than to the average concentration over a yearly interval as originally proposed.

Before Pennsylvania took action on the permit stipulations, review copies were circulated to the staff of ORSANCO and to the signatory states downstream from Shippingport. This was followed by a meeting of all interested parties, on the basis of which the Sanitary Water Board reached its final conclusions. These were presented in a report to the ORSANCO commissioners.[7]

The conditions stipulated in the Pennsylvania permit were: (1) daily maximum concentration of radioactive materials to be released should not exceed one-tenth the maximum permissible value as set forth in *Handbook 52* (this meant that the plant effluent would meet drinking water standards even without dilution by river); (2) the yearly average concentration of radioactive materials was not to exceed one-fourth of the daily maximum value; (3) the plant effluent must not produce a rise in river temperature of more than 2°F.; (4) the Duquesne Light Company would continue area monitoring and submit periodic reports; and (5) in the event of an accident, the plant was to be shut down and immediate notification given to the state agency, which would assume responsibility for alerting downstream water users.

The ORSANCO commissioners were informed that although the Shippingport operation was expected to start within a month (around November 1, 1957), facilities for storage of wastes to permit radioactive decay were of such capacity that some six months might elapse before any radioactivity would be released to the river. No dissent was registered by any of the signatory states with respect to the Pennsylvania requirements, the consensus being that they provided appropriate safeguards so far as interstate waters were concerned.

Radiation Monitoring Activities

During the years of indecision with respect to jurisdictional responsibilities, the ORSANCO states sought to prepare themselves for participation in dealing with radiation problems. Pollution-control personnel were trained in measurement of radioactivity, and specialized laboratory equipment for this purpose was acquired. In addition, steps were taken to formulate radiation-control programs, notably by Pennsylvania, Kentucky, New York, Illinois, Indiana, and Ohio.

Familiarity with the techniques of radioactivity monitoring had reached the point in 1957 where four of the states were prepared to undertake

7. ORSANCO, minutes of meeting, October 1, 1957, p. 162.

routine surveillance procedures. Meantime, ORSANCO, through its representative from the Public Health Service, had promoted the conduct of a radioactivity background survey in the Ohio Valley. Specialists from the Public Health Service were assigned to determine at some thirty-four locations what the conditions were with respect to "natural" or background radiation. The object was to obtain baseline data from which it would be possible to assess the effect of future atomic-energy installations.

Interstate surveillance. After this background survey had been completed, ORSANCO undertook a continuing compilation of data on radioactivity levels in the Ohio River and its tributaries from some seventy locations. This was accomplished by arrangements made with the Atomic Energy Commission and its contractors and licensees, the Public Health Service, and the several state agencies.

In addition to this surveillance of conditions in flowing waters, ORSANCO initiated in 1958 an assay of radioactivity accumulation in the sediments, biota, and fishes of the Ohio River and some of the major tributaries. This was carried out under a contract with the University of Louisville until July, 1965, when demands on the Commission budget had reached the point where radioactivity appraisal, costing $10,000 annually, had to be deferred. The contract also provided that the university evaluate the significance of all radioactivity data compiled by ORSANCO from various sources. The university was uniquely qualified to undertake this exacting task by having on its faculty Dr. A. T. Krebs, an internationally recognized authority on radiobiology and a consultant on such matters to the U.S. Army.

Quarterly reports submitted by the university indicated that the radioactivity content of water of the Ohio Valley was far below the level considered to have any public health significance, and, in fact, had been diminishing since the cessation of nuclear testing. For example, during 1964 the values of gross beta activity ranged from 0 to 33 micromicrocuries per liter.[8] The Public Health Service Drinking Water Standards establish 1,000 micro-microcuries as a permissible upper limit.

8. Laboratory techniques for the measurement of radioactivity in water are focused primarily on a count of gross alpha and gross beta radiation emissions.

At the risk of oversimplification it may be said that the nature of atomic radiation is such that the alpha measurement can be regarded in most cases as an approximation of radioactivity originating from natural sources. The fluctuations in beta count are indicative of radioactivity created by man, and reflect the impact of fallout from bomb testing and discharges from nuclear-energy installations.

Unlike chemical analysis of water, where concentrations are measured as weight per unit volume of water, the radioactivity analysis provides a measure of the

The findings with respect to the accumulation of radioactivity in samples of river sediments and in the plankton and fish showed ranges, respectively, of 0 to 69, 0 to 1.5, and 0 to 155 micro-microcuries.[9] According to Dr. Krebs, these values were about the same as those reported elsewhere in the United States and did not present a hazard to the well-being of man.

Public Alarm over Radioactivity

In February of 1960 people in Wheeling, West Virginia, became alarmed about the operation of the atomic reactor at Shippingport (54 miles upstream) and the potential hazard of radioactive contamination of their drinking water supply. This concern was aroused when the Wheeling *News Register* (January 31, 1960) carried a story on the current annual report of the Atomic Energy Commission and headlined it "Atomic Waste Dumped Into Ohio River—AEC Reveals 'Pollution' above City." Public attention centered on the headline, rather than on the AEC statement that radioactivity in the Shippingport wastes was "well within values for maximum permissible concentrations," and that no rise in concentration was noted in the Ohio River.

The newspaper ran a daily series of what it termed "startling disclosures." A February seventh story said: "The chief ingredient of the atomic waste discharge into the Ohio River above Wheeling is tritium—the material used in the hydrogen bomb." When scientists at local colleges were asked for statements, one said he found no cause for worry; but six others called for an immediate halt to the dumping of atomic wastes into the river.[10] One of the scientists wrote a letter to U. S. Congressman Arch T. Moore, Jr., of West Virginia, expressing his concern, and Mr. Moore responded by scheduling a public hearing in Wheeling with the Atomic Energy Commission for the purpose of discussing all aspects of the situation. Among others, ORSANCO was asked to appear.

Meanwhile, a distributor of water-softening devices in Wheeling purchased newspaper space for display of a notice that his equipment would

---

rate of atomic disintegrations per unit volume (milliliter or liter) of water. The accepted unit for measuring the rate of radioactivity is the curie, established at 2,200 billion disintegrations per minute. Because of the extremely small amounts of radioactivity present in streams, concentrations are expressed in micro-microcuries per liter. One such unit is equivalent to 2.22 atomic disintegrations per minute in about one quart of water.

9. ORSANCO, *Seventeenth Annual Report,* 1965, p. 20.
10. Wheeling *News Register,* February 11, 1960.

"remove practically all of the important radioactive isotopes, especially those of strontium, barium and the rare earths caused by any atomic waste dumped into the Ohio River."

By this time public concern had reached the point where the City Council, among other things, called on ORSANCO to make a study of the dumping of atomic wastes into the Ohio River at Shippingport, and to report on the extent of pollution caused by such wastes and on any potential danger.

In response, the Commission submitted a memorandum[11] detailing its actions relating to atomic-energy developments, all of which had been set forth earlier in annual reports sent each year to the Clerk of Council of Wheeling and to local newspapers. The memorandum described how decisions had been reached concerning permissible discharges from the Shippingport operation. It went on to say that the most recent review of the operation, only three weeks earlier, led to the conclusion that the radioactivity produced was less than anticipated. In fact, the Pennsylvania authorities had commended the Duquesne Power and Light Company, the operator of the facility, for engineering competence and accomplishment "in operating safely and with a minimum of hazard to public health the world's first commercial nuclear power station."

Quoted in the memorandum was a confirmation of this conclusion by Joseph O. Lieberman, chief of the environmental sanitary engineering branch of the Atomic Energy Commission. On January 27, 1960, five days before the Wheeling newspaper headlined its story, Dr. Lieberman had said in an address at a conference at the University of Illinois, "It is significant to note that in the first *year* of plant operation [at Shippingport] the total quantity of radioactivity discharged into the Ohio River was . . . much less than the permissible discharge for a single month."

In addition, ORSANCO cited a report it had received from the U. S. Public Health Service, which had been analyzing the radioactivity data obtained by the several agencies that maintain observations on conditions above and below Shippingport. This report stated: "Operation of the Shippingport Nuclear Power Station has produced no measurable increase in the radioactivity in the Ohio River. There is no detectable radioactivity at downstream points attributable to Shippingport. This confirms expectations based on operating records and the analysis of effluents being discharged." The Wheeling City Council was informed further that the State of Ohio corroborated the finding of no detectable

11. See report of the Executive Director, *Record of Commission Activities,* 1959–60, p. 116.

radioactivity from its independent analyses of the Ohio River at East Liverpool, a point only 8 miles downstream from Shippingport.

The Wheeling hearing. Several weeks later, on March 18, Congressman Moore convened a hearing before a standing-room-only audience in the Wheeling City Council chambers.

Dr. Charles R. Dunham, director of the division of biology and medicine for the AEC, testified first that the additional radiation in the Wheeling water supply was approximately one thirty thousandth (1/30,000) of the exposure that an individual would obtain from nature if he lived to be 70 years of age.[12] Dr. Lieberman of the AEC then stated that Shippingport contributed only 1/15 of the amount of radioactivity that could be added to the river with complete safety, and that the plant had been operated for two years without harmful effect on man or the environment.[13] James G. Terrill, deputy chief of the division of radiological health of the Public Health Service, described the conservative limits that had been prescribed in the permit under which the plant operated and asserted that waste disposal constituted no problem. Dr. Krebs, radiobiologist consultant for ORSANCO, pointed out that monitor data showed radioactivity concentrations in the river so far below maximum permissible limits that, in fact, it might be regarded as negligible. Replying to a question on health hazards, Dr. Dunham said: "The risk is an extremely small one. There is either one chance in a million—or no chance at all—that someone eventually will be harmed by atomic wastes in the river water."[14] The result of the hearing and the information it provided were summed up in a newspaper editorial a few days later, that said, in part:

"From what we know of this operation [Shippingport], it would appear that there is nothing to fear. The more understanding of the subject we have, however, the more intelligent will be the judgment we form . . . It is well to bear in mind, however, as we contemplate further exploration of the subject, the necessity of distinguishing between the fantastic and the realistic."[15]

One lesson to be drawn from this experience with radioactivity— which is but one of the characteristics of river quality that affect use— is that monitoring of river conditions must be regarded as a prime responsibility of a pollution-control agency. What ORSANCO is doing in this area is described in the next chapter.

12. Martins Ferry, Ohio, *Times Leader*, March 19, 1960.
13. *Wheeling Intelligencer*, March 19, 1960.
14. *Ibid.*
15. *Ibid.*, March 24, 1960.

16

River-Quality Surveillance
and Robot Monitoring

If river pollution is to be effectively managed, one of the requisites is systematic acquisition and assessment of information on quality conditions. ORSANCO endeavors toward this end have been rewarding, and have attracted attention in this country and abroad, notably in connection with the development of an electronic sentinel called a robot monitor.[1]

Shortly after the Ohio Valley program was inaugurated, the staff concluded that a proper understanding of river behavior would require something more than sporadic surveys. Quality conditions in the Ohio River system, which comprises a main stem of 981 miles and 19 major tributaries, reflect a host of varying impacts from natural and man-made influences—wastewater discharges from thousands of municipalities and industries, periodic releases of dilution water from storage reservoirs, the operation of navigation dams, and changes in rainfall and runoff. Without continual diagnosis of river conditions, there would be no suitable basis for evaluating quality trends and the potentialities for influencing them. Furthermore, without knowledge of conditions before and after remedies have been applied, there is no way of gauging the appropriateness of regulatory decisions.

From these considerations emerged the concept of establishing the means for observation of chemical and bacteriological changes in various parts of the river system. The monitor program had three purposes: to co-ordinate the acquisition of data on quality characteristics; to evaluate the data for judging performance of pollution-abatement efforts; and to guide the prescription of additional control measures.

1. "River-Quality Surveillance Techniques in the Ohio Valley," *Revue Suisse d'Hydrologie,* Vol. XXII, 1960, pp. 420–39. "Ein Fluss-Roboter für die Kontrolle der Wassergüte," *Die Wasserwirtschaft,* April 1961, pp. 85–90. "An Electronic Monitor System for River-Quality Surveillance and Research," *Proceedings,* International Conference on Water Pollution Research, London, September 1962 (Oxford–London–New York: Pergamon Press, 1964), pp. 63–77.

When the Commission approved this venture in 1951, there was some question about how such an ambitious undertaking might be executed within the limitations of an already strained budget. The first step taken by the staff, which was armed with little more than enthusiasm, was to solicit the interest of managers of public and private water companies. To these men, river conditions were more than a matter of academic concern, for each day they faced the practical problems of processing water from the river.

The staff appeal produced a good response and led to the formation, in January, 1952, of a Water Users Committee. Each member agreed to furnish results obtained from daily analyses of samples of river water. This task, in addition to special monitor undertakings, has been faithfully performed ever since.

Initially eleven stations comprised the "water users" network. The addition of volunteer stations monitored by chemists at industrial plants and power companies brought the number up to seventeen in 1965. Conduct of committee activities, including expenses of quarterly meetings with the staff, has averaged $1,400 annually, over the years.

Other monitoring points were established in co-operation with the U.S. Geological Survey of the Department of the Interior, which has long been authorized to match funds with state agencies for the measurement of chemical characteristics of streams. The first six points were established in 1954, making it possible to obtain quality information at or near state lines and other places where the services of volunteer monitors were not available. This operation was launched with $5,000 from each agency.

During the following five years the co-operative contract was amplified to the point where ORSANCO was committing as much as $25,000— almost 20 per cent of its appropriations from the states—for this work. Later it became possible to co-ordinate these joint monitoring activities with similar activities subsidized by some of the signatory states. This permitted reduction of the annual allotment to $10,000 without any decrease in the amount of data made available. In 1965 ORSANCO was contributing funds for the joint operation of eleven Geological Survey stations. Six of these are on the Ohio River and five on tributaries.

Adventure in "Imagineering"

The manually-operated monitor program was useful in securing basic data for assessing river quality, but it left something to be desired. Manual sampling and chemical testing are time-consuming procedures.

Furthermore, it was not practical to maintain such services on an around-the-clock schedule. These considerations prompted exploration of possibilities for automatic instrumentation and the ultimate development of a robot-monitor device.

Detailed investigations started in 1956 with consultation among a number of instrument companies in the United States and abroad. The outcome was disappointing; few firms displayed any enthusiasm, and many required developmental fees far beyond Commission resources. River monitoring was regarded as a novelty, and except for the interest displayed by ORSANCO there was no ostensible market. Furthermore, the staff ideas were, as one manufacturer put it, "somewhat ahead of the art of instrumentation."

The only automatic analytical devices available at that time were ones designed primarily for quality or process control in industrial applications. Many of them were capable of performing continuous analyses, but they required daily manual checking and adjustment. Further, use of the instruments was confined to liquid or gas streams whose composition, unlike that of river water, remained quite uniform.

Appraisal of possibilities. Thus the stage was set for a staff venture in "imagineering." Several types of instruments were purchased or borrowed with a view toward learning something about the possibilities of adapting them to unattended river monitoring. The City of Cincinnati permitted a trailer-type laboratory to be located adjacent to the municipal water-pumping station so that a direct tap could be made to an intake from the Ohio River. This assured an appropriate sampling of river water, and, since this same water was being routinely analyzed by city chemists, reliable data was available for comparison with results from the instruments under test.

The instruments that were studied could be broadly classified into two groups: those based on the application of photometers, and those employing electrodes or transducers. Photometric analyzers operate on principles involving measurement of the intensity of light transmission. The instruments available varied from relatively simple color-measuring devices to rather complex spectrophotometers. Some of them measured the concentration of a substance in a solution directly; others did so indirectly by measuring the effect of a chemical reaction resulting from addition of a reagent. Among the devices tested were those for measuring fluorides, hardness, turbidity, and phenolic compounds.

Instruments of the electrode or transducer type employ sensing elements that deliver their information output in the form of a generated voltage or a varying electrical impedance. Electrode systems may consist of something as simple as a pair of metallic plates, or may involve a complex assembly of permeable membranes and cells containing an electrolyte. The transducers likewise may vary from simple impedance elements, whose output changes in a known manner with the quality characteristics under observation, to more elaborate devices with pulse-producing ionization chambers. The transducer devices can be employed for measuring hydrogen-ion concentration (pH), oxidation-reduction potential (ORP), conductivity, chlorides, and dissolved oxygen (D.O.).

Decision and design. An automatic system employing electrode and transducer-sensing components seemed to offer the greatest promise for river monitoring. These devices were capable of providing continuous "output" signals, which would permit interrogation of the monitor whenever and as often as required, whereas the photometric instruments could provide only an intermittent signal. Also there was the probability of monitors being located in areas where it would be inconvenient to replenish the chemical reagents in photometric instruments.

This conclusion was fortified by an electronics consultant whose services had now been retained to supplement staff research.[2] He designed the circuitry and structural arrangements and then built what is now called a modular, multiple, automatic analyzer. The function of the unit is revealed by the name chosen for it—a robot monitor. Coincident with its development, evaluation studies were made on commercially available telemeter equipment, data-logging devices, and telephone circuits that could be adapted for remote transmission of signals from the analyzer.

The ORSANCO monitor was designed to accommodate measurement of ten different water-quality characteristics from as many as forty locations. At present, instruments have been devised to measure and transmit data on dissolved oxygen, chloride-ion concentration, hydrogen-ion concentration, specific conductance, oxidation-reduction potential, and temperature of water, as well as solar radiation in the area where the monitor

2. The ORSANCO robot monitor is based on an original conception of the author. However, translation of his notions into practical realities was made possible by the dedication of William L. Klein, staff chemist, who was responsible for detailed execution of the project, and by the creativeness of Carl Schneider who not only served as consultant but engineered design of the robot monitors and supervised their fabrication in the shops of his company, Engineering Specialties of Cincinnati, Ohio. Throughout several years of experimentation a number of instrument companies were most generous in responding to requests for advice and in providing opportunities to evaluate emerging developments in sensors and electronic components.

is located. Feasibility studies have been made for a unit to measure gross-beta radioactivity.

How it works. The robot-monitor system consists of three separate but integrated components: a group of electronic analyzers combined with a transmitter (see Figure 8), a telemeter interrogator and receiver, and a data-logger and transcriber.

The analyzer component with its transmitter is a self-contained unit that can be located at any point along a stream. As river water circulates through the unit, the cells containing the electronic sensors respond to

Recorder and
telemeter transmitter

Electronic
measuring instruments

Flow cells
and detectors

Figure 8. The combined analyzer and telemeter-transmitter unit of the ORSANCO robot monitor. These units, which are located at various points along the river, measure changes in water quality for relay to head-quarters in Cincinnati.

changes in quality. These changes are converted into electrical impulses for relay to ORSANCO headquarters in Cincinnati.

The telemeter component in Cincinnati is connected with the analyzer units at river locations by means of a leased telephone-wire circuit. At a predetermined interval (every hour at present), the telemeter interrogates each monitor station in sequence, and then stands by to receive a report on the quality characteristics being measured. Signals received through the telemeter circuit actuate data-logging devices. One of these is a transcriber that automatically types the information received on a tabulation sheet. This provides a visual record of quality data. At the same time a paper-tape punch is also activated; it codes the data in a form that can be fed into an electronic digital computer, which is programmed to perform a variety of evaluation processes.

In September, 1960, the prototype analyzer, along with the telemeter and recording equipment, was placed "on stream." Its performance justified expectations and ten additional analyzer units were constructed. By July, 1965, a total of thirteen units were in operation. Meantime, a so-called mobile monitor was constructed for survey purposes and special investigations. It is a portable version of the robot analyzer equipped with a strip-chart recorder. It will accommodate any two units of the standard modular analyzers for measuring quality characteristics.

As time goes on, it is anticipated that sensors will be added to measure other quality characteristics. Also being contemplated is the possibility of circuitry arrangements in the existing robots for production of a "river-quality index" number. Such a number would represent a weighted composite of various measurements now performed by the monitor and would be automatically computed at the monitor site and transmitted to central headquarters. Thus it would be possible to secure immediate and continual grading of river quality in such simple terms as Grade A, B, etc. Execution of this intriguing possibility is not so much a problem in electronics as one of selecting and weighting quality characteristics to arrive at a meaningful index number. Staff studies are being made on development of an index-number system.[3]

Network Operation and Data Processing

In 1965 the monitor network (see Figure 9) consisted of four integrated components: (1) 17 Water Users Committee manual stations

3. See Robert K. Horton, "An Index-Number System for Rating Water Quality," *Journal,* Water Pollution Control Federation, Vol. 37, No. 3 (March 1965), pp. 300–06.

operated on a voluntary basis by the managers of municipal and private waterworks; (2) 11 manual stations operated under contract arrangements with the U.S. Geological Survey; (3) 13 robot-monitor units installed and maintained by ORSANCO, ten of which relay data directly to headquarters and three record information only at the site; and (4) 15 sampling points for periodic assay of radioactivity in water, in river sediment and biota, and in fish, operated under contract with The Potamological Institute of the University of Louisville.[4]

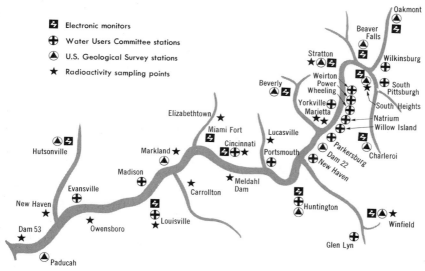

Figure 9. The ORSANCO network of monitor stations on the Ohio River and some major tributaries.

Measurement of detergent concentration has been given separate attention. Acting on invitation of the Commission, the Chemical Industry Committee inaugurated weekly sampling of the Ohio River at one point in 1954 and at another in 1957.[5] These analyses are supplemented by a checking of detergent content at twenty other points by the U.S. Geological Survey.

Manual vs. automatic monitoring. The robot monitors complement the manually operated components of the network. Each has merits that

4. This work has been temporarily discontinued because of budget limitations.
5. See Paul J. Weaver and Francis J. Coughlin, "Monitoring the Ohio River for Synthetic Detergent Content," *Journal of American Water Works Association,* Vol. 52, No. 5 (May 1960), pp. 607–12.

cannot be duplicated by the other. The robot monitors perform tests continuously and maintain day and night vigilance. They produce data routinely, rapidly, and economically, but sensors are not yet available for direct measurement of alkalinity, fluorides, hardness, iron, manganese, nitrates, or phosphates. Only a manned station can provide data on bacteriological conditions and threshold-odor values. However, manual monitoring is costly and time-consuming.

Flow analysis and forecasts. In addition to compiling information on quality conditions, the monitor operation is geared to assemble current and historical data on river-flow (quantity) variations. The historical record for this purpose is obtained from the Surface Water Branch of the U.S. Geological Survey, which maintains stream-gauging stations throughout the Ohio Valley. Records from some of these stations on the Ohio River embrace a period of thirty-seven years. This hydrologic information is used by ORSANCO primarily for frequency-of-occurrence studies to reveal how often various quantities of dilution water may be expected to be available, as well as for assessing relationships between river flow and quality changes.

Having envisioned use of the electronic monitor as a tool for management of river quality, the staff concluded that the benefits from continuous monitoring would be enhanced if the information on quality could be coupled with knowledge of the quantity of flow at the time measurements were made. Flow data developed from stream gaugings made by the Geological Survey does not lend itself to this purpose because it cannot be made available until the following year when annual compilations have been completed.

The matter of obtaining immediate data on daily flow was discussed with hydrologists of the U.S. Weather Bureau, which operates a Flood Forecast Center at Cincinnati. Here techniques have been developed for prediction of river-stage information during periods of high water. Would it be possible, ORSANCO asked, to expand this service to provide daily information on flows at selected points in the river system?

The answer was yes. The only reason for not doing it was because no one previously had exhibited any interest in such information. As a result, a unique service was inaugurated in 1959.[6] Each day, the Cincinnati

6. Arrangements for this service were developed by the late Roy M. Lundquist, hydrologist-in-charge of the Cincinnati office of the U.S. Weather Bureau with the support of Ralph F. Kresge, hydrologic engineer for the eastern area of the bureau. The river forecast procedure used by Mr. Lundquist is based on a daily evaluation of runoff from rainfall or melting snow combined with known or reported river conditions, together with reports of reservoir releases. The entire system of unit areas is then integrated into stream flow and stage forecasts for successive points downstream.

office of the Weather Bureau furnishes to ORSANCO a telephoned forecast on river flow for twelve locations along the Ohio River and some of its tributaries. These forecasts provide an estimate of both quantity and velocity of flow for the current day, as well as predictions for the next three days. The velocity report has special usefulness because it can be used for calculating the time of travel when accidental spills occur.

The prompt integration of flow information with quality data has improved the diagnostic capabilities of the robot monitor system. Furthermore, the availability of a daily flow forecast will permit programming the discharge of waste effluents with hydrologic variability.

The value of the flow forecasts in facilitating quality diagnosis was dramatically evidenced in December, 1960, following a highway accident in which cans of cyanide were spilled from a truck into an Indiana creek. The creek flowed into the Ohio River a dozen miles upstream from Louisville, Kentucky. Learning of the accident from a routine report of the highway patrol, a radio station created some consternation in Louisville by broadcasting an alarm that the river was poisoned and city water should not be used.

Kentucky and Louisville officials contacted ORSANCO because the accident occurred in Indiana. Knowing the volume of flow in the Ohio River as of that morning, the staff calculated that dilution was sufficient to accommodate some 1.7 million pounds of cyanide before a potential hazard would be created; the highway patrol had estimated the spill at not more than 1,000 pounds. Furthermore, the velocity of flow was such that the prism of water in the vicinity of the spillage would not reach the city for at least 18 hours. This prompt diagnosis ruled out immediate cause for public apprehension. Meantime, chemists from the Indiana and Kentucky pollution-control agencies were rushed to the area, and their tests confirmed the absence of any hazard. In fact, the spill had been so small and was dissipated to such an extent in the creek that when the flow entered the Ohio there was virtually no trace of cyanide.

Data compilation and appraisal. Operating the network constitutes only one phase of river-quality surveillance. Evaluating the data with respect to current and prior conditions is the fundamental aim of the program. Items of data, like bricks, have only limited usefulness until they are arranged in some orderly fashion. To give meaning to the hundreds of thousands of items of analytical information assembled each year, ORSANCO has devised a variety of numerical tabulations, graphical representations, and appraisal summaries.

Numerical tabulations have been designed to consolidate in a standardized form on a single sheet all quality and related flow data for an entire year at each monitor station. In addition, each sheet contains information on location of the sampling point, size of drainage area above the point, the number of years of record, and details on flow computation and analytical methods. From time to time these sheets are collated and published for general distribution.[7]

One graphical method of data presentation that has been developed is called the "qualigram" (see Figure 10). These graphs are isometric representations that reveal at a glance the observed ranges of a quality characteristic as well as the frequency of occurrence of specific values in various stretches of the river. Their construction is similar to that of the flow-duration curve commonly used in hydrologic studies. The qualigram makes it possible to visualize in a composite form the aggregate knowledge derived from thousands of data items. This relieves the river analyst of the statistical drudgery and leaves him free to concentrate on evaluation.[8]

Following installation of the robot-monitor system, which has vastly increased the amount of data to be compiled and analyzed (the robots alone supply some 500,000 items annually), a program for electronic data-processing was placed in operation. Among other things, this has facilitated the annual publication of an appraisal of river-quality conditions and trends.[9]

The volume of data from the robot-monitor system is of such magnitude that manual processing is physically and economically impossible. It would take 150 man-years to produce manual summaries of data collected during the course of one year, showing daily averages, maximums, minimums, and standard deviations for all quality characteristics at all stations. By way of contrast, the cost for computer time to produce the kinds of summaries indicated for data collected in 1964 was $4,200.

Tracing unusual incidents. An important use of the robot monitor is the tracing of spills and accidental discharges. By noting changes in certain quality characteristics, the duration and effect of some substances in a stream can be determined. With this information, coupled with

7. Two volumes are in published form, and a third is being collated for the ORSANCO archives. The published volumes are *Water Quality and Flow Variations in the Ohio River 1951–55,* and *Water Quality and Flow Variations—Ohio River and Tributaries 1956–57.* Copies are distributed at no cost to state and federal agencies, municipalities, libraries, and tax-supported institutions. The cost to others is $2.00.

8. See Edward J. Cleary, "The Qualigram—A Visual-Aid Device for River Data Appraisal," *Public Works,* August 1960, p. 120.

9. What is encompassed in such an account can be seen in the 1965 annual report of ORSANCO, one-third of which is devoted to findings on river conditions and an appraisal of their significance. The 1966 report is even more detailed.

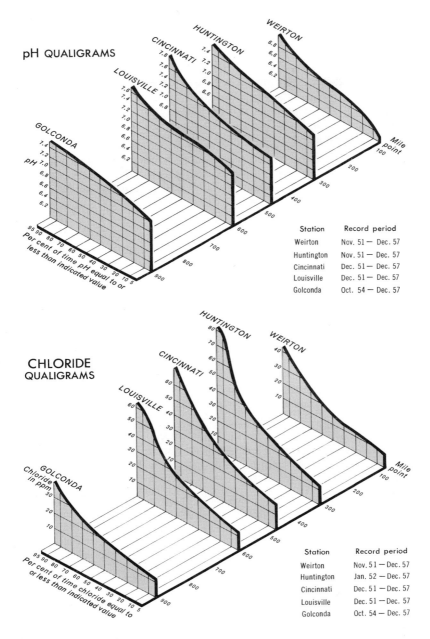

Figure 10. A graphical portrayal of river-quality variations developed by ORSANCO called the "Qualigram." The two graphs shown here depict pH and chloride concentration conditions at selected points on the Ohio River.

Weather Bureau flow forecasts, downstream water plants can be alerted and advised regarding the time a spill may be expected to arrive at the intake and its probable influence.

One incident involved the city of Huntington, W. Va., which was treating its water with permanganate for taste and odor control. A certain substance was spilled upstream that would have reacted with permanganate to turn the water red at the Huntington treatment plant. The plant operator was advised of the time of arrival of the spilled material so that he had time to substitute another method of treatment during the critical period. As a result, the finished water was unaffected. The operator reported that it would have cost $1,000 to correct the adverse effect on the finished water had he been unaware of the spill.

The detection of unusual incidents on a tributary of the Ohio made it possible to alert one industry to the need for greater attention to its waste-discharge practices. Robot-monitor readings showed that in the space of one hour, the pH of the river rose from 7.5 to 11.4, and decreased to less than 2 during the next 20 hours. When the state agency was informed of this situation, it launched an investigation which revealed that a company was sporadically discharging an effluent whose pH varied from 1.0 to 13.0 in a period of less than an hour. These extreme variations were corrected by incorporation of a multistage pH control system in the company's waste-treatment facilities.

The monitor is also useful in cases of widespread and unusual dissolved oxygen conditions. On one occasion when a dry, hot spell was ended by intense rainstorms throughout the Ohio Valley, the dissolved-oxygen content of streams was severely depressed for a period of about three days. Because the monitor network showed that the effects on oxygen levels extended throughout a considerable portion of the valley, the situation was diagnosed as one caused by natural forces—probably the sudden washout into the streams of decaying vegetation and other oxygen-demanding debris.

Cost of monitoring. Collection and laboratory analysis of river samples by conventional methods is a costly procedure.[10] For a single sample, the cost of measuring only five constituents is at least $10; if analyses are made for thirty constituents, the cost may go as high as $120. At these

10. Edward J. Cleary, "Sleuthing the Behavior of a River," *Transactions,* American Society of Civil Engineers, Vol. 125, Part 1, 1960, Paper No. 3052, p. 1053, with discussions on Rhine River practices by Bernd Dieterich, Federal Department of Atomic Energy and Water Economy, Bonn, Germany; and on Thames River experience by George E. Walker, Thames Conservancy, London, England.

costs, control agencies are forced to limit the number and duration of their sampling programs for the assessment of stream conditions.

With respect to the cost of operating the manual component of the ORSANCO monitor network, the accompanying tabulation provides an annual summary of data items received, the out-of-pocket expenses associated with their assembly, and the dollar value of the data. The "value" placed on the data represents what the actual cost would be if ORSANCO had to fund analytical services equivalent to those contributed by the Water Users Committee at no charge, and if ORSANCO had to pay the entire cost of services shared by the Geological Survey.

	No. of data items	Out-of-pocket expenses	"Value" of data	"Value" per item
Water Users (17 stations)	31,570	$ 2,664	$71,376	$2.26
U.S.G.S. (11 stations)	9,900	10,000	20,000	2.02
28 stations	41,470	$12,664	$91,376	$2.20

This accounting shows that the value attached to each item of data averages $2.20. When ORSANCO funds devoted to the project are matched against value received it becomes apparent that the Commission acquires the equivalent of $7.22 of data for each dollar it contributes. The value of data received from each of the 28 manual stations averages $3,000 annually.

The cost of data acquisition using the robot-monitor network may be judged from the following analysis based on experiences with the 13-station system.

Amortization expense (assuming a 7-year life of equipment and a 4% interest rate on a total investment of $136,000)	$17,000
Operation and maintenance	14,000
Leased-circuit rental	6,000
Total annual expense	$37,000

This system produces around a half million items of data per year. Thus the cost per item averages 7½ cents, as compared with $2.20 for the manually-operated stations. In brief, for those quality characteristics that can be measured automatically, the cost on the average is only about 3½ per cent that of manual sampling and analysis.

Appraisal of the robot monitor. In 1965 the commissioners of ORSANCO requested a staff appraisal of the robot monitor system with respect to these questions: Is the system serving the purpose for which it was developed? What specific contributions to pollution control practice have resulted or can be expected from operation of the system? To what extent is expansion of the system merited? Is it adaptable to the needs of other pollution-control agencies? The answers provided may be summarized as follows:

The purpose of the monitor system is to provide information on quality conditions on a continuous, around-the-clock basis. This goal has been attained, and sections of the Ohio River and certain tributaries have been placed under 24-hour vigilance.

One measure of the contribution made by automatic monitoring to pollution-control management may be expressed in terms of economies realized in the collection of water-quality data. The ORSANCO system produces half a million items of data a year. The cost per item is about 7½ cents. With conventional, manually-operated sampling and analysis programs the average cost per item of data is $2.20. Without the automatic system it would not be feasible to monitor streams in a region such as the Ohio Valley on a 24-hour basis.

In terms of specific application, the robot monitor is being used to study cause-and-effect relationships with regard to quality changes, to minimize the effects of spills and accidental discharges on downstream water uses, and to implement the tailoring of waste-treatment practices to river-quality conditions. In brief, it can be said that the essential contribution lies in the opportunity it provides to apply a systems type of operation to water-quality management problems. Usefulness and versatility of the system will be increased as field stations are added and equipment for measuring additional quality characteristics is developed.

The robot monitor has attracted widespread interest, and several local, state, and federal agencies have installed one or more units. A multi-unit station installation was being made on the Potomac River in the spring of 1966 by the U.S. Department of Health, Education, and Welfare. Prior to this the federal government ordered units for surveillance studies in the Raritan Bay area of New Jersey and several places on the West Coast. The Interstate Sanitation Commission is operating a single unit in New York Harbor. And the Municipality of Metropolitan Seattle has installed four units in waterways adjacent to its sewage-treatment plants. It should be pointed out, however, that operating such a system is neither simple nor inexpensive. Acquiring the equipment is but a first step. And to justify the investment required by its installation and maintenance, the user must be prepared to engage in the continuing evaluation of data and diagnosis of river conditions.

Part III

Perspective on Performance

It has never been difficult to design
elaborate constitutions or covenants;
the difficulty has always been in making
them work. It is very easy to draft
on paper great changes or great innovations, for paper offers no resistance.

Mme. de Sabron

17

Goals and Their Attainment

Thus far this chronicle of the Ohio Valley crusade for clean streams has dealt with circumstances leading to creation of the interstate compact, and then with development of the strategy and tactics for an action program. This third part of the book is intended to provide perspective for appraising the utility of the ORSANCO compact. It deals with what has been accomplished in terms of its goals, with the legal aspects of compacts and the obligations of signatory states, with the constraints on performance, and with the functioning of the commissioners and staff.

Experience with this type of institutional device for regional pollution control is limited and has received only scant documentation. In fact, there are only three other interstate compact agencies whose orientation and structure are similar to that of ORSANCO—the Interstate Sanitation Commission (New York, New Jersey, and Connecticut), the Interstate Commission on the Potomac River Basin, and the New England Interstate Water Pollution Control Commission. Each of these agencies, however, is in some way unique. Therefore, while ORSANCO experiences may not be analogous to all compacts, they broadly illustrate the potentialities of this particular kind of arrangement in coping with matters that are regional in scope.

In this chapter the program is discussed, first, in terms of reliance upon co-operative response and the consequent limited exercise of legal proceedings. This provides the background for viewing in some detail the progress made by the states toward the attainment of specific goals.

Co-operation in Achieving Goals

When the interstate compact proposal was first advanced for the Ohio Valley in 1935, the idea was regarded as one of questionable merit. On the one hand, the states were dubious about the effectiveness of an instrumentality dependent for the advancement of its mission primarily on a pledge of faithful co-operation by the signatory parties. On the other hand, they were chary about becoming parties to an agreement creating an agency that might seek to emulate the role of a "supergovernment." Lack of experience with compacts for dealing with regional pollution problems left proponents of this approach with little more than theoretical assurances for gaining acceptance of their proposal.

The promise they held out was the obvious benefits that could be derived through an agency harnessed to the task of co-ordinating and supplementing individual efforts directed toward achievement of mutual objectives. And they argued that it would be possible for such functions to be carried on effectively without intruding on prerogatives of the states. The ORSANCO experiences amply justify the validity of these assumptions. As detailed in Part II of this book, the mission of the compact is being accomplished through the employment of means to foster co-ordinated action and by the pooling of resources to provide services that have supplemented state endeavors.

Not the least of the supplementary services assigned to ORSANCO was securing participation in the eight-state program of many entities in the valley whose interests are affected by or could contribute to its conduct. For this purpose ORSANCO contrived such arrangements as: organizing managers of municipal and industrial water supply plants for assembling data on river-quality variations, from which has grown a valley-wide monitoring network; establishing industry action committees that opened lines of communication with the corporate citizenry of the valley to promote their support; enlisting newspaper, radio, and television media in creating public understanding and motivating interest.

The promotion of these endeavors prompted the observation that "education and cajolery" have been among the principal tools employed by ORSANCO to attain its objectives.[1]

Exercise of police powers. ORSANCO experience is not definitive on the question of whether the existence of an enforcement provision in a compact is a contributing factor to its effectiveness, inasmuch as program goals in the Ohio Valley are being attained with little resort to the use of legal proceedings.

However, it can be said that fears expressed by some that limitations attached to the enforcement clause of the compact (Article IX) would deny employment of police powers thus far have not been sustained.

1. This viewpoint was expressed by Abel Wolman and John Geyer in their "Consultants Report on Future Activities and Compact Revision," prepared for the Interstate Commission on the Potomac River Basin, Washington, D.C., 1958, p. 49.

This provision, it may be recalled, requires that at least two of the three commissioners in a state in which the Commission seeks to intervene must assent to such an action. Critics claimed this injected a type of veto power that would stymie any exercise of enforcement proceedings. As detailed elsewhere (see Chapter 10), in those cases where the Commission did assert its enforcement powers, this action was endorsed by unanimous consent—not only by the commissioners representing the state where legal proceedings were to be initiated, but by the entire membership as well.

The viewpoint of a corporation lawyer regarding Commission procedures and the enforcement clause is of interest. Responding to a query from an industry manager regarding the authority of ORSANCO, he commented as follows: "The power of the Commission is clear and unambiguous. To date the Commission has not had to use its powers to accomplish its objectives, and in many instances each individual state carries out, through the machinery within the state, pollution-abatement programs favored by the Commission. This is a practical working arrangement since in many states the representatives of each state on the Commission are also members of the pollution control machinery of the particular state. . . . The fact that these voluntary methods of accomplishing results have been used by the Commission since 1948 does not eliminate the possibility that the Commission may in the future elect to use the legal powers vested in it by the compact. . . ."[2]

It would be fair to say that thus far the conscientiousness of the states in meeting obligations imposed by the compact, coupled with application of persuasive measures by the Commission in lieu of litigation, has minimized the need for enforcement proceedings in advancing program objectives. Support for this view is to be found in an examination of the status of specific goals as related to the strategy and tactics employed for their attainment.

Status of Program Objectives

When reasons were first advanced for establishment of the compact, the most compelling, so far as public interest was concerned, was the promise it offered for co-ordinated action throughout the region in halting the indiscriminate discharge of sewage and industrial wastes. Initial atten-

2. Letter dated February 28, 1958, from William Foster, senior general counsel, United States Steel Corporation, to Henry F. Hebley, research consultant to Pittsburgh Consolidation Coal Company. At that time Messrs. Foster and Hebley were members of the ORSANCO Coal Industry Advisory Committee.

tion was to be focused on the Ohio River. Conditions on its tributaries were to be remedied in turn. While pollution caused by acid mine drainage was severe in some parts of the basin, it was agreed that this was a less universal and certainly a more complex problem to contend with than the elimination of contamination contributed by municipalities and industries. These priorities of public concern, amply supported by professional opinion of what should be done, determined the strategy and tactics of the ORSANCO mission.

The specific goals that were established can thus be identified as separate but related components of the comprehensive regional program. Some of them were derived from explicit directives in the compact, notably the provision in Article VI that all sewage be given at least the equivalent of primary treatment before discharge into waters of the district. Others have stemmed from policy declarations and decisions of the Commission, reflecting a consensus of state viewpoints on the manner by which the implicit aims of the interstate agreement might be realized.

Execution of the program has been flexibly adapted to take advantage of whatever favorable circumstances presented themselves for advancement of the total mission. In many instances the program components have been advanced simultaneously, paced only by the availability of state and Commission resources. For example, at the same time that Commission investigations and hearings were being conducted to expedite construction of municipal sewage-treatment works, steps were being taken to implement a river-quality monitoring program. Meanwhile, industry committees were organized and discussions initiated on procedures for the control of industrial wastes. Other endeavors were directed toward establishment of criteria, the development of a hazard-alert system, and prevention of oil pollution.

Major goals and progress toward their attainment may be sketched as follows:

Halting discharge of untreated sewage into the Ohio River. By 1965, sewage-treatment facilities handling wastewaters from 99 per cent of the sewered population (3,700,000 people) were in operation. In 1948, less than one per cent of the sewage received treatment. All of the plants were designed to meet standards promulgated by ORSANCO following technical investigations and public hearings conducted in the early fifties. River-quality monitoring is providing information for decisions soon to be reached on the need for upgrading treatment requirements.

Securing treatment of sewage by all municipalities in the district.
Action within the borders of each of the signatory states has resulted in
this record: treatment works serving 94 per cent of the 11,400,000
urban sewered population are now in operation.[3] By way of contrast, at
the time the compact was signed only 38 per cent of the urban population
was served with treatment plants. Capital investment for sewage disposal
facilities in the entire district now totals over a billion dollars—an outlay
averaging $100 for every man, woman, and child. Nine-tenths of this
investment was locally financed. Federal aid did not become available
until 1956, by which time three-quarters of the municipal construction
program was nearing completion. (Appendix 11 shows the status of
facilities for sewage treatment and industrial waste control as of July 1,
1965.)

Controlling industrial-waste pollution. More than 1,700 industrial
establishments discharge effluents directly into streams of the Ohio Valley district. Today, 90 per cent are inventoried as having provided
facilities to comply at least with minimum interstate requirements. However, because the inventory makes no differentiation between large and
small establishments, the record should not be construed to mean that
90 per cent of the industrial pollution is abated. Meantime, the wastewaters from additional thousands of industries connected to community
sewer systems are now being treated in the newly built municipal plants.

The minimum requirements for industrial-waste control, as detailed in
Chapter 11, were established by ORSANCO as the initial step toward
satisfying clean-stream necessities. The second step involves promulgation
of supplemental control measures for each industry "tailored" to meet
river-quality standards. It cannot be said, however, that progress in the
control of industrial wastes has as yet measured up to aspirations. The
work advanced by a majority of industries is marred by the tardiness of a
few. This accounts for situations in some parts of the valley where discharges of sludges and color-producing or floating materials reveal continuing evidence of gross pollution. Furthermore, accidental spills and
carelessness, notably with regard to handling oil and chemical products,
create localized conditions of pollution from time to time.

Mitigating mine acid drainage. Despite legal obstacles that had to be
overcome because of an almost universal attitude of defeatism concerning

3. About half of the municipal sewage receives "secondary" treatment (which
is capable of removing up to 95 per cent of the pollutional constituents); another
quarter receives "intermediate" treatment and the remainder "primary" treatment
(which provides 35 to 40 per cent removal).

availability of technical means for controlling mine drainage, ORSANCO finally succeeded in 1960 in modifying this viewpoint and promulgated basic regulations. Heretofore, in several of the signatory states as well as in an early policy declaration of the interstate agency itself, mine drainage qualified for blanket exemption from regulation until "practical means" for control had been demonstrated. The change in ORSANCO policy resulted from a study of mine-drainage practices, which revealed that if certain precautions were taken the pollutional effects of acid drainage from active mines could be mitigated. This declaration by the interstate agency, which was endorsed by its coal-industry advisory committee, encouraged changes in state legislation that have removed mine drainage from an exempt category of industrial-waste discharge. Still unanswered, however, is the question of what can be done about curbing pollution from so-called abandoned mine operations. A substantial amount of federal research funds has now been allocated to finding a solution to this perplexing problem. ORSANCO also participates in a federally sponsored technical committee guiding development of a mine acid remedial project for the Monongahela River, which is a large contributor of acidity to the Ohio River.

Preventing oil pollution. Adoption of an interstate oil-control measure in 1958 was coupled with the issuance of a manual of precautionary practices required on boats, at terminals, and at other installations where oil products are used, transferred, or stored. As an aid in promoting compliance, ORSANCO and its Petroleum Industry Advisory Committee produced a film, *Oil on the River,* for those engaged in handling oil products and for state regulatory agency personnel. With some 16 million tons of oil products transported annually on the Ohio River alone, and with the ever-present hazard of accidental discharges from shore-based facilities, the prevention of oil pollution requires constant vigilance. Toward this end, periodic reconnaissance by aerial and boat patrol is undertaken by the ORSANCO staff. Violations traceable to shore-based installations are referred to state regulatory agencies. Those involving marine transport and defective floating equipment are referred to the U.S. Coast Guard, which has jurisdiction over shipping operations.

Status of River-Quality Conditions

Progress in securing installation of wastewater control facilities, with the resulting reduction in the visibly offensive and obvious manifestations of pollution, is one measure for charting the attainment of goals. The river-quality monitoring system operated by the Commission makes possible an appraisal of results in another and more significant manner. It permits assessment of the invisible aspects of quality improvement. This is accomplished by measurement and evaluation of the chemical, bacteriological, and radioactive characteristics of the river under varying conditions. Thus, by matching these findings on quality against established criteria,[4] a professional judgment can be made of the effectiveness of remedial measures already applied and of what additional controls may be needed and where.

Following are the highlights of Ohio River findings based on an evaluation of 1964–65 monitor data.[5] Broadly speaking, quality characteristics were such as to satisfy drinking-water criteria for dissolved solids, chlorides, fluorides, nitrates, methylene-blue active substance (an indicator of the apparent concentration of synthetic detergents), and radioactive materials.

Bacterial conditions, measured by the density of coliform organisms, met the criterion for water-supply purposes (monthly-average counts of 5,000 per 100 ml or less) 100 per cent of the time at Wheeling, 92 per cent of the time at Cincinnati, 67 per cent at Louisville, 60 per cent at Huntington, and 39 per cent at Evansville.[6] The criterion for recreational purposes—daily values of coliform less than 2,400 and monthly-average values less than 1,000—is close to realization during the recreational season in the Wheeling, Huntington, and Cincinnati areas. At other locations additional improvement in river conditions is required.

The density of coliform bacteria provides one measure of the sanitary quality of river water. However, the analytical methods for making this determination are not specific because they measure coliform bacteria common to the soil as well as fecal coliforms associated with sewage discharges. A more meaningful test for measuring the impact of sewage discharges on bacterial density in rivers is being advocated. The test, which is specific for identification of fecal organisms, is being given trial by the ORSANCO Water Users Committee, for comparative examination of identical samples to determine the ratio of fecal organisms to the total count. Results thus far indicate that for the Ohio River the fecal count is one-tenth to one-third of the total count.

4. See Appendix 10 for a tabulation of ORSANCO criteria.
5. See ORSANCO, *Seventeenth Annual Report*, 1965, for an appraisal of river-quality conditions in 1964 and a comparison with those ten years ago.
6. See "Bacterial Quality Objectives for the Ohio River," adopted by the Ohio River Valley Water Sanitation Commission, April 4, 1951.

Conditions related to the maintenance of fish life,[7] as measured in terms of temperature, pH, and dissolved oxygen, were these: river temperatures were satisfactory in all reaches; pH levels were within recommended limits except for a small percentage of time in a short stretch of the upper Ohio River; dissolved-oxygen concentrations met the criterion for 100 per cent of the time at Cincinnati (mile 463) and at South Heights (mile 16), 95 per cent of the time at Huntington (mile 304), 94 per cent at Stratton (mile 55), and 89 per cent at Louisville (mile 601). Just below Cincinnati (at Miami Fort—mile 490), this level was met only 77 per cent of the time.

Concentrations of nitrates and phosphates in the river have shown no appreciable increase since 1954, when monitoring of these constituents was initiated. These constituents are known to have a fertilizing influence on the growth of algae and other aquatic plant life; however, no precise relationship of these chemicals with algal productivity has been established.

From the standpoint of hardness content, Ohio River water may be characterized as varying from "moderately hard" to "very hard" in terms of U.S. Geological Survey classifications.[8] In 1963–64 the monthly-average concentrations showed an improvement (reduction) of 8 per cent over those ten years earlier. Hardness-producing constituents originate from natural geological conditions and mine drainage, as well as from wastewater discharges. The relative magnitude of each of these contributing sources, and therefore the potentialities for managing hardness levels, has not yet been determined.

Iron and manganese concentrations in the upper portion of the river exceed limits recommended for drinking water. There has been no appreciable reduction in concentration levels of these substances over the past ten years. However, all water supplied to consumers is first processed in filter plants that have the capability of reducing both iron and manganese content.

7. Recommendations of the ORSANCO Aquatic Life Advisory Committee. See *Journal,* Water Pollution Control Federation, Vol. 28, No. 5, May 5, 1956, pp. 678–90.

8. Hardness is a chemical characteristic that causes reduction of the lathering capacity of soap and the deposition of scale in boilers. It may be defined as the total concentration of calcium and magnesium ions in the water plus those of other polyvalent metals such as iron, aluminum, zinc, etc. The U.S. Geological Survey classifies water with a hardness of 61 to 120 milligrams per liter as "moderately hard"; if it is greater than 180 mg/1 it is "very hard." The monthly-average concentration of hardness in various stretches of the Ohio River now ranges from 80 to 230 mg/1, averaging 139.

Sulfate concentrations, in terms of monthly-average values, at times slightly exceed the criterion for drinking water in one reach of the Ohio River upstream from Parkersburg. However, in most reaches, particularly downstream from Parkersburg, there has been a reduction in sulfate content during the past ten years.

Radioactivity levels in the Ohio River are less than a tenth of the permissible limit for drinking water and may be regarded as equivalent to natural levels. ORSANCO also measured radioactivity accumulation in plankton, fish, and silt from fifteen locations, all of which were very low. In addition, analyses were performed on rain water to assess the contribution of "fallout" to the river. A trend toward lower values during the past three years has been noted.

From monitor data on six of the major streams tributary to the Ohio River, the following findings emerge. With respect to acidity values, all of these streams except the Allegheny and Monongahela met the criterion considered satisfactory for maintaining a harvestable crop of fish. Dissolved oxygen on all tributaries except the Allegheny fell short of meeting desired conditions at certain times; on some occasions the Kanawha River was devoid of oxygen, but conditions showed improvement over previous years. Conductivity and chloride values were satisfactory on all streams except the Muskingum. Iron and manganese concentrations were high on the Allegheny and Monongahela. Temperature values were below limiting values, and radioactivity levels were far below permissible concentrations.

To sum up, the record reveals substantial progress toward attainment of the goals established for the ORSANCO program. However, the ultimate measure of success in the pursuit of the eight-state mission will be found in stream-quality conditions. Findings from the monitoring network reveal general improvement in several quality characteristics compared with conditions that prevailed ten years ago. But they also confirm that more control needs to be exercised, through the installation of additional facilities in some areas and also in the improvement of performance of existing treatment works. There are certain stretches of streams in the valley, notably on the tributaries, that cannot yet qualify as being clean enough to satisfy water-use requirements.

18

Legal Scope and
Validity of the Compact

Pollution of waterways that pass through or are contiguous to several states is one of the more recent problems of a regional nature that states have sought to resolve by establishing compact commissions. The compact is an old instrumentality for co-operative action, but it was not until 1935 that this approach was pioneered in the field of pollution control.

Prior to this time the only avenue for settlement of interstate pollution problems was through adversary proceedings in the Supreme Court of the United States. Always time-consuming, generally expensive, and often unsatisfactory in results, such litigation was considered only as a last resort for those who were seeking a remedy. The limitations of legal action were emphasized by the Supreme Court in the case of *New York v. New Jersey,* 256 U.S. 313 (1921), involving pollution of New York Bay, when it said:

> We cannot withhold the suggestion inspired by the considerations of this case, that the grave problem of sewage disposal presented by the large and growing population living on the shores of New York Bay, is one more likely to be wisely solved by cooperative study and by conference and mutual concession on the part of representatives of the states which are vitally interested than by proceeding in any court however constituted.

Perhaps even more important in focusing attention on the compact method as an appropriate device for co-operation along the lines suggested by the Supreme Court was an essay by Felix Frankfurter and James Landis in 1925.[1] Discussing interstate adjustment to newly emerging problems, Frankfurter and Landis said:

> ... We are dealing with regions, like the Southwest clustering about the Colorado River, or the States dependent upon the Delaware for water, which are organic units in the light of a common human need like

1. See "The Compact Clause of the Constitution—A Study in Interstate Adjustments," *Yale Law Journal,* Vol. 34, No. 7 (May 1925), pp. 685–758.

water-supply. The regions are less than the nation and are greater than any one State. The mechanism of legislation must therefore be greater than that at the disposal of a single State. National action is the ready alternative. But national action is either unavailable or excessive. For a number of interstate situations Federal control is wholly outside the present ambit of Federal power, wholly unlikely to be conferred upon the Federal government by constitutional amendment and, in the practical tasks of government, wholly unsuited to Federal action even if constitutional power were obtained.

With all our unifying processes nothing is clearer than that in the United States there are being built up regional interests, regional cultures and regional interdependencies. These produce regional problems calling for regional solutions. Control by the nation would be ill-conceived and intrusive. A gratuitous burden would thereby be cast upon Congress and the national administration, both of which need to husband their energies for the discharge of unequivocally national responsibilities. As to these regional problems Congress could not legislate effectively. Regional interests, regional wisdom and regional pride must be looked to for solutions. . . . Collective legislative action through the instrumentality of compact by states constituting a region furnishes the answer.

These ideas were taken up in 1935 when New York, New Jersey, and later Connecticut negotiated a compact establishing the Interstate Sanitation Commission. Its role was to unite the efforts of those three states in a continuing administrative program for abatement of pollution in the harbor waters of the area and in the tributary streams.

Growth of Compacts

The regional interdependencies of water pollution, the inadequacy of litigation for resolving interstate conflicts, and the indisposition of the states toward federal intervention were factors that commended application of the compact method for the regulation of pollution. Following closely the lead taken by the states in the New York Harbor area, the Ohio Valley states began negotiations to establish a compact agency.

Shortly thereafter came the Interstate Commission on the Potomac River Basin (established in 1941 by Maryland, Pennsylvania, West Virginia, Virginia, and the District of Columbia) and the New England Interstate Water Pollution Control Commission (created in 1941 by Massachusetts, Connecticut, Rhode Island, and later joined by New York, New Hampshire, Vermont, and Maine). For each of these compacts Congressional consent was sought and obtained.

Frequently identified with these compact agencies was the Interstate Commission on the Delaware River Basin (INCODEL), which operated from 1936 until 1963. It differed from the others in that it was established by reciprocal legislation enacted by New York, New Jersey, Pennsylvania, and Delaware rather than by a compact, so that Congressional consent was unnecessary. The interstate water-quality standards produced by this agency became embodied in statutory and administrative agreements among the pollution-control authorities of the four states, as the agency itself had no regulatory enforcement powers. When the new Delaware River Basin Commission superseded INCODEL in 1963, it adopted these standards as a starting point in its program and is now engaged in revising them. The Delaware commission, unlike its predecessor, is a compact agency created with the consent of Congress. The signatory parties include not only the four states but the federal government as well, which makes this compact unique among interstate agreements. The Delaware commission has broader functions and powers for regional development of water resources than any other compact agency (see Chapter 22).

In 1958 the Congress gave approval to the formation of the Tennessee River Basin Water Pollution Control Compact, involving the seven states of Alabama, Georgia, Kentucky, Mississippi, North Carolina, Tennessee, and Virginia. On March 1, 1963, an organization meeting was held by the three states whose legislatures had by then ratified the agreement— Tennessee, Kentucky, and Mississippi. A temporary chairman was appointed, but no budget was adopted. As of the middle of 1966 none of the additional states had signed the agreement and the agency is not yet functioning.[2]

At the present time a draft of a proposed interstate compact on water-resources development and pollution control is being circulated by the

2. Delays that have attended formation and implementation of the Tennessee compact are explained, in part, by Richard H. Leach in an article titled "The Status of Interstate Compacts Today," in *State Government,* Spring, 1959. Said Professor Leach: "Congress does not create all the obstacles in the way of interstate compact use. Executive departments and agencies also erect obstacles of their own. The opposition of the United States Public Health Service to the Tennessee River Basin Water Pollution Control Compact ... [is] a well-known case in point."

At the 1960 National Conference on Water Pollution, I called attention to the intent of the Congress, as expressed in the Federal Water Pollution Control Act, that encouragement be given to the formation of interstate compact agencies. I noted that all of those in existence resulted from the initiative of the states and came into being prior to enactment of the federal act in 1948. And I concluded: "If the federal authorities have given any encouragement to the formation of new interstate agencies, the results have not yet manifested themselves." *Proceedings,* The National Conference on Water Pollution (Washington: U. S. Government Printing Office, 1961), p. 270.

Interstate Advisory Committee on the Susquehanna River Basin.[3] Three states—New York, Pennsylvania, and Maryland—are involved. The advisory committee consists of four members from each state, two of whom are appointed by the governor and two by the legislature.

In addition, there are in existence two informal interstate "agreements" concerned with pollution control and three formal compacts that are authorized to include pollution control within their purview. A Great Lakes Drainage Basin Sanitation Agreement was inaugurated in 1928, the present members being Wisconsin, Minnesota, Illinois, Michigan, Ohio, Pennsylvania, New York, and Indiana, and efforts have been under way to convert this agreement into a formal, Congressionally-approved compact agency. In 1935 an Upper Mississippi Drainage Basin Sanitation Agreement was concluded by the states of Minnesota, Iowa, Wisconsin, Illinois, and Missouri.

Congressionally-approved agencies whose powers embrace pollution control but so far have not been actively identified with such endeavors include: Red River of the North Compact (1938), which includes North Dakota, South Dakota, and Minnesota; the Bi-State Development Agency (1950), representing Illinois and Missouri; and the Klamath River Basin Compact (1957) between California and Oregon.

Powers of Enforcement

Only two of the pioneer pollution-control compact agencies—the Interstate Sanitation Commission for New York Harbor and ORSANCO—are clothed with authority to enforce compliance with their provisions. However, the new Delaware River Basin Commission is provided with such powers, as is the not-yet-operative Tennessee River commission.

The Interstate Sanitation Commission is directed to place the tidal and coastal waters within the New York Harbor district under one of two classifications for which statutory standards were prescribed in the compact.[4] Class A includes waters used primarily for recreational purposes,

3. The Susquehanna Advisory Committee has a small staff and maintains an office at 2101 North Front Street, Harrisburg, Pennsylvania.
4. The statutory requirements are set forth in Article VII of this compact (which has been published as Public Res. No. 62, 74th Cong., 1st Sess., approved Aug. 27, 1935). They are as follows:
    It is agreed between the signatory States that no sewage or other polluting matters shall be discharged or permitted to flow into, or be placed in, or permitted to fall or move into the tidal waters of the district, except under the following conditions and restrictions:
    (1) All sewage discharged or permitted to flow into Class A waters of the district shall first have been so treated as:

shellfish culture, and development of fish life; Class B includes all other water areas. The agency is given the power to issue orders for compliance and enforce them. No such action can be taken, however, unless it receives the assent of a majority of the commissioners from each state.

The Ohio Valley compact, as has been described, establishes minimum standards for treatment for all sewage that is discharged into the interstate waters of the district. The commissioners are vested with authority to promulgate such higher standards as may be determined by investigations and hearings, and they are also directed to prescribe requirements for treatment or modification of industrial waste based on investigations and hearings. Enforcement authority is limited by a provision that no order against a violator shall go into effect unless and until it has received the assent of at least a majority of the signatory states, as well as the assent of not less than the majority of the commissioners of the state in which the violator is located.

The Tennessee compact includes a limitation on the exercise of enforcement power similar to that in the Ohio Valley compact.

The new compact for the Delaware River Basin contains no such restriction. It states simply (in Article 5.4): "The Commission may, after investigation and hearing, issue an order or orders upon any persons or public or private corporation, or other entity, to cease the discharge of

---

(a) to remove all floating solids and at least 60 per centum of the suspended solids; and (b) to effect a reduction of organisms of the B. coli group (intestinal bacilli) so that the probable number of such organisms shall not exceed one per cubic centimeter in more than 50 per centum of the samples of sewage effluent tested by the partially confirmed test: *Provided, however,* That in the case of discharge into waters used primarily for bathing, this bacterial standard need not be required except during the bathing season; and (c) to effect a reduction in the oxygen demand of the sewage effluent sufficient to maintain an average dissolved-oxygen content in the tidal waters of the district and in the general vicinity of the point of discharge of the sewage into those waters, at a depth of about five feet below the surface, of not less than 50 per centum saturation during any week of the year.

(2) All sewage discharged or permitted to flow into Class B waters of the district shall first have been so treated as:

(a) to remove all floating solids and at least 10 per centum of the suspended solids, or such additional percentage as may by reason of local conditions be necessary to avoid the formation of sludge deposits in the Class B waters of the district; and (b) to effect a reduction in the oxygen demand of the sewage effluent sufficient to maintain an average dissolved-oxygen content in the tidal waters of the district and in the general vicinity of the point of discharge of the sewage into those waters, at a depth of about five feet below the surface, of not less than 30 per centum saturation during any week of the year.

sewage, industrial or other waste into waters of the district which it determines to be in violation of such rules and regulations as it shall have adopted for the prevention and abatement of pollution."

Legal Validity of Compacts[5]

In general, and also with specific reference to the Ohio Valley compact, the Supreme Court of the United States has rendered decisions that are regarded as favorable to the implementation of interstate compacts. And in no instance has a compact been held unconstitutional or invalid.

Principles enunciated. One fundamental principle established by the U.S. Supreme Court with respect to interstate compacts is that questions relating to their validity or interpretation are federal questions. Thus in the matter of *Delaware River Joint Toll Bridge Commission* v. *Colburn,* 310 U.S. 419, 84 L. Ed. 1287 (1940), which involved the exercise of the right of eminent domain under a compact for erection of a bridge, the court expressly stated that construction of a compact sanctioned by Congress involved a question of federal title, right, privilege, or immunity which, when specifically set up and claimed in a state court, could be reviewed on certiorari.

It has also been clearly established that the Supreme Court is the final arbiter of all questions as to validity or construction of compacts, even if state constitutional issues are involved. In *Kentucky* v. *Indiana,* 281 U.S. 163, 74 L. Ed. 784 (1930), the Court asserted that, in such situations, the states cannot determine their rights *inter sese* and that the Supreme Court "must pass upon every question essential to such a determination although local legislation and questions of state authorization may be involved."[6]

In the case of *Hinderlider* v. *LaPlata River & Cherry Creek Ditch Company,* 304 U.S. 92, L. Ed. 1202 (1938), the Supreme Court upheld the validity of a water-allotment compact that had been approved by Congress, notwithstanding the necessity of reversing a decision of the highest court of the State of Colorado holding the compact to be in violation of certain provisions of the state constitution.

5. This section is based in large part on a memorandum by Leonard Weakley, legal counsel of ORSANCO.

6. Mitchell Wendell, counsel for the Council of State Governments, points out that, "*Kentucky* v. *Indiana,* although handled by the Court and most other people as though it were a compact case, really involved an administrative agreement rather than a compact. Consequently, that Court opinion is strictly speaking not controlling on any compact issue." Personal communication to the author.

Position of the Ohio Valley compact. The most recent case that confirms both the foregoing principles and provides additional support for the administration of compacts is that of *State of West Virginia* ex rel. *Dyer* v. *Sims,* 341 U.S. 22, 95 L. Ed. 713 (1950). The history of this case is as follows: Edgar B. Sims, the West Virginia state auditor, refused to issue the warrant for the disbursement of funds appropriated by the legislature to cover West Virginia's proportionate share of ORSANCO expenses for 1949. He had approved the first payment in 1948, but he later displayed qualms about the propriety of the legislature in approving participation in the Ohio Valley compact. A writ in mandamus was requested of the Supreme Court of Appeals of West Virginia by N. H. Dyer, a West Virginia member of the interstate commission, seeking to compel the auditor to issue the necessary warrant.

The Supreme Court of Appeals of West Virginia ruled in a three to two decision that ratification of the Ohio River Valley Water Sanitation Compact by the Legislature of West Virginia in 1939 was unconstitutional. The West Virginia court interpreted the compact as: (1) requiring the state to incur a financial obligation in violation of debt limitations imposed by its constitution; and (2) resulting in a delegation of police power that is contrary to general principles of constitutional law.

The issue thus presented was regarded in legal circles throughout the nation as basic to the stature of all compacts, namely: could a state avoid or subvert obligations that it had assumed in becoming a signatory party to such an agreement? ORSANCO took the question to the Supreme Court of the United States.

The Supreme Court of the United States granted the motion for a writ of certiorari, finding that under the *Colburn* case previously cited there was no question as to its jurisdiction to review the proceeding in the state court. The Supreme Court then proceeded to spell out the extent of its authority with respect to interpretation and validity of interstate compacts in the following language:

> . . . A state cannot be its own ultimate judge in a controversy with a sister state. To determine the nature and scope of obligations as between states, whether they arise through the legislative means of compact or the "federal common law" governing interstate controversies (*Hinderlider* v. *LaPlata Co.,* 304 U.S. 92, 110), is the function and duty of the Supreme Court of the Nation. Of course every deference will be shown to what the highest court of a state deems to be the law and policy of its state, particularly when recondite or unique features of local law are urged. Deference is one thing; submission to a state's own determination of whether it has undertaken an obligation, what that obligation is, and whether it conflicts with a disability of the state to undertake it is quite another.

The Supreme Court of Appeals of the State of West Virginia is, for exclusively state purposes, the ultimate tribunal in construing the meaning of her Constitution. But two prior decisions of this Court make clear that we are free to examine determination of law by state courts in the limited field where a compact brings in issue the rights of other states and the United States.

Turning to the issues specifically raised by the decision of the West Virginia state court, the U. S. Supreme Court concluded that the Ohio River Valley Water Sanitation Compact involved a conventional grant of legislative power and was a reasonable and carefully limited delegation of power to an interstate agency. In addition, the Court concluded that the provision of the compact with regard to contributions by the signatory states had been drawn in the light of various debt limitations of state constitutions and did not create an obligation in conflict with the language of that particular section of the Constitution of West Virginia. The decision of the state court was therefore reversed, and the case remanded for further action.

In the concurring opinion, Mr. Justice Jackson used the following language:

> West Virginia, for internal affairs, is free to interpret her own Constitution as she will. But if the compact system is to have vitality and integrity, she may not raise an issue of ultra vires, decide it and release herself from an interstate obligation. The legal consequences which flow from the formal participation in a compact consented to by Congress is a federal question for this Court.
>
> West Virginia points to no provisions of her Constitution which we can say was clear notice or fair warning to Congress or other states of any defect in her authority to enter into this compact. It is a power inherent in sovereignty limited only to the extent that Congressional consent is required. (*Rhode Island* v. *Massachusetts,* 12 Pet. 657, 725; *Poole* v. *Fleeger,* 11 Pet. 185, 209.) Whatever she now says her Constitution means, she may not apply retroactively that interpretation to place an unforeseeable construction upon what the other states to this Compact were entitled to believe was a fully authorized act.
>
> Estoppel is not often to be invoked against a government. But West Virginia assumed a contractual obligation with equals by permission of another government that is sovereign in the field. After Congress and sister states had been induced to alter their positions and bind themselves to terms of a covenant, West Virginia should be estopped from repudiating her act. For this reason, I consider that whatever interpretation she may put on the generalities of her Constitution, she is bound by the compact, and on that basis I concur in the judgment.

In the opinion of ORSANCO's legal counsel, the decisions referred to, and particularly the language used in the *West Virginia* case, put to rest many of the questions that come to mind with respect to the legal scope and validity of compacts. He concludes that this instrumentality "provides a basis for interstate adjustments having considerably more substance than the more familiar pattern of co-operative action through so-called agreements which, not being supported by Congressional approval, are not capable of satisfactory enforcement and which, being terminable at any time by the unilateral action of any participating state, must be recognized, from a practical point of view, as having limited durability."

19

Constraints upon Performance

Any assessment of the ORSANCO program invites recognition of the constraints on performance as well as the incentives that guide its development. The incentives, which have been detailed in previous chapters, stemmed from a conviction that the appropriate way to deal with regional pollution problems in the Ohio Valley was for the states involved to determine jointly what should be done, and then individually shoulder responsibility for doing what was required.

Having been so emphatic in their preference for the exercise of state initiative as an alternate to federal intervention when the compact was being negotiated during the thirties, the Ohio Valley states were now challenged to "put up or shut up" after the document was signed. Therefore, a sense of pride in demonstrating that performance would equal promise may be regarded as one of the pervading motivations in making the compact work.

How well the states have performed may be judged from the record. Less apparent, perhaps, are the problems that had to be overcome. The following comments on administrative, jurisdictional, and financial difficulties may help to illuminate some of the less obvious aspects of this regional enterprise. The constraints imposed upon the execution of the ORSANCO program are grouped into three categories—those associated with state administrative functions, those occasioned by divided responsibilities, and those of a limited budget.

State Administrative Problems

When the compact was signed in 1948, not all the states were equipped with legislation that could be considered suitable for the expeditious pursuit of interstate pollution-control endeavors. For example, Kentucky found it desirable to rewrite its legislation completely, and Ohio took steps to revise its laws, notably to remove a provision that exempted

231

municipalities on interstate streams from installing sewage-treatment works until all other communities upstream had provided facilities. By 1953, when certain deficiencies in the West Virginia statutes had been corrected, the signatory states felt they had substantially improved their legislative tools.

From the beginning the states faced problems in adjusting their resources and personnel to the extra demands imposed by the ORSANCO program. The state agencies could not, of course, devote their efforts exclusively to Ohio Valley affairs. Each one in varying degree had commitments to fulfill in other watersheds. This engendered problems of priority assignment. It would be unrealistic to presume that a regional responsibility, regardless of its merit, could always take precedence over equally pressing matters in other areas of a signatory state.

Inadequacy of state budgets has been a major limiting factor in how far and how fast efforts could be deployed. On the totem pole of state budget appropriations, pollution-control activities traditionally have been "low man." A national study[1] by the Public Administration Service reveals that, with few exceptions, state support for this activity is less than a PAS recommended "minimum" level of expenditure, and pitifully deficient when compared to the "desirable" level. The situation for the ORSANCO states is shown in the following tabulation prepared from the PAS study.

Among the Ohio Valley states the conclusion can be drawn that in order to maintain control programs commensurate with a "desirable"

Comparison of Pollution–Control Expenditures with
Recommended Levels in ORSANCO States

State	Reported expenditures		Public Administration Service recommended levels	
	1957–58	1964–65	Minimum	Desirable
Illinois	$ 226,158	$ 412,791	$1,450,000	$ 2,225,000
Indiana	158,228	329,275	556,000	965,000
Kentucky	104,294	207,648	237,000	410,000
New York	337,479	643,602	2,200,000	3,320,000
Ohio	341,715	454,708	1,285,000	1,960,000
Pennsylvania	469,000	807,000	1,420,000	2,170,000
Virginia	154,237	284,199	374,000	673,000
West Virginia	76,193	198,420	201,000	291,000
Total	$1,867,304	$3,337,643	$7,723,000	$12,014,000

1. *Staffing and Budgetary Guidelines for State Water Pollution Control Agencies.* A 1964 survey report of the Public Administration Service (1313 East 60th Street, Chicago, Ill.), sponsored by the Division of Water Supply and Pollution Control, U. S. Public Health Service.

level of performance the state budget should be five times greater than the 1964–65 figure in Illinois; about four times greater in Ohio; three times as much in Indiana; and doubled in Kentucky.

Illustrating the administrative complications faced by the states in their efforts to satisfy regional requirements was the situation in Pennsylvania. Prior to accepting Ohio Valley obligations, this state was committed to a long-range program developed by its Sanitary Water Board. This plan called for concentrating efforts on successive cleanup of individual watersheds, the work to be done progressively from east to west across the state. ORSANCO territory lies in the western area. For several years, therefore, Pennsylvania's response to advancing its components of the Ohio Valley program had to be fitted in with completion of certain commitments in other parts of the state. This explains why initial efforts in Pennsylvania were confined to the main stem of the Ohio River before emphasis could be given to such tributaries as the Monongahela and Allegheny rivers. Furthermore, as a member of the Delaware and Potomac interstate commissions, Pennsylvania had obligations to these agencies.

New York had a somewhat similar problem. It was constrained in dealing with pollution in that area of the ORSANCO district under its jurisdiction (the upper Allegheny) by a state program that required studies, public hearings, and classification of streams prior to issuance of clean-up orders. Certain streams in the state had been accorded a higher priority than the upper Allegheny and its tributaries. Although Pennsylvania, whose interests on the Allegheny are downstream from New York, might have preferred faster action in cleanup on this stream, the fact was that New York's position was analogous to Pennsylvania's in that other areas had a program priority.

The difficulties imposed by limitations of budget and staff were typified by the situation in West Virginia. Jurisdictional responsibilites of this state with respect to the compact area include not only a populated and industrialized section of the Ohio River, but several heavily industrialized major tributaries as well. Until recently, the pollution-control program in West Virginia was serviced by a staff averaging six professional employees.[2] Yet, in the ORSANCO district alone, West Virginia was

2. Inadequate staff continues to influence the conduct of pollution-control endeavors in West Virginia. Under a reorganization in 1961, resulting from consolidation of several resources activities under a department of natural resources, a total of 17 employees have been assembled to deal with *all* aspects of water. In his annual report for 1963–64, Bern Wright, director of the water-resources division stated: "... the staff is the largest in the history of the agency, but additional personnel are needed to render the service demanded by the public. Low salaries remain the biggest obstacle to hiring and keeping engineers and chemists."

faced with implementing construction of sewage-treatment plants at 192 communities and control facilities at 246 industrial establishments. Presumably it was the strain of this endeavor and the less-than-satisfactory salary conditions prevailing in West Virginia that resulted in turnover of the directorship of the state pollution agency four times in a span of twelve years. A similar story of a heavy burden being carried by a small staff could be told for Kentucky. However, state appropriations in both West Virginia and Kentucky have been increased in the past few years, and additional funds from federal grants-in-aid have become available.

The challenge of matching state efforts to interstate-compact aspirations is accentuated each time additional regulations are adopted by ORSANCO and thrust upon the states for execution. This was evident when regulations for curbing acid drainage from active mines were promulgated in 1960. In Ohio, where mine drainage had previously been exempted from regulation, the state agency was not in a position to promptly shoulder the new burden. It was only by re-alignment of staff duties that attention could gradually be applied to the new activity.

These experiences are not novel. Every state signatory to the Ohio Valley compact is constrained in varying degree with similar administrative and budgetary problems. Therefore, the commissioners could be gratified that under these circumstances the states did accomplish so much in advancing ORSANCO goals. It is no small thing to secure the construction of sewage-treatment plants serving some 1,300 communities with a combined population of 11 million and the installation of control facilities at more than 1,500 industrial establishments in the valley.

Reconciliation of Multiple Interests

The commissioners have had to reconcile multiple interests in guiding development of the regional program. They cannot be unmindful, for example, that operations of ORSANCO should be conducted in a manner to minimize intrusion on state prerogatives. Furthermore, since at least one commissioner from each state is also directly responsible for executing interstate directives within his state, the commissioners cannot always be expected to be enthusiastic about proposals that add individual burdens or may require departure from established practices. For these reasons, there are occasions when proposals that in the abstract may appear meritorious are subject to modification or deferment.

An instance of jurisdictional sensitivity is reflected by the negative reaction of the commissioners to a proposal that ORSANCO consider establishment of a river-warden patrol on the Ohio River. This suggestion reflected the view that, since interstate regulations have been promulgated and many control works have been installed up and down the river, the prompt challenging of violations could be regarded as a logical next step in advancing the mission of the compact agency. However, several commissioners feel that policing operations by ORSANCO might symbolize in spirit, if not in fact, an infringement of regulatory functions.

A similar sensitivity was displayed earlier with regard to establishment of a regional hazard-and-alert program. The proposal called for inauguration by ORSANCO of a clearinghouse so that industries experiencing accidental discharges or spills could notify central headquarters, which in turn would relay an alert to downstream water users. However, since it is Commission policy not to engage in direct contact with any municipality or industry except by request of the state in which it is located, there was some question about approving a hazard-and-alert program, although there was agreement that in principle it had merit. Finally, several interstate pollution incidents associated with spills led to a trial of the proposed procedure.

The staff has exhibited great care in conducting such operations so as to avoid any semblance of jurisdictional overlap with the states. Whenever an industry notifies Commission headquarters of a spill, and the staff has made an assessment of its impact on river-quality conditions, this information is relayed immediately to the state in which the spill occurred, along with recommendations as to who should be notified downstream. It is then the option of the state agency to determine whether it will contact those who may be affected in its area of jurisdiction or instruct ORSANCO to do so. In situations where a spill may affect parties in different states, each of the states concerned is notified. In no case, however, does the interstate agency establish contact with local parties without first having consulted the state agencies.

The challenge faced by the commissioners is, on the one hand, to avoid intrusion on state prerogatives and, on the other, to encourage a broadening of ORSANCO services to strengthen efforts for the attainment of regional objectives. Supporters of the compact rejected notions that it would lead to the creation of a regional "supergovernment." But they did expect the interstate agreement to provide a mechanism for accomplishing co-operatively in the region what the states could not undertake independently. Such activities as establishment of quality criteria and standards, monitoring and surveillance of river conditions, and maintenance of a clearinghouse for hazard-and-alert functions represent the kinds of service that a regional agency is uniquely qualified to provide. However, it must be acknowledged that some of these services were not originally conceived as components of the interstate pollution-control program. Rather, these activities stem from experiences that have led to the identification of opportunities for ultimate achievement of the mission of ORSANCO. Simply stated, that mission is to prevent pollution originating in any state from injuriously affecting the various uses of interstate water.

Problems of a Limited Budget

Program aspirations normally are tied to the size of the budget. The ORSANCO experience is somewhat unusual, for much of what the agency accomplishes is made possible by enlisting voluntary aid and taking advantage of co-operative undertakings. The necessity to husband the Commission's limited resources created incentives to be continually on the lookout for ways to do things with a minimum outlay of its funds.

Indeed, it may be said that some of the most productive aspects of the ORSANCO operation have developed from the probing of ways to enlist aid for its endeavors. One example is the support received from the U. S. Weather Bureau in adapting its flood-forecast techniques to produce a daily report and forecast of volume and velocity of flows at various points in the Ohio River and certain tributaries throughout the year. Development of this unique service has made it possible for ORSANCO to improve its hazard-and-alert predictions when spills occur and, in addition, to obtain data essential for the enhancement of quality monitoring and management procedures. Because this information is useful for other purposes and could be made available as a by-product from other operations of the Weather Bureau, the cost to ORSANCO is nothing.

Similarly, ORSANCO started its ambitious venture of monitoring river quality with only a modest allotment of funds. But by exploitation of a mutual interest in such information among municipal and industrial water users, as well as the U. S. Geological Survey, ORSANCO has been the recipient of about $7.00 worth of data for every dollar that it expends for this purpose.[3]

Another example relates to conduct of public-education efforts to prevent littering of streams with debris from boats and marinas. Initially, ORSANCO used spot annnouncements over radio and television stations, the time for which was furnished as a public service at no cost. This effort

---

3. Edward J. Cleary and David A. Robertson, "Ohio River Water Quality and Flow," *Journal of American Water Works Association,* Vol. 50, No. 3 (March 1958), p. 399. Here are summarized expenditures for quality data compared with value of services rendered by co-operating parties.

was supplemented with a poster campaign, and the aid of U. S. Coast Guard personnel was enlisted to distribute the posters at hundreds of marinas and boat clubs.

Meantime, the staff had designed a plastic bag with a facsimile of the anti-litter poster. However, the budget would not cover the purchase of sufficient bags (at five cents each), nor were there means for making the bags available to boaters. Both of these problems were overcome by securing co-operation of the ORSANCO Petroleum Industry Advisory Committee. Several member companies offered to finance the purchase of thousands of the bags and distribute them free wherever their products were dispensed to boatmen along rivers of the valley. The U. S. Coast Guard and state boating enforcement officers are also participating in this campaign by presenting a litter bag each time a boat is boarded for a check of safety equipment.

These examples illustrate why it is not possible to provide a meaningful relationship between expenditures and accomplishments.

The funding for ORSANCO activities must be regarded as rather puny and, in fact, has been described as a "bargain-basement" type of operation. As shown in the accompanying summary, annual appropriations have varied from an initial $40,000 to a high of $242,400; the average over the eighteen-year period has been $179,129 annually. For thirteen years, federal-aid grants have supplemented state appropriations, the state-federal ratio being about two to one for the eighteen-year period.

ORSANCO *Annual Appropriations—State and Federal*

Year	State	Federal	Total
1948–49	$ 40,000	$ —	$ 40,000
1949–50	100,000	29,000	129,000
1950–51	100,000	24,538	124,538
1951–52	100,000	26,084	126,084
1952–53	100,000	—	100,000
1953–54	100,000	—	100,000
1954–55	130,000	—	130,000
1955–56	130,000	—	130,000
1956–57	130,000	69,802	199,802
1957–58	130,000	112,424	242,424
1958–59	130,000	110,659	240,659
1959–60	130,000	110,258	240,258
1960–61	130,000	107,645	237,645
1961–62	130,000	111,473	241,473
1962–63	130,000	108,238	238,238
1963–64	130,000	105,019	235,019
1964–65	130,000	104,654	234,654
1965–66	130,000	104,530	234,530
	$2,100,000	$1,124,324	$3,224,324

One way of conveying a "feel" for the cost of operating the commission is to place it on a per capita basis. There are 20 million people in the Ohio Valley whose interests are allied to realization of the mission of this regional agency in safeguarding water resources. If every person were equally and individually assessed to support the activities of ORSANCO, he would pay less than a penny a year—actually only 84/100ths of a cent!

It would be fair to say that state appropriations for ORSANCO have not matched the program aspirations of the compact agency. Currently, of course, the budget needs are even greater than they were a decade ago when state funds were pegged at a ceiling of $130,000. Since then, administrative expenses have increased substantially by virtue of higher costs for travel, postage, office supplies, and rent, as well as salary adjustments.

When a compact was being negotiated in 1938 the delegates concluded that operations of the interstate commission would justify annual funding of from $200,000 to $250,000.[4] Not until 1958—two decades later when the purchasing power of the dollar had greatly depreciated—did the ORSANCO budget reach $242,000, which was the highest it has ever gone. The increase came from federal funds, which have averaged about $104,000 over the past decade.

Money now available to operate the Commission is not adequate to maintain a program equivalent to that of even a few years ago. In 1966 some activities had to be curtailed. They included radioactivity monitoring, robot-monitor expansion, and public-affairs projects. As a result, the commissioners are recommending to the governors of the eight states that appropriations to ORSANCO be increased by 40 per cent.

4. *Proceedings,* Third Conference of Delegates Appointed to Draft an Ohio River Valley Water Sanitation Compact, May 24, 1938, p. 52.

20

Functioning of
Commissioners and Staff

A compact among states is a pledge of good faith. How well that pledge is redeemed depends on the sincerity, the ingenuity, and the moral fiber of those entrusted with its implementation. ORSANCO has not lacked for dedicated servants, as is borne out by the story of what has been achieved. Behind those accomplishments are the commissioners, who review, modify, and serve as the arbiters of policy and procedures, and the staff, who initiate proposals and translate the commissioners' decisions into action programs. This chapter describes how they function.

How the Commissioners Function

Responsibility for the transaction of Commission business and the conduct of meetings centers on the chairman. He appoints standing committees composed of commissioners who are assigned to oversee such operating functions as budget presentation, audit of finances, personnel matters and bylaws, as well as ad hoc committees. He also appoints an engineering review committee, which is not restricted, however, to Commission members. In addition, the chairman is the ex-officio head of an executive committee, consisting of one commissioner from each state and the federal government. The members of the executive committee are selected by caucus among the three members who represent each entity.

The executive committee is rarely called into action. It is designed to serve as a standby group to counsel the chairman on questions that might arise between regular meetings of the entire membership. Since regular meetings are held every four months—and for the first twelve years were scheduled every three months—there have seldom been compelling reasons for the chairman to call upon the committee for interim decisions.

An important function that might have been assigned to the executive committee—namely, the screening of regulatory proposals before they reach the agenda for final decision—has by informal delegation been placed under the purview of the engineering committee. Many early decisions faced by the interstate agency involved an appraisal of the technicalities of control measures, as well as consideration of the practicality of their enforcement by the state agencies, and the commissioners considered it logical to be guided on such matters by a committee composed of the chief sanitary engineers of the states and the three technical representatives of the federal agencies.

Stature of engineering committee. The engineering committee responded so well to its initial tasks that it was considered superfluous to refer matters to an executive committee for additional study. The engineering group schedules a full-day meeting prior to Commission meetings so that it can review and clarify issues that otherwise might burden the agenda. Not all of the members of the engineering committee are commissioners,[1] but each one, nevertheless, occupies a key position in his state for executing interstate directives. It is deemed essential, therefore, that full consideration be given to the viewpoints of the engineers prior to decisions by the Commission.

All commissioners are welcome at the committee's meetings. Those who attend have an opportunity to become intimately informed on technical phases of regulation-making, as well as on details of state compliance procedures and problems. There have been occasions when commissioners who do not find it convenient to participate in sessions of the engineering committee have felt that its recommendations might benefit from additional review by the executive committee. In response to this, chairmen have from time to time scheduled executive committee meetings on the evening preceding regular meetings. But this arrangement leaves something to be desired. Members of the executive committee who also serve on the engineering committee are not happily disposed to sit through an evening meeting rehashing matters on which they have been working all day. Furthermore, the executive committee members themselves, while agreeing that such briefing sessions provoke informative discussions, also acknowledge that they find it tedious to cover much the same ground the following day for those who attend only the regular meetings.

Frequency of meetings. After twelve years of meeting quarterly, and after many activities became fairly well routinized, the commissioners concluded in 1960 that three meetings annually might be sufficient. They

1. The reason for this is that in several states the health officer or other official to whom the chief sanitary engineer reports is the official designee as commissioner.

felt also that the time saved in reduced travel could then be devoted to longer sessions when required. Actually, few commissioners find it possible to be away from their offices for more than a day. The change to three meetings yearly does not appear to have handicapped the conduct of business because experience has provided precedents to facilitate decisions on many matters.

What can be said in favor of more frequent meetings is that they offer opportunity to improve orientation and involvement of new commissioners. This reflects the view that in an undertaking whose welfare depends on the personal enthusiasm and dedication of those who are guiding it, the greater exposure a commissioner has to its aspirations the better equipped he is to nurture their development.

Tenure of officers. One aspect of ORSANCO procedure that has been questioned by some commissioners is the custom of annual rotation of the chairmanship among the states. This has been traditional practice, which was instituted as a means for symbolizing the equal responsibilities of each state for providing leadership to the joint undertaking. Now that the rotation is going into its eighteenth year, the connotations of this practice are regarded of lesser significance than experience with Commission affairs and aptitude for the role of chairman.

Several past chairmen have indicated that one year in office is too short a time to make the fullest contribution to this assignment. It is their view that the agency should not deny itself the benefits that accrue from a chairman's familiarity with the task, and that a two-year tenure in this post might be considered a minimum.

Concerning other officers, the ORSANCO organization provides for annual election of a vice-chairman, secretary, treasurer, assistant treasurer, legal counsel, and executive director. Among the officers, only the chairman and vice-chairman are commissioners. All others, with the exception of the legal counsel and the secretary, are chosen from the staff. The secretaryship is an honorary post held by F. H. Waring, who acted as secretary throughout all the negotiations leading to the compact beginning in 1936.

How the Staff Functions

Day-by-day discharge of Commission business involves the staff in a variety of administrative and professional activities. The staff executes policy and directives. It evaluates proposals to be acted on by the Commission. It acts as the spokesman for the agency at conferences. And it is responsible for all operations relating to financial and legal affairs, recruitment and assignment of personnel, and maintenance of an office.

After completing a term as chairman, one of the commissioners jocularly remarked: "I am awed by the demands imposed on a small staff in trying to satisfy the desires of twenty-seven bosses." Such a situation could be awesome if commissioner-staff activities actually relied on a "boss" rather than a "partner" relationship. Regarded as a partner—albeit a hired one—the staff of ORSANCO is provided with incentives and a minimum of restraints in advancing the goals of the Commission.

The staff is expected to be the initiator of recommendations—and is always encouraged to participate in decision making. This intimate identification of the staff with the welfare of the enterprise obviously engenders personal as well as professional satisfactions, as evidenced by the fact that the executive director, the assistant director, and the office manager have been associated with the Commission since its establishment eighteen years ago.

Staff size and duties. At no time has the full-time staff exceeded eleven people. Half of these are in a professional category, and the remainder serve in a secretarial or record-keeping capacity. Services of legal counsel are obtained on a retainer basis and are primarily consultative in nature. For a few years a technical consultant was retained on a part-time basis.

Staff resources have often been stretched to match the scope of program activities. On the professional level, staff duties embrace engineering investigations, analysis of legislation, supervising research projects, conducting advisory committee activities, maintaining liaison with state and federal agencies, operating a river-quality monitor network, and servicing a public-affairs program.

In addition, there are the normal requirements associated with public-agency operations. Handling of correspondence and requests for information are unusually demanding, not only because the interests of eight states and twenty-seven commissioners are involved, but primarily as a result of the emphasis placed on educational efforts and public-affairs projects. Financial accounting, along with preparation of reports required in connection with the use of federal funds, requires almost the full time of the office manager. These and other necessities such as maintaining records, preparing minutes, writing bulletins, and meeting visitors, command a substantial amount of staff time.

As might be expected in a small organization, adaptability of personnel to a variety of tasks is a staff requisite. The director, for example, not only acts as administrative officer but also serves as chief engineer and until recently handled all public relations activities as well. The assistant director supervises technical studies and budget preparation, is the custodian of pension and insurance matters, serves as assistant treasurer, and shares responsibility for liaison activities with other agencies and advisory committees.

The treasurer is also the office manager and supervisor of secretarial personnel. The chemist-biologist conducts river surveillance and aquatic-life investigations, is responsible for robot-monitor equipment, and coordinates operations relating to accidental spills and the issuance of hazard alerts. In this latter and increasingly important activity he is now assisted by a sanitary engineer whose primary duties, however, are data processing associated with river-quality evaluation. The chemical engineer conducts technical investigations, advises on treatment requirements, maintains status records on control facilities, and also serves as Commission liaison member to industry advisory committees. Recently the staff was augmented by a research specialist who is assigned to mine acid drainage control, systems-engineering developments, and preparation of project proposals.

The notion that the Commission would require only a minimum staff had its origin in the belief that the states, with their cadre of specialists on pollution control, might be in a position to satisfy technical and investigatory requirements of the interstate agency. In fact, when the initial operating policies were drafted, it was asserted that: "The Commission does not propose, in the immediate future, to operate a laboratory or engage in any research activities, but instead will endeavor to . . . work through state agencies, the U. S. Public Health Service, or established research agencies."

The aim of this policy was to prevent duplication of efforts and facilities. However, it was made before there was adequate comprehension of the scope of the interstate program and the requirements this would impose in the way of providing services and professional direction. Certainly there was no conception of the role the Commission would play in sponsoring such endeavors as organizing public-affairs activities, operating a regional water-quality surveillance network, and developing robot-monitor equipment.

Supplementing staff efforts. Contractual arrangements have made it possible to undertake certain projects without increasing the staff. But this could be done only after the ORSANCO budget had been augmented with federal funds. For a small organization there are manifest advantages in contracting for certain types of work because it permits retaining the services of specialists for limited engagements and it offers flexibility for gearing expenditures to budget allotments.

However, it must not be presumed that contracting procedures free the staff of responsibilities associated with a project. Quite to the contrary, such arrangements involve preparation of specifications on the objectives of the work to be performed and often call for "riding herd" on the project to insure desired returns. For example, one contractor became so absorbed with certain scientific aspects of his endeavor that his final report focused on these almost to the exclusion of relating their significance to the specific aim of the project. It required considerable staff time to obtain reorientation in presentation of the findings.

Productivity of staff endeavors has been multiplied through participation in co-operative investigations and research. A happy example was ORSANCO sponsorship of an inventory of aquatic-life resources of the Ohio River. The conservation commission of Kentucky, whose domain includes 700 miles of the river, and which was already started on an inventory of tributary streams, had a special interest in the interstate project. Accordingly, the state director of conservation, who was also an ORSANCO commissioner, was favorably disposed to contributing personnel and services to promote execution of this undertaking.

Conduct of co-operative projects calls for continual probing of opportunities for collaboration and for patience in adapting to the interests and commitments of the collaborators. As a consequence, accomplishments may take longer. But sacrifices in time are offset by gains in economy and in securing talent and facilities that otherwise might not be obtainable. An example of a research project that was made possible by co-operative effort was the study of chemical oxidation of phenol waste. Laboratory facilities and testing were provided by the State of Ohio. A steel-producing company participated by building the pilot-plant processing equipment adjacent to its coke ovens and maintaining a flow of phenol wastewaters through the unit as required by the investigators. Three owners of proprietary treatment processes were invited to utilize the pilot plant to permit a comparison of the efficacy of the processes under identical conditions. ORSANCO supplied the project director, guided preparation of a report on the work, and then published the findings as a public service.

Similarly, an investigation on the Wabash River to develop facts for determination of sewage and industrial waste-treatment requirements provided opportunity for a pooling of services. The collaborators included two state agencies, three federal agencies, several industries, and a research organization representing the paper and pulp industry. The role of ORSANCO was to provide a project director who co-ordinated various elements of the undertaking and then prepared a report on the findings.

Staff recruitment. With so small a staff a major consideration in recruitment is to seek people who not only are competent in their specialty but can also adjust to a "jack-of-all-trades" role. Maturity of viewpoint and experience are favored because there are only limited opportunities for on-the-job training. Recognizing the competition that exists for qualified professional personnel among federal agencies, industry, and consultants, the commissioners have endeavored to maintain salary scales, pension and fringe benefits, and vacation and sick-leave privileges that are commensurate with the job market. However, decisions have been tempered by the view that an agency financed by the states should not depart too widely from state personnel practices, although it is acknowledged that these have not been distinguished in matters relating to compensation.

Staff role in decision-making. When asked by a student of public administration what role the staff was expected to play in the decision-making aspects of Commission affairs, a commissioner once summed it up in this fashion: "The staff is expected to propose, and the commissioners will then be obligated to dispose."

How this concept has worked out in practice can be illustrated by again referring to the chloride control regulation (Chapter 12), and detailing the steps that led to its adoption. Based on an evaluation of the trend of water-quality variations in the Ohio River, the staff concluded that increases in salinity might pose a future pollution problem. Accordingly, the director acquainted the engineering committee with the findings and proposed that it recommend to the Commission that a detailed study be initiated.

This procedure permitted the state engineers to make a judgment on what priority should be accorded to the question of salinity control and, in turn, recognized the prerogative of the commissioners to make the decision on where staff effort should be applied. The Commission approved the recommendation and directed that the staff apply itself to the matter. At the same time it invited its industry advisory committees to furnish the staff with whatever information they wished to have weighed, and to prepare themselves for an expression of views on whatever proposals were advanced.

When the staff completed its studies, an oral report was presented, first to the engineering committee, then to each of six industry committees. These presentations occupied a period of more than a year, during which there was a detailed exchange of views, attempted clarification of issues, and development of additional facts. Because the proposals advanced for exercising control departed from conventional regulatory procedures and suggested practices that might serve as a precedent for control of wastewaters other than those containing chloride, the staff report created much controversy.

Eventually the engineering committee found common ground with the staff on recommendations to be presented to the Commission. However, some of the industry committees were not in harmony with these recommendations. Therefore, after the commissioners received the staff report along with the engineering committee endorsement, they arranged to hear the views of those who were not in agreement. Because of the technical nature of certain disagreements, an ad hoc committee of commissioners was appointed to resolve differences. After several conferences with the staff and deliberation on additional information supplied by the industry groups, this committee developed a reconciled version of the control measure. The engineering committee found it acceptable, after which it was adopted by the Commission.

Not all of the proposals on technical matters and policy that have been brought before the commissioners have involved issues as original and complex as those relating to chloride control. However, all proposals that originate with the staff go through a similar series of procedural steps in the formulation of Commission decisions. Some proposals, of course, are initiated by the commissioners themselves. These are referred to the staff and to the engineering committee for review and recommendations subsequent to final consideration by the Commission.

From this account of procedure it may be appreciated that the challenge to the staff, as indeed must be the case in any operation involving group decisions, is to clarify and outline the pros and cons of issues, to offer alternate approaches for resolving questions, and to detail the consequences that attend various choices.

From this description of the functions of the commissioners and the staff it is apparent that the operational aspects of a compact agency are rather complex. But they are not unnecessarily so, for the task assumed by an interstate agency is one of considerable complexity. It is a task, nevertheless, that the ORSANCO experience suggests is not beyond the capabilities of a compact agency.

PART IV

Prospects for Tomorrow

It is not the wake of the ship of state
that I shall contemplate, but her
bow-wave riding toward the horizon
whither the forces of change
are driving us.

Gordon M. Fair

21

Churnings of Change

Profound changes have occurred since eight states in the Ohio Valley launched their co-operative enterprise for regional river cleanup in 1948. As a result, ORSANCO is confronted with circumstances far different from those which prompted its establishment and have guided its program up to now. This invites examination of the thrust and dimensions of these happenings, along with considerations of what might constitute an appropriate response to them. Broadly speaking, these changes may be viewed as falling into two categories: those resulting from local accomplishments throughout the region in reduction of pollution, and those imposed by the emerging dominance of federal policymaking and funding of pollution-control endeavors.

Of paramount significance with respect to ORSANCO's mission is the progress made toward completion of the most urgent and most difficult component of its program. At all major, and most minor, sources of sewage discharge, communities have shouldered the complex task of acquiring disposal plant locations, installing huge interceptor sewers to bring wastewaters to these central sites, and constructing treatment works and sludge disposal facilities. As a result of this billion-dollar outlay by municipalities—90 per cent of which was locally financed—the most costly elements of their contribution to the regional undertaking have been taken care of. Installation of interceptor sewers alone has in some cases amounted to four times the cost of treatment units. Consequently, whatever additional treatment facilities may be required in the near future to upgrade quality conditions should constitute only a fraction of capital investments already made, and part of this will be eligible for federal funds.

Meantime, the equally compelling task of curbing industrial pollution has reached the point where almost 90 per cent of the establishments are reported by the states as providing control facilities that comply at least with interstate minimum requirements. While this does not mean that nine-tenths of the industrial load has been removed, it does represent a substantial reduction at least in gross pollution.

In brief, the concerns of ORSANCO are no longer dominated by the task of securing construction of basic facilities. What now compels attention are such matters as insuring proper performance of some 3,000 municipal and industrial waste-control plants, upgrading their capability where required, improving guardianship of water quality through amplification of monitoring and surveillance, and taking steps to correlate reservoir releases and expected hydropower operations with river-quality variations.

In other words, the states in the Ohio Valley have advanced their regional program from the stage of dealing with fundamental elements of "abating" pollution to the point where opportunities exist to put into practice techniques for "managing" river quality. In fact, one of the essential tools for this purpose—equipment for continuous, automatic measurement and transmission of river-quality variations—was developed by ORSANCO and has been operated for more than six years. From a technical standpoint, ORSANCO is now in a position to guide the application of a systems-engineered approach for quality management in the Ohio Valley. However, it does not appear that the signatory states are presently disposed, either temperamentally or financially, to undertake active support of such an enterprise.

This posture of suspended incentive can be attributed, at least in part, to uncertainties created by the intensification of federal influence in affairs that traditionally were under the dominion of state governments. The conditions that prevailed when the ORSANCO compact was activated and throughout the first decade of its operations no longer hold. A vastly different social, economic, and political climate now surrounds pollution-control endeavors.

Socially, the public has been aroused to regard the prevalence of pollution as a national disgrace, and this has generated pressure for national action as a painless way to remove the stigma. Economically, the affluence of the nation is such as to dismiss doubts that this desire cannot be quickly satisfied. And, politically, responsiveness of the Congress to hasten corrective action has placed increasing reliance on legislation broadening federal jurisdictional authority, propped up with ever greater commitment of federal funds to bring about desired reforms. The changed climate has produced a fog of uncertainty among the states. Just what is their position? In what direction should they proceed? Indecisiveness on these points obviously influences their viewpoints with respect to widening the future role and functioning of interstate agency relationships.

At this point it becomes appropriate, therefore, to provide some background on the evolution and present status of federal involvement in water pollution control.

Evolution of Federal Policies and Actions

Although the federal government has long exercised a dominant influence in water-resources developments associated with navigation, irrigation, flood prevention, and hydropower, its involvement with control of water pollution is relatively new.[1] President Truman signed the first federal water pollution control act on the very day that the Ohio Valley interstate compact commission was activated—June 30, 1948. Administration of this pioneer national legislation, which had a long and stormy history of prior rejection on ideological and constitutional grounds, was assigned to the Public Health Service in the Department of Health, Education, and Welfare. Eight years later a new pollution control act broadened the basis for federal enforcement proceedings and, in addition, authorized grants-in-aid to communities. Amendments in 1961, in 1965, and again in 1966 successively amplified both jurisdictional powers and the commitment of funds. In 1966 administration of pollution control was transferred from HEW to the Department of the Interior.

The 1948 act. The enactment of Public Law 845 (80th Congress) represented a compromise approach to the then controversial question of whether or not it was appropriate for the national government to assert a direct role in water pollution control. The decision was yes—but with clearly defined qualifications. This legislation envisioned a partnership relation wherein federal activities would abet and supplement state efforts, but not supersede them unless a state actually defaulted in meeting its obligations. The preamble declared it to be national policy "to recognize, preserve and protect the primary responsibilities and rights of the states in preventing and controlling water pollution." To this end, the act offered to the states technical aid and services, and it authorized $1 mil-

---

1. Prior to 1948 the federal identification with water pollution rested solely on the Rivers and Harbors Act of 1899, on a Public Health Service Act of 1912, and the Oil Pollution Act of 1924. The 1899 act (33 U.S. Code 407) prohibited the discharge into navigable waters of refuse and debris, other than that flowing from sewers. The 1912 act authorized establishment of a Streams Investigation Station at Cincinnati for fundamental research on water pollution. The act of 1924 was concerned with prevention of oily discharges in coastal waters only.

lion for improving state administrative capabilities. Another provision sanctioned blanket consent of Congress for the creation of interstate compacts and urged federal encouragement for their formation. Enforcement procedures were authorized, but with the limitation that resort to federal legal proceedings would require the consent of the state in which pollution was alleged to originate.

For diametrically opposed reasons neither the states nor the advocates of federal control were satisfied with this 1948 legislation. The states welcomed the promise of technical services and financial help, but they resented the provision authorizing federal enforcement measures, limited as they were. Proponents of federal intervention, on the other hand, saw little virtue in a law that did not clothe the national government with overriding police powers, especially in situations involving interstate pollution. They pointed out that in only a few cases had the states shown a disposition to enter into regional agreements for handling such matters. Furthermore, they claimed that interstate agreements were poorly suited for their intended mission. There was validity to the charge that the states displayed little initiative in utilizing compacts for pollution control—only three (New York Harbor, Potomac River, and New England) were in operation prior to 1947. But it was premature to offer a judgment on the effectiveness of compacts because those dealing with pollution had not been in existence long enough to provide an adequate record of experience.

Action in 1956. Five years after its passage, the 1948 act was renewed for another three years, although it was generally conceded that its influence on expediting stream cleanup was less than satisfactory. Then in 1956 the law was rewritten. The new legislation (P.L. 660, 84th Congress) substantially broadened the base of federal activities. Among other things, it strengthened enforcement potentialities by providing that "whenever the Surgeon General . . . has reason to believe" that water pollution is occurring, he can call a conference with the state or states involved and prescribe remedial measures. If state action failed to secure compliance from the offenders within a specified time, then the federal government was authorized to proceed on its own initiative to institute legal proceedings.

In addition, the 1956 act authorized $50 million annually for grants-in-aid to subsidize one-third the cost of municipal sewage plants, but not in an amount greater than $600,000 for a single project. This was an acknowledgment that federal fiats would continue to lack vitality without infusions of federal subsidy, and that securing action to abate pollution required something more than the capability for waving a big stick. Testimony of the American Municipal Association made this quite plain. Its spokesmen, representing thousands of communities, in effect said this: if you expect municipalities to comply with federal edicts to build sewage-treatment plants, then the Congress has the obligation to provide funds for their construction. It appeared, therefore, that without the sugar of subsidy to sweeten attitudes toward compliance, the federal effort was not destined to achieve speedier results than those being obtained by many states without the use of subsidies. In retrospect, the accomplishments prior to 1956 in California, New Jersey, Michigan, Indiana, Ohio, Pennsylvania, Illinois, and Wisconsin may be regarded as exceptionally creditable. In the latter two, for example, with only modest outlays for administration, the state agencies had promoted construction of treatment plants serving more than 90 per cent of their sewered population.

The 1956 legislation reaffirmed the original declaration of Congress to recognize, preserve, and protect the primary responsibilities and rights of the states in controlling water pollution, and authorized funds up to $3 million annually for distribution among them for improving administrative capabilities. And once again the Congress called upon the Surgeon General to encourage the formation of interstate compacts, a matter on which there had been no manifestation of federal agency interests thus far. The act also provided for the federal government to undertake comprehensive river-basin investigations and projects for the assembly of basic data, as well as to expand research programs and the training of personnel.

During the following five years, enforcement proceedings under the act were initiated in twelve cases involving interstate pollution, four of which were on the Missouri River where virtually no treatment programs had as yet been started. Meanwhile, the grant program was credited with having generated local expenditures of $5.00 for every dollar of federal subsidy. The Public Health Service reported that contract awards for municipal sewage treatment increased from an average of $222 million annually for the five-year period before the grants were offered to $360 million for the five-year period after the subsidy program started. In this same period federal expenditures for research were quadrupled (from $440,000 annually to $1,651,000), and funds for enforcement proceedings were increased more than fivefold—from $250,000 to $1,347,000 yearly.[2]

Changes in 1961. Added stature was given to the federal program by further amendments in 1961 (P.L. 87–88). Enforcement authority,

2. *A Study of Pollution—Water.* Staff report to the Committee on Public Works, U.S. Senate, 88th Cong., 1st Sess., June 1963, p. 40.

which heretofore had been limited to interstate streams, was broadened to include all "navigable" waters and, with the consent of a state governor, could even be extended to intrastate waters. In addition, authorization was given for increasing municipal grants-in-aid from $50 million to $100 million yearly, this to be done in annual increments of $10 million. Research funds were increased from $5 million annually to $25 million, and approval was granted for the establishment of seven regional research laboratories. Financial support for state programs was also increased from $3 million to $5 million annually. And, finally, direct responsibility for administering the act was transferred from the Surgeon General of the Public Health Service to the Secretary of Health, Education, and Welfare.

The transfer in administrative supervision was significant in two respects. It foreshadowed the end of Public Health Service direction of water pollution control, which formally occurred in 1965 with the establishment of a new office in HEW called the Federal Water Pollution Control Administration. Before this took place, however, and while the PHS was still charged with executing the program, direction of all pollution-control activities was assigned to an assistant secretary of HEW. Soon thereafter, the program took on aspects of being operated by two distinct and independent entities. One of these appeared to dominate affairs with emphasis on enforcement proceedings, while the other dealt with the more prosaic aspects of planning, researching, and allocating funds. The stepped-up tempo of enforcement actions (which totaled twenty-five cases in the next five years) caused a build-up of tensions among the states who claimed that the manner of conducting these proceedings ignored the intent of Congress by seeking to supersede rather than support the exercise of state responsibilities.

Amendments in 1965. Seeking further to accelerate action nationally, the Congress passed the Water Quality Act of 1965 (P.L. 89–234). Developed under the leadership of Senator Edmund S. Muskie and Representative John Blatnik, this bill amended prior legislation in several significant particulars. It broadened federal jurisdiction through a provision requiring the establishment of standards of quality for all interstate waters. And the states were handed a deadline date—June 30, 1967— to establish such standards and submit a plan for their implementation following public hearings. If a state does not comply, or if its standards are not approved as consistent with the purposes of the act, then the Secretary (originally the Secretary of Health, Education, and Welfare, but after the 1966 reorganization the Secretary of the Interior) is empowered to call a conference of the parties involved, following which federal standards will be promulgated. If a governor of a state is not satisfied with these standards, the Secretary shall then convene a hearing board of five or more persons, and its recommendations on standards will be final.

Another provision increased the authorization of grants for municipal sewage-treatment facilities from $100 million annually to $150 million, and it liberalized allotments in favor of large communities. Previously, federal grant offerings were based on 30 per cent of the estimated cost, but were not to exceed $600,000 for a single project and $2,400,000 for a joint, multi-municipal installation. The 1965 amendment raised the grant ceilings to $1,200,000 for a single project, and $4,800,000 for a joint undertaking. Also authorized was an annual appropriation of $20 million for four years for projects to demonstrate methods of minimizing pollution of waterways during periods of heavy rain when combined sewers (those used for conveying sewage as well as stormwater) become surcharged and their flow goes directly into streams, by-passing treatment plants.

Additionally, the act relieved the Public Health Service of its responsibilities for administering water pollution control and placed such activities in a new echelon in the hierarchy of the Department of Health, Education, and Welfare, called the Federal Water Pollution Control Administration.[3] According to a Senate committee report[4] the changeover in administrative responsibility was said to be desirable because the basic orientation of the Public Health Service was "toward cooperative health programs with the states" instead of "toward the broader problems associated with the conservation of waters for public water supplies, propagation of fish and aquatic life and wildlife, recreational purposes, agricultural, industrial and other uses."

Developments in 1966. When President Johnson signed the previously described Water Quality Act on October 2, 1965, he stated that this bill was only the prelude to "additional bolder legislation." Such legislation

3. A few months later this new agency, the FWPCA, was lifted from the jurisdiction of the Department of Health, Education, and Welfare and placed in the Department of the Interior. This was accomplished through Reorganization Plan No. 2 of 1966 prepared by the President and transmitted to the Senate and House of Representatives in Congress assembled, February 28, 1966, pursuant to the provisions of the Reorganization Act of 1949 (63 Stat. 203, 5 U.S.C. 133z). The Congress offered no objection to the plan and it became effective 90 days later (Order No. 2895, 31 F.R. 6877, effective May 10, 1966).

4. "Federal Water Pollution Control Act Amendments of 1963," Report No. 556, Committee on Public Works, U.S. Senate, 88th Cong., 1st Sess., October 4, 1963.

was not long in coming. Thirteen months later, the President signed the Clean Waters Restoration Act of 1966 (Public Law 89–753). This bill is an amendment to the 1965 act, based on a Senate-House compromise version of separate bills introduced by Senator Muskie and Representative Blatnik.

The boldness of the new legislation is exemplified by the authorization of $3.4 billion for construction grants for municipal sewage treatment for the fiscal years 1968 through 1971—an increase of $1.1 billion over the original House version, and a decrease of $2.45 billion from the Senate version. The scheduling of appropriations is designed to provide $450 million for 1968; $700 million for 1969; $1 billion for 1970; and $1.25 billion for 1971.

The former dollar limitation on individual grants and combined grants is eliminated, and in all cases the authorized federal share for either a single or combined project is at least 30 per cent of the total cost. If a state agrees to match 30 per cent of the total cost, the federal share is increased to 40 per cent. However, if a state also agrees to establish intrastate water-quality standards (states must establish only interstate standards under the 1965 act), and in addition matches 25 per cent of the total cost of a municipal project, the federal share will be further increased to 50 per cent.

Grants totaling $20 million annually for three years are authorized for demonstration projects by states, municipalities, or interstate agencies to develop methods for treating discharges from combined stormwater sewer systems, as well as for development of new or improved methods of joint treatment for municipal and industrial wastewaters. The federal share for such undertakings is limited to not more than 75 per cent of the cost of a project. In addition, the act authorizes grants to persons conducting research on ways of preventing water pollution by industries; a grant of this kind is not to exceed either $1,000,000 or 70 per cent of the cost of the individual project.

To provide incentive for development of comprehensive pollution-control planning for entire watersheds, the act offers assistance in the financing of such undertakings up to a total cost of the expenses of a planning agency for a period of three years. Requests for such aid must be made by a governor of a state, or a majority of the governors when the interests of more than one are involved. The planning agency so established must provide for representation of appropriate state, inter-state, local, or (when appropriate) international interests in the water-shed or a portion thereof.

Federal enforcement procedures are broadened by authorizing the

Secretary of the Interior, at the request of a majority of the conferees at a hearing, to request any person alleged to be causing pollution to file a report on the nature of the discharges. Failure to comply could result in a civil penalty of $100 a day for each day the failure continues.

Other sections of the law provide for a study of pollution by water-craft, and pollution of estuarial waters. Another section amends the Oil Pollution Act, 1924 (43 Stat. 604; 33 U.S.C. 431) by making it unlawful to discharge oil into territorial waters of the United States. Individuals convicted of violations are punishable by a fine not exceeding $2,500 or imprisonment for up to one year, or both, and the owners and operators of a boat or vessel are liable for a penalty of up to $10,000.

When President Johnson signed the bill on November 3, 1966, he optimistically said: "We now possess the tools to reach out into our environment and shape it to our will. . . . Pollution is not a problem of the individual cities or even the individual states. It is a problem of the entire watersheds and water basins. There is where the problem must be fought. The new measure will allow us to do that. It enlarges and it strengthens the comprehensive approach that is already begun. It creates new incentives for our states and for our cities. It strengthens their partnership with industry and with the Federal Government. It enables us to work together on sound and practical plans for controlling pollution once and for all."[5]

Other federal programs. Although prime responsibility for pollution control is vested in one agency—formerly the Public Health Service, and now the Federal Water Pollution Control Administration in the Department of the Interior—several other federal agencies sponsor programs concerned with water-quality protection.

For example, the relationship of quality-enhancement opportunities in multipurpose planning of water resources was formally recognized in 1961. At that time an amendment to the Federal Water Pollution Control Act (P.L. 87–88) directed that additional storage to permit low-flow augmentation of streams be given consideration in the planning of reservoirs by the Corps of Engineers as well as by the Bureau of Reclamation. Such extra storage at federal expense is authorized where it can be demonstrated that benefits would be widespread or national in scope.

The Geological Survey, the Fish and Wildlife Service, and the Bureau of Mines in the Department of the Interior, have long been identified with water-quality matters. The Geological Survey has been engaged in

5. As reported in *Highlights,* November, 1966, a monthly newsletter published by the Water Pollution Control Federation, Washington, D.C.

the collection of basic data on streamflow and quality for more than half a century, and quite recently was assigned the task of co-ordinating all federal-agency activities in such matters. The Fish and Wildlife Service, which has participated actively in ORSANCO affairs through a Presidential appointment to the membership of the interstate commission, reviews all federal water-resources development projects with respect to their influence on aquatic life. The Bureau of Mines is engaged in research on mine acid drainage control measures.

In 1965 the Department of the Interior was given a unique assignment in regional pollution control affairs when President Johnson directed the Secretary to develop a plan for the Potomac River that would "clean up the river and keep it clean." This endeavor presumably cuts across all existing jurisdictional arrangements, which include several federal agencies and state agencies, as well as an interstate agency already involved in planning and executing pollution-control activities for the region.

Financial aid for building municipal sewage-disposal projects, in addition to the grants offered since 1956 under the Federal Water Pollution Control Act, has been made available from several other programs. Under the Public Works Acceleration Act (P.L. 87–658), which became effective in September, 1962, a total of $112 million was allocated by municipal sewers and treatment plants before this program went out of existence two years later. At the present time, (December, 1966) funds for local governments are made available by the following legislation:

Appalachian Regional Development Act (P.L. 89–4), which is administered by the Department of Commerce, authorizes $6 million for construction of community waste disposal facilities until June 1967. In addition, there is a general fund of $90 million for aid to depressed communities, some of which could be applied to sewage disposal projects.

Public Works and Economic Development Act (P.L. 89–136), also administered by the Department of Commerce, allocates $500 million over a four-year period for all types of public works in economically depressed areas. These grants may cover up to 80 per cent of the cost of a project.

Housing and Urban Development Act (P.L. 89–117), administered by the Department of Housing and Urban Development, authorizes an expenditure up to $200 million to pay one-half the cost of water supply and sewage disposal projects.

Consolidated Farmers Home Administration Act (P.L. 89–240), administered by the Department of Agriculture, has a $50 million annual fund. It is authorized to make a 50 per cent matching grant to public or quasi-public organizations that are incorporated to provide residents of open country and rural villages (up to 5,500 population) with domestic water and waste disposal systems.

Because these funds are being disbursed under the auspices of agencies whose mission and methods are not identical, a situation has developed that does not comfort those who yearn for more tidy arrangements in federal-state relationships in pollution control. Housing and Urban Development funds are allocated directly to the cities. Procedures of the Department of Commerce likewise involve direct dealing with local applicants. The Department of Agriculture uses county agents.

Local units of government now have a wide variety of sources they can tap for federal aid. It would appear that their only concern is to make certain they select the agency that offers the best deal, since the subsidies may range from 30 to 80 per cent of the estimated cost of the project, depending on the source. There is at least one community in the Ohio Valley that faces this happy dilemma of choice. Since it is also involved in legal proceedings with ORSANCO for failure to comply with interstate sewage-treatment requirements, it has asked for (and been given) an extension of time while the funding possibilities are being examined.

Recently Senator Edmund S. Muskie, chairman of the Subcommittee on Intergovernmental Relations of the Senate Government Operations Committee, and Secretary of Commerce John T. Connor concluded that, "we need a sewer man at the federal level."[6] The situation is such, according to Senator Muskie, that it is nearly impossible for a mayor seeking federal assistance to decide where to turn or what conditions he would have to meet to secure federal approval of a project. He indicated that the confusion and lack of co-operation between agencies has reduced the value of the various programs.

A summing up. What becomes apparent from this recital of the evolution of federal involvement in pollution control is that it has been proliferating and it is becoming ever more pervasive. A twenty-fold increase in budget appropriations for funding the operations of what is now the Federal Water Pollution Control Administration—from $2.2 million in 1956 to $47 million proposed for fiscal year 1967—tells part of the story. The requirement set forth in 1965 for establishment of quality standards on all interstate waters added another chapter of expanding federal influence. And now the 1966 act authorizes successive increases in federal subsidies to municipalities from $150 million annually to $1,250 million by 1971. One question this raises is: will the huge sums of money being committed for pollution abatement produce results com-

6. Reported in *Water Control News,* Nov. 28, 1966, Vol. 1, No. 28, p. 6, published by Commerce Clearing House, Inc., Chicago, Ill.

mensurate with expenditures without a more effective gearing of federal, state, and regional administrative machinery for program implementation?

Hearings recently completed by a subcommittee of the Science and Astronautics Committee of the House, headed by Representative Emilio Q. Daddario, on the status of water, air, and land pollution and proposals for remedial action, support the views that corrective legislation may well have outrun both the factual bases for action and adequate machinery for development and regulation.[7] Mr. Daddario has pointed out: "Sober consideration of the waste products problem is a responsibility of us all, but it is not an issue which should be treated in an atmosphere of crisis where blame is placed on ill-considered remedies hastily enforced. . . . Much significant legislation for control of environmental pollution has been passed. . . . What remains to be seen is how political, economic, and technical institutions can organize themselves for an efficient and equitable response to this public purpose."

This is how matters stood at the end of 1966. On the one hand there has been a snowballing of political efforts to legislate pollution out of existence, and on the other there is evidence to suggest that these enthusiasms may not fit the realities faced by administrators, engineers, and scientists working on the problem.

State Reaction to Federal Action

While all these legislative developments and appropriations of money have stimulated national interest in advancing stream cleanup, they have also presented perplexing problems of accommodation in the sensitive area of state and federal jurisdiction. Certain federal efforts have not been distinguished in fostering the partnership relation envisioned by the Congress. There has been growing concern among state agencies that their initiative, as well as their authority, is being emasculated by undue emphasis on the assertion of federal prerogatives. They are not at all assured that execution of the Federal Water Pollution Control Act has conformed as closely as it might have with the policy declaration of the act, whose premise is that the national government will supplement—

7. *Hearings* before the Subcommittee on Science, Research and Development of the Committee on Science and Astronautics, U. S. House of Representatives, 89th Cong., 2nd Sess., July, August, and September, 1966, 2 vols. It seems appropriate to mention here that the author supplied a memorandum on water pollution at the request of Abel Wolman, consultant to the subcommittee, based on material already written for this book, some of which is now incorporated in the Wolman report presented at the hearings.

not supersede—responsibilities of the states. Furthermore, they feel that public confidence in the role of the states has suffered.

Mitchell Wendell, counsel to the Council of State Governments, has commented on this latter point:[8] "The most characteristic distortion resulting from the sudden popularization of anti-pollution campaigns is the assertion that nothing worthwhile was done until the federal government galloped onto the scene a few years ago, and that all of whatever progress is now beginning to appear must be attributed in one way or another to that appearance. From the 'Clean Water' television clips, to the newspaper and magazine articles, to the reports of the Federal Water Pollution Control Administration and Congressional committees, we are told either by innuendo or direct statement that nothing has been done to keep our water bodies from deteriorating, and that gross neglect has made most of them open sewers." He also noted that while these highly dramatic ways of presenting the problem may serve to "heighten the air of crisis that seems helpful in getting a reluctant or apathetic public to vote more money for treatment works and accept more regulation . . . one of the unfortunate side effects of the process has been to create a vast misimpression of the relative responsibilities and achievements of federal, state and local governments in the field of pollution control."

Among the matters protested by the states was the manner in which the so-called "conference" provisions of the act were carried out, when enforcement proceedings were stepped up in 1961. The conference provision originated from suggestions made by the states during early Congressional hearings; it was conceived as offering a means through which the parties concerned could be brought together for resolving viewpoints prior to, and hopefully without the necessity of, formal proceedings to reach agreement on proposed federal compliance actions. Instead, the federal authorities elected to conduct the conferences virtually as public hearings, generally in the ballroom of a large hotel and with advance publicity geared to generate the attendance of hundreds of people. Furthermore, these conferences were shrouded with the atmosphere of an adversary proceeding, in which the federal representatives appeared to cast themselves as the savior of streams with the states placed in the role as opponents of such good intent. At least, this is the way it seemed to most of the states, who regarded this approach as contrary to their understanding of the conference technique.

Mixed emotions must be expressed, therefore, over the zeal with which

8. Mitchell Wendell, "Governmental Coordination in Water Resources Management," presented at 16th Semi-Annual Meeting of the Manufacturing Chemists Association, New York City, November 22, 1966.

enforcement activities have been pursued thus far. The actions had a salutary effect in showing that federal authorities were prepared—as well as eager—to step into situations where it might be presumed that state efforts were not matching needs. But in some cases it appears there were other motivations. And too often it became evident that the conferences did more to alienate relationships with the states than they did to generate united support.

The states signatory to the Ohio Valley compact had reason to be disillusioned when the enforcement unit of the Public Health Service initiated proceedings on the Monongahela River, a major upstream tributary in the compact district, for this action ignored the opportunity that existed for conduct of a federal-state conference through the mechanism of an interstate agency on which the federal authorities were already represented.

Some details concerning the Monongahela proceeding, followed by an account of a later conference on the Mahoning River, will reveal why the ORSANCO states have had a jaundiced outlook on the motivation of federal enforcement activities.

Monongahela affair. At the Monongahela conference called in Pittsburgh on December 17–18, 1963, the ORSANCO views were summarized in a statement by Chairman Joseph R. Shaw who said, in part:[9]

"If there is any reason for the Secretary of the Department of Health, Education, and Welfare to feel uninformed or dissatisfied with any aspect of the Ohio Valley program, why was this not disclosed at a regular meeting of the Commission? The Department has its own representative—in the person of the Surgeon General of the Public Health Service—serving as a member of this Commission. The Surgeon General or his representative has participated in meetings of ORSANCO since its organization 15 years ago, and has had a voice in development of the interstate program.

"In calling this conference, the Acting Secretary of the Department of Health, Education, and Welfare, in a letter dated October 14, 1963, wrote as follows: 'The purpose of the conference, as specified by Section 8 (c) (3) of the Federal Water Pollution Control Act, is to consider the occurrence of pollution of interstate waters subject to abatement under the Act; the adequacy of measures taken toward abatement of the pollution; and the nature of delays, if any, being encountered in abating pollution.'

9. See ORSANCO, *Sixteenth Annual Report,* 1964, p. 5.

"These items of consideration," said Chairman Shaw, "in so far as they relate to waters within the Ohio Valley district, are documented in the minutes and records of ORSANCO and in annual reports prepared for the Governors of the signatory states and the President of the United States. Such information is—and always has been—readily available to the Department of Health, Education, and Welfare through its own representative on the Commission.

"It is difficult to understand, therefore, why the Department has not availed itself of these well-established channels of communication and the meetings conducted regularly by the Commission, to express its interests. The fact that the Department has chosen not to exercise its prerogatives under the interstate compact—a course of action that seems inconsistent with the declared policy of Congress—is the greatest single source of confusion that enshrouds these proceedings."

The conference resulted in "conclusions and recommendations" with which all the conferees expressed harmony and which, in fact, could have been agreed upon by an exchange of correspondence. These were: pollution of an interstate nature does exist in the Monongahela Basin; the states and ORSANCO have made appreciable progress in abatement and presented acceptable programs for further control; cognizance is taken of plans to bring about such controls by the end of 1966, subject to delays should court actions be encountered and modified by the fact that economically depressed communities may require financial assistance; and a technical committee of state, interstate, and federal representatives should be formed for assessing the amount of pollution from coal mines and developing a remedial program, including an estimate of costs.

Mahoning River misadventure. Regarded by the Ohio Valley compact states as even more disturbing in its implications was a later summons by the Secretary of Health, Education, and Welfare to the states of Ohio and Pennsylvania and to ORSANCO to participate in an enforcement conference on the Mahoning River on February 16–17, 1965. This stream in Ohio is a tributary to the Beaver River, which flows through Pennsylvania.

As a matter of background, it should be said that in 1954, the State of Ohio developed a comprehensive program for pollution abatement on the Mahoning. This program not only had been reviewed by Pennsylvania and ORSANCO and found acceptable but, in addition, had been formally approved by the Surgeon General of the Public Health Service as meeting objectives of the Federal Water Pollution Control Act. By 1965, Ohio had gone a long way toward completing the program. All the municipalities had constructed treatment works, and with the completion of tune-up operations at one plant, requirements for all sewage discharges were to be satisfied within a few months. Concerning control of industrial wastes, some 70 per cent of the establishments in this heavily industrialized area were listed by the state as meeting requirements, and further compliance, with exception of some cases involving spent-acid disposal, was scheduled for 1966.

Why this situation now claimed justification for federal intervention was far from clear because at no time had the Commonwealth of Pennsylvania registered any complaint either to Ohio or to ORSANCO. Following submission of evidence by all parties relating to the status of compliance and improvement in river conditions, the ORSANCO conferees concluded that in view of the progress being made there appeared to be no practical or legal basis for federal interest or concern. The conferees representing Pennsylvania and Ohio reached similar conclusions. However, the federal conferee, after acknowledging "significant progress in pollution abatement in the Mahoning basin," concluded that additional treatment requirements should be imposed immediately. The viewpoints of all the conferees were then submitted to the Secretary of HEW for his deliberation. Nine months later, on November 15, 1965, the Secretary issued his mandate. Apparently unimpressed with the conclusions of the majority, he adopted only the recommendations of the federal conferee and laid down a timetable for the State of Ohio to implement them.

Ohio responded by informing the Secretary that his requirements were regarded as unrealistic in scope and could hardly be carried out within the prescribed time limits. Furthermore, it was pointed out that the Secretary's action, which was taken a month after Congressional adoption of the Water Quality Act of 1965, gave no cognizance to the standards-setting provision of this new act. Declaring its intent to comply with this new act, the state concluded: "It is our hope that the establishment of water-quality standards for the (Mahoning) river will officially provide the basis for future treatment requirements."[10]

10. In accord with procedures set forth in the Water Quality Act of 1965, the State of Ohio conducted a public hearing on July 26, 1966, as a basis for developing standards to be submitted to the Secretary of the Department of the Interior. The staff of the Ohio Pollution Control Board proposed a program to achieve conditions at the Pennsylvania state line consistent with ORSANCO criteria, except that higher river temperatures would be permitted. (See Appendix 10 for ORSANCO criteria). A statement from the Commonwealth of Pennsylvania at the hearing indicated general concurrence with the proposals but requested that consideration be given to adding a limiting value for iron and reducing the temperature limit as well as the levels for cyanide and fluoride. Final decisions on standards have not yet been made by the Ohio authorities.

Significance of Change

These two episodes of federal-state relationships in the Ohio Valley and the tensions they produced are symbolic of circumstances for which better accommodation must be sought. While these events are referenced to the ORSANCO program, the issues they present are relevant to future endeavors elsewhere in the nation. As is the case in some other types of federal-state relationships, the emerging trend in matters pertaining to water pollution control is one of attenuation of state autonomy. As a result two things are happening. State agencies are deprived of opportunities to put forth their best efforts because they are embroiled in jurisdictional matters and thus rendered less effective, or they are diverted from matters they regard as having priority in order to satisfy a bewildering array of federal directives.

Challenge of standards-setting. For the states the most challenging directive of the 1965 Water Quality Act is the one requiring the establishment of interstate water-quality standards. It is the laudable intent of the standards-setting requirement to come to grips with the issue of defining pollution-control goals and developing timetables for their attainment. However, the generalized manner in which the standards section is drafted has provoked perplexing questions for administrative decision. And the time allotted by the law for the states to complete this task—1½ years—appears unrealistic considering the fundamental importance of such an undertaking, the complexities involved in its execution, and the burdens already straining state agencies.

The section dealing with standards says that they "shall be such as to protect public health or welfare, enhance the quality of water, and serve the purposes of this act." It further stipulates that the states, following public hearings, are to adopt criteria for interstate waters along with a plan for implementation and enforcement of the criteria. Then it says that if the criteria and plan are acceptable to the Secretary they "shall thereafter be the water-quality standards applicable to such interstate waters or portions thereof."[11]

11. This vital matter of what might constitute appropriate standards is hardly clarified in "Guidelines for Establishing Water Quality Standards for Interstate Waters," which was issued to the states by the Federal Water Pollution Control Administration on May 9, 1966. In fact, a number of attorneys general from the states and federal legal representatives met in a conference at Ann Arbor, Michigan, on July 20, 1966, in an effort to resolve "conflicts" in the interpretation of the guidelines. It appears that the federal authorities themselves are uncertain and will not reach conclusions on what standards will be acceptable until they have opportunity to review what the states propose.

One source of confusion stems from apparent lack of distinction in the federal act between criteria and standards. The ORSANCO states faced a similar problem in the early fifties, when they tackled the matter of interstate standards for the Ohio River. The following distinction was evolved: criteria are yardsticks of reference for appraising the suitability of water for various uses; they reflect professional judgments based on existing knowledge, and are subject to modification as new information becomes available. Standards, on the other hand, are the specifications developed to maintain conditions that will satisfy the "best use" classification assigned to a particular stream or stretch thereof.

Varying standards were established for different stretches of the Ohio River, depending on what was determined to be the optimum use of the river in that stretch. These determinations were based on an analysis of present and anticipated uses, coupled with consideration of preferences expressed at public hearings and the practicality of satisfying them. After a decision had been made concerning the uses to be safeguarded, the applicable criteria were employed in drafting the standards. This procedure recognizes that the establishment of water-quality standards for a specific situation is a public policy issue and not simply a matter of bureaucratic pronouncement. Development of standards has sought to give cognizance to both tangible and intangible value judgments, in an endeavor to balance benefits with costs.

A provision of the federal act, setting forth instructions upon which judicial review of standards shall be based, is more illuminating about what should be considered in their development. Here it is stipulated that if an alleged violator of the standards should seek to obtain a legal opinion on their validity or applicability, a determination will be made as follows:

> The court, giving due consideration to the *practicability* and to the *physical* and *economic feasibility* of complying with such standards, shall have jurisdiction to enter such judgment and orders enforcing such judgment as the *public interest* and the *equities* of the case may require. [Italics added.]

These instructions outline rather precisely the essential factors to be weighed, in addition to quality criteria, when drafting standards. In fact, they spell out the considerations that have emerged as paramount issues in the history of litigation on pollution. Furthermore, these are the considerations that have been implicitly—and in some cases explicitly—set forth in most state legislation, and which influenced procedures adopted by ORSANCO.

It seems relevant, therefore, to comment on the criticism aimed at state agencies for "spending too much time" in reaching determinations on pollution-control requirements. What is overlooked is that through experience these agencies long ago learned how the courts analyze such requirements, and they have sought to resolve the complex issues of practicability, physical and economic feasibility, the public interest, and the equities involved prior to promulgating regulations. As a result, state agencies have been successful in minimizing cause for judicial review of their actions. Court action is not only a costly procedure but a slow one. It has not been unusual—in the Ohio Valley—for legal proceedings in pollution abatement to stretch out over a decade. And during that time nothing tangible is achieved in terms of improving conditions in a stream.

ORSANCO evolved its approach to establishing standards from a statutory provision in the compact (Article VI), which asserted that no single standard for the treatment of sewage or industrial wastes was applicable in all parts of the region because of "such variable factors as size, flow, location, character, self-purification, and usage of waters within the district." But the compact also stipulated that regardless of these physical, hydrological, and use considerations, all sewage discharged into interstate waters must be treated to provide at least "substantially complete removal of settleable solids, and removal of not less than forty-five per cent of the total suspended solids"—which, in effect, requires the installation of so-called primary treatment facilities. Standards requiring a higher degree of treatment in specific stretches of streams can be promulgated, but only after completion of investigations and public hearings that take into account the "variable factors" pertaining to the situation.

This sequential procedure has permitted prompt action in dealing with gross and obvious pollution while awaiting completion of the detailed investigations related to the formulation of standards for a higher degree of treatment. Presently, 94 per cent of the sewered population in the valley is served by disposal plants, three-quarters of which are equipped with facilities to provide treatment of a higher degree than the minimum afforded by primary plants. Meantime, endeavors are continually underway to upgrade standards still further as required.

This same two-step approach was applied by ORSANCO in the control of industrial-waste discharges, although this procedure for industrial wastes was not originally spelled out in the compact. (See Chapter 11.) Minimum requirements applying to all discharges were promulgated with the proviso that these control measures would be upgraded on the basis of continuing investigations. Some 90 per cent of the industries are now reported by the signatory states as complying at least with these basic standards. Additional requirements have been developed and applied, while work is going forward to identify further needs.

What these comments seek to emphasize is that standard-setting can proceed on a two-step basis. There are certain requirements that may be specified as universally applicable to wastewater discharges in every stream (or lake) without waiting for the completion of any studies or surveys. They represent the minimum conditions to be met regardless of any other circumstances, and are justified solely on the basis of preventing gross and indiscriminate pollution. The second step in establishing appropriate standards involves the development of more detailed specifications to supplement basic requirements. This takes time because it often calls for the assembly of scientific, technical, and economic data that is not readily available. And then the findings must be analyzed and recommendations developed for presentation at public hearings.

The states are confronted with two major problems in their efforts to comply with the federal directive for establishing standards. One stems from lack of clarity concerning how the standards should be formulated and how they will be judged by the Secretary. The other problem is a limited capability in most states to deploy the requisite manpower and resources for doing an acceptable job in the time that has been allotted.

Portent for the future. A critical appraisal of the current situation in water pollution control must lead to the view that the churnings of change have now produced a mixture of governmental endeavors in which confusion often seems to be the principal ingredient. At least the evidence is not convincing that thus far conditions have been conducive for effective meshing of federal and state activities, or that opportunities for the attainment of mutual objectives have been adequately exploited. Unfortunately, responsibilities have become so blurred in some instances that contentiousness is absorbing energies that could more profitably be applied to co-ordination of efforts.

Legislative preoccupation with expansion of the role of the federal government has submerged consideration of the potentialities of other institutional arrangements for dealing with pollution problems. Since billions of dollars are to be spent for this purpose, and since there are admitted shortcomings in both federal and state regulatory practices, it would be in the national interest to explore what might be accomplished with regional associations for the management of water quality.[12]

12. These views were outlined by the author at a water conference sponsored by the Dayton (Ohio) Chamber of Commerce on September 24, 1964, which gave recognition to the 50th anniversary of the Miami Conservancy District.

The concept of management implies much more than promulgation of prohibitions, which is at best a crude tool with which to fashion a river-quality control program. There is little reason other than lack of appropriate institutional arrangements to continue to rely exclusively on the issuance of regulations governing discharge of effluents at individual sources for the mitigation of pollutional effects, when there are a variety of technological means—such as scheduled low-flow augmentation, mechanical aeration of streams and programmed discharge of effluents—which alone or in combination offer opportunities for maintaining desired quality conditions at lower social costs.

Watershed agencies of the type pioneered in Ohio,[13] now being operated in parts of Texas[14] and those permitted by recently enacted legislation in Michigan,[15] suggest one means of managing water-quality programs. Such instrumentalities can be set up to plan comprehensively, to construct and operate a variety of facilities designed for the specific needs of a watershed or region, and to finance them through service charges that would relate benefits to costs in a more meaningful manner than is presently possible.

Interstate compact agencies offer another means. Their potentialities have not been adequately probed as a mechanism for the design, financing, and operation of regional management programs. In this connection, attention is invited to the compact establishing the Port of New York Authority,[16] and to the manner in which this agency operates various regional transportation services on a self-liquidating basis—a function it has performed since 1925 without dependence on the tax resources of the signatory states or the federal government. The new Delaware River Basin Commission, created by an interstate-federal compact, holds similar promise for water-resources management on a regional scale.[17]

13. For details see Arthur E. Morgan, *The Miami Conservancy District* (New York: McGraw-Hill Book Co., 1951). A more recent and generalized account of conservancy district accomplishments in Ohio is to be found in: L. Bennett Coy, "They Kept the Promises They Made in an Attic," in *The Ohio Banker,* December, 1965.

14. One example is the Sabine River Authority with offices in Orange, Texas.

15. The "Local River Management Act," (No. 253), State of Michigan, 72nd Legislative Regular Session, 1964.

16. Activities of this agency are outlined by Richard H. Leach and Redding S. Sugg, Jr., in *The Administration of Interstate Compacts* (Baton Rouge: Louisiana State University Press, 1959). See also "The Port of New York Authority—A Public Agency Created by Interstate Compact," a paper presented by Sidney Goldstein, general counsel of the authority, at the Symposium on Atomic Energy and State Governments, Dallas, Texas, April 17, 1958.

17. Conceptual and practical aspects of quality management are detailed in *Development of a Water Quality Management Program for the Delaware River Basin,* a report of the board of consultants, Harvey O. Banks, Edward J. Cleary, Allen V. Kneese, July, 1963, prepared for the Delaware River Basin Commission.

Experience in the Ohio Valley can reveal only certain capabilities of the interstate compact for regional water-quality control, because the mission of ORSANCO is limited to the co-ordination of regulatory activities. However, there are sufficient reasons to believe that the compact can be adapted to render even greater service. How this might be done is discussed in the next chapter.

22

Response to New Challenges

What might be the role of the Ohio Valley compact agency under the dispensations wrought by change? Do the prospects suggest that it should occupy a larger place, a smaller place, or no place at all in the future scheme of things?

The proposition advanced in this final chapter is that conditions favor expanding the influence and tasks of the interstate agency as an instrumentality for regional management of river quality. The usefulness of ORSANCO as a co-ordinating and service agency is a matter of record, and the experience it has accumulated provides a basis for determining what kinds of additional action would be productive in satisfying emerging needs in the Ohio Valley. Furthermore, by arranging for appropriate federal linkage with the regional agency, opportunities are presented to improve federal-state relationships, which are becoming ever more complex. Having displayed the initiative two decades ago to devise a mechanism for co-operative action, and then having evidenced the capability of making it work, the Ohio Valley states should not hesitate to take a new look at their interstate compact and see how it might be fitted for more effective service.

Proliferation of federal activities should not obscure the fact that it is the states who furnish the primary line of defense in the war on pollution, and that a regional agency responsive to their interests is of strategic importance in this mission. The events of recent years adequately confirm the view that the states—and the federal government—will find merit in supporting interstate compacts for the attainment of mutual goals. Whatever doubts may have been harbored on this score deserve re-examination in view of what was outlined by the President of the United States on water pollution in his 1966 message dealing with conservation, which will be discussed in some detail later. Suffice it to say at this point that the President emphasized the "crucial" need for experimenting with new organizations, and he singled out interstate compacts and conservancy districts as types of instrumentalities for this purpose.

Seizing New Opportunities

Uncertainty among the commissioners of ORSANCO concerning the future place and posture of their interstate agency—notably among those who had newly come on the scene—prompted the staff director in 1964 to offer an assessment of what had transpired since 1948 and from this to develop perspective on the job ahead.[1] The theme of his report was that the substantial progress already made in abating pollution in the Ohio Valley, coupled with increasing commitment of federal efforts to expedite river cleanup, had created unusual opportunities to advance the usefulness of ORSANCO—provided adjustments were made to take advantage of these circumstances. Some activities could be undertaken within the framework of the existing compact simply by expanding certain service responsibilities and providing the financial resources to support them. But for exploitation of other opportunities to enhance performance, changes would probably have to be made in the compact itself. Matters seen as inviting current attention of ORSANCO included a closer relationship with federal comprehensive planning projects, and greater emphasis on management and custodial functions such as quality monitoring, treatment plant inspection, and river patrol.

Planning. There were two significant developments under way in the Ohio basin at that time. One was a broad endeavor launched by the Corps of Engineers, which encompassed all aspects of long-range development of water resources. ORSANCO had been invited to participate as an "observer" but not as a member of the co-ordinating committee, which included representatives from six federal agencies and eleven states in the basin. The other was a $7 million, seven-year planning project that had been initiated by the Public Health Service in accord with provisions of the Federal Water Pollution Control Act, which called for development of comprehensive programs for pollution control in all river basins.

With respect to these planning endeavors, it appeared that ORSANCO had a great deal to offer—not only was it in a position to furnish appraisals of water-quality variations, but it had potentialities for influencing them. In turn, what was being developed claimed attention by ORSANCO to insure appropriate consideration by the planners of the impact of their proposals on future river-quality conditions.

Custodial functions. Participation in long-range planning, though important, was rated well below attention to current needs. What was

1. Report of Edward J. Cleary at the sixteenth annual meeting of ORSANCO. See Appendix A of the minutes of the meeting of May 14, 1964.

stressed, in particular, was the expansion of custodial functions and the opportunities for doing so. It was pointed out that the mission of ORSANCO involved responsibilities that went beyond developing standards and promoting construction of physical facilities to comply with them. While these activities were fundamental to the inauguration of a pollution-control program, there were continuing necessities to be satisfied, which hinged on the conduct of a variety of custodial functions. They included monitoring and evaluation of stream quality, inspection of treatment plants, maintenance of a hazard-and-alert system, prompt handling of citizen complaints, and river patrol for detection of violations and prevention of littering.

Perhaps in no other region of the nation are some of these operations further advanced than in the Ohio Valley. But the importance and magnitude of the task justified far greater support than it had been possible to marshal thus far either individually by the signatory states or jointly under the auspices of ORSANCO.

Of primary concern was the limited capability of state regulatory agencies to adapt to an ever-increasing burden of plant inspections. Each year a greater number of sewage-treatment and industrial-waste control facilities were going into operation and laying claim for performance auditing. However, budgetary constraints handicapped the states in assigning adequate staff for this task.

Along the Ohio River alone there were now some 335 installations whose operations required regular scrutiny. Improper operation of some facilities was apparent from visual observation of river conditions and was also to be inferred from occasional erratic variations in quality recorded by robot monitors. There were reasons to believe that carelessness—and sometimes even evasion of control responsibilities by municipalities and industries—could explain why cleanliness in certain stretches of the Ohio River was not measuring up to expectations.

Concerning river patrol, results from sporadic aerial and boat surveillance supported the view that much was to be gained from visual inspections. Sources of unrecorded pollution had been discovered, violation of regulations had been uncovered, and pictorial evidence had been assembled for use by the states in expediting corrective action.

With respect to monitoring, it could be said that the existing program on the Ohio River provided considerable data on quality characteristics, but the information available for evaluating the condition of major tributaries was not adequate. And measurement of quality in certain stretches of the main stem deserved further amplification.

Another quality-control deficiency that could be cited was the lack of appropriate means for determining compliance with regulations relating to the discharge of substances that could be toxic or harmful to humans, animals, or aquatic life. While the ORSANCO criteria set forth a bioassay procedure for determining toxic risks to fish, no such relatively simple test is available for evaluating potential hazards to humans. And even the bioassay test is not yet being widely applied by either those who are expected to comply with toxicity control regulations or by the regulators themselves. This situation was not unique to the Ohio Valley—it is universally true. In fact, it could be said that no greater challenge presents itself in the administration of water-pollution control than determining compliance with toxicity requirements.

These were the highlights of the director's view of the situation, and of what might be done within the framework of the existing compact to advance the mission of ORSANCO. As for revision of the compact to exploit other opportunities for regional service, it was indicated that this was a matter that merited detailed exploration at a subsequent meeting.

The director's report was referred to a review committee of commissioners. It recommended[2] approval of staff participation in basin-planning activities. But it cautioned restraint in matters involving the interstate agency in operations of a custodial nature. Concerning possible revision of the compact, the committee felt it was important for ORSANCO to analyze its present role, and specifically to consider broadening its functions to encompass additional water resources interests.

Some commissioners displayed enthusiasm for widening the scope of the compact to embrace planning and management of all water resources in the valley.[3] Others insisted that with so much still to be done in controlling pollution it would be folly to permit ORSANCO to be diverted from this single task. This argument was reinforced by pointing out that Congress had recently passed the Water Resources Planning Act,[4] which promised future establishment of federal-state basin planning commissions. ORSANCO, it was contended, should only be concerned with improving its capability as an action agency for river-quality control. The outcome of this discussion was a request to the staff to explore the matter and make a report.

Alternate Proposals for Broadening Compact Functions

A staff memorandum outlining three proposals for broadening interstate activities was submitted to the commissioners in December 1965.

2. Report of the Long-Range Planning Committee, ORSANCO, minutes of meeting, January 14, 1965, Appendix B.
3. ORSANCO, minutes of meeting, September 8–9, 1965, p. 5.
4. This is P.L. 89–80 which was signed by the President on July 22, 1965, and which went into full operation on July 1, 1966.

The suggested alternates dealt with: (1) creation of an entirely new compact to administer all aspects of water use and development; (2) expansion of ORSANCO service responsibilities; and (3) restructuring of the compact to establish a regional association for water-quality management that would be empowered to finance, construct, and operate such physical facilities as the public interest might favor, and that would foster the organization of watershed associations on the tributaries to the Ohio River. These proposals are set forth in more detail below.

(1) *Water Resources Compact.* A pattern for an agency embracing total water-resources planning and management is provided by the Delaware River Basin compact. The federal government is a signatory member and thereby an equal partner with the states in prescribing policy and execution of the regional program. Members of the Delaware commission are the governors of four states and a member of the Cabinet of the President of the United States who represents all federal interests.

Among other things, the Delaware commission is empowered to: (a) adopt and keep current a comprehensive plan for development of water resources and insure that all new projects or facilities having a substantial effect upon waters of the basin are carried out in conformance with this plan; (b) work with and through existing federal, state, and local agencies—or directly when necessary—in planning, constructing, operating, and maintaining dams, reservoirs, and other facilities, as well as conduct other programs, for the purposes of flood-damage reduction; water-quality improvement; municipal, industrial, and agricultural water supply; recreation and fish and wildlife improvement; hydroelectric power generation; soil conservation, forestation, and watershed management; (c) make future allocations of the waters of the basin among the four states and their political subdivisions in accordance with the Supreme Court doctrine of equitable apportionment which takes into account alternative sources, relative needs, and changing uses; and (d) regulate the volume of withdrawals or diversions in areas where water shortages threaten to develop, or in areas where an actual emergency shortage has developed.

Financing for the Delaware River Basin Commission activities is authorized from two sources: general public funds, and direct-user charges. A governmental unit (federal, state, or local) will provide public funds for facilities without anticipation of repayment where the benefits are widespread and in the general public interest. Where the beneficiaries can be specifically identified and the benefits are measurable (as, for example, in the sale of hydroelectric power) use charges can be levied. Accordingly, the commission operations may be financed by a current expense budget to be apportioned among the signatory parties; by appropriations, grants, or loans from federal or state governments; by issuance of revenue bonds; and by charges for products and services.

(2) *Expansion of Service Responsibilities.* This proposal set forth additional service functions that might justifiably be undertaken within the framework of the existing compact. It was a reiteration of the opportunities suggested by the director a year earlier, and outlined in the first part of this chapter. Since conduct of these activities required no changes in the compact—a procedure that might take a couple of years—the only apparent reasons why they could not be programmed would be reluctance of the commissioners to authorize the undertakings, or insufficient funds to execute them if they were approved.

(3) *Regional Quality Management Association.* What the staff favored as offering practical promise in the Ohio Valley for accommodating to current needs—as well as having the flexibility for adjustment to future requirements—was a state-federal compact structured exclusively for regional management of water quality.

For this purpose the compact would create an instrumentality—which could be known as the Ohio River Valley Association (ORVA)—with broad operating responsibilities as well as co-ordinating functions. Its governing board would include representatives of the governors of the signatory states, representatives of appropriate federal agencies appointed by the President of the United States, and a representative of each watershed association or conservancy district in the valley that had responsibilities for water quality. In addition, some form of legislative participation would be provided for municipalities and industries, as well as agricultural, recreational, and conservation interests, perhaps through establishment of a parliament-type assembly. Financing procedures would be based on the principles employed for the Delaware River Basin Commission, which was previously described.

The major task of ORVA would be to devise and operate a systems-engineered quality management program for the region. In so doing it would need to obtain consideration of its program in whatever planning projects were undertaken in the valley, and it would promote the integration of quality control measures with all other components of federal and state water-resources developments. It appeared logical that ORVA should undertake responsibility for execution of all quality management activities on the main-stem Ohio River, and serve as a co-ordinator to stimulate the execution of similar functions on the tributaries to the Ohio. Concerning the latter, ORVA would seek to foster formation of tributary and watershed associations, which would then be represented on its governing board. And it would rely on these agencies to implement sub-basin quality improvement programs approved by state pollution agencies, but adapted to local needs and circumstances and modified only so far as might be required to satisfy agreed-upon main-stem and regional system quality objectives.

To fulfill these purposes ORVA would need broader authority than is now reposed in agencies oriented only to regulatory or planning functions. It would have to be empowered to finance, design, construct, and operate quality management facilities that could not or would not be undertaken by other governmental units or private enterprise. An example of the type of special facilities that might be built and operated by ORVA would be those providing mechanical aeration of streams.[5] There are situations where this technique for maintaining desired oxygen levels in streams during periods of drought could prove to be more economical than requiring additional treatment at upstream effluent discharges. The beneficiaries—communities and industries who would otherwise have to make provision for occasional high-degree treatment—could then be assessed their proportionate amount for the lower-cost alternative.

Similarly, the regional association would be prepared to provide off-site disposal facilities for difficult-to-treat wastes in areas where enough industries would find it advantageous to utilize such a service. This might prove feasible, for instance, in places where there are concentrations of small metal-plating establishments whose toxic wastes could be trucked or piped to a central disposal works and handled for a fee. Pollution-control authorities, as presently constituted, are not in a position to undertake such service functions.

And, of course, operation of a systems-engineered quality control program would permit ORVA to make effective application, where applicable, of proportioning industrial wastewater discharges with variations in river flow, based on principles enunciated in the ORSANCO chloride-control regulation (see Chapter 12).

Another function of the regional association would be to advance the development of means to bring about the correlation of reservoir releases and hydropower operations with river quality conditions. For example, the Corps of Engineers operates many multipurpose reservoirs on tributaries of the Ohio River. However, augmentation of stream flow from these reservoirs during dry periods is not yet systematically geared to quality needs. There are potentialities for accomplishing this, at least in part, if a regional agency operates a network of electronic quality monitoring stations whose continuous output of data on changing conditions

5. See Edward J. Cleary, "The Re-aeration of Rivers," *Industrial Water Engineering,* June, 1966, pp. 16–21.

can be integrated into reservoir flow-routing schedules. Likewise, the operation of hydropower installations can be made responsive to improving river quality during periods of critically low dissolved oxygen, one method being to vent air or oxygen through the turbines. However, these techniques cannot be applied in a meaningful way unless co-ordination is provided by an agency with responsibilities for quality management.

This outline of what might constitute the organization and functions of an Ohio River Valley Association prompts the recollection of something that transpired thirty years ago when a citizens group in Cincinnati first began generating ideas on how to go about controlling pollution in the Ohio River. They received a suggestion in 1935 from the federal Public Works Administration (PWA) calling attention to the possibility of creating a "regional authority" for this purpose. At that time, as part of the effort of the national government to prime the pump of economic recovery, the PWA was offering grants-in-aid of 45 per cent of the cost of a project to stimulate public-works construction, provided the recipient (local, state, or other governmental entity) would finance the remainder. Because effectiveness of pollution control in the Ohio River depended on every community providing sewage treatment, the PWA saw merit in establishing a regional agency to facilitate the financing of a valley-wide construction program. An agency qualified to issue revenue bonds (to be retired from collection of sewer-service charges) would have been eligible for PWA grants to cover almost half the total cost of the facilities it constructed.

In view of the diversified background and practicality of those Cincinnatians who were promoting an Ohio Valley compact, it seems odd that there was no discussion of this idea or of the desirability of empowering the interstate agency to participate in financial and operating responsibilities. The record of the compact negotiations provides no clue as to why such a proposal was not given consideration. Perhaps the reason lay in an intuitive recognition that with the states not yet conditioned to embrace the concept of co-operative action through a compact, it would be foolhardy to inject notions of an interstate association.

There are reasons to believe that installation of municipal sewage-treatment works could have been expedited if the compact commission had been clothed with powers to assist in building facilities. Communities complying with cleanup directives in the Ohio Valley did so under considerable stress. Those that were slow defended their tardiness by reciting the problems involved in raising money. Financing local public-works projects is an intricate business. And with major undertakings, such as sewage-disposal works, considerable time is required to consummate arrangements.

A procedure might have worked out whereby the interstate agency could have made an agreement with a community to advance funds for the construction of works, and, in return, the community would guarantee repayment through collection of service charges levied on users of the facility. Several advantages over the conventional methods of local community financing might have been realized. If bonds issued by ORSANCO could have been backed with the full faith and credit of eight states, they would have been eligible for a lower rate of interest than those issued by a single municipality. Furthermore, because the interstate agency undoubtedly would have been engaged in financing more than one project at a time it could have combined its bond offerings to take advantage of whatever economies this might afford. And finally, the spreading of risk over a number of projects would have contributed to the attractiveness of the ORSANCO bond offerings to investors. In brief, the compact agency might have facilitated financing for individual communities and passed on to them the savings derived from whatever superior position the agency could command in the money market.

Acting in a fiscal capacity, ORSANCO might even have broadened its service capabilities to offer lease-back arrangements for treatment facilities. Under such a plan a community or industry could have contracted with the interstate agency for financing and installing facilities, and then made monthly, semimonthly, or yearly payments until the investment was amortized. Industries might have found this plan attractive from a corporate tax standpoint, insofar as they could charge off the cost of pollution control as an operating expense while conserving capital resources for other purposes. Lease-back facilities, had the Commission been able to offer them, would have answered both the real and fancied claims of those polluters who pleaded current difficulties in undertaking capital investments for treatment works.

It could also be presumed that, with fiscal-agency powers, ORSANCO could have fostered the installation of joint treatment facilities among adjacent communities, as well as for industries and municipalities, where such works would have provided economies in cost and operation. A few joint enterprises were undertaken in the Ohio Valley, the motivation being basically of local origin.

Leadership for the most notable joint undertaking—a $100 million venture through which Pittsburgh and sixty-nine satellite communities participated in constructing an interceptor sewer system and treatment works—came from the City of Pittsburgh and officials of Allegheny

County. This project, the largest in the valley, is designed to serve a population of 1.4 million.

Perhaps the most imaginative joint project was that undertaken by the Union Carbide and Carbon Corporation and the city of South Charleston, West Virginia. The company provided leadership for the organization of a private corporation to build and manage treatment facilities to handle both sewage and industrial wastes.[6] As described in *Engineering News–Record:*[7] "South Charleston and Carbide joined forces several years after the city acting alone failed in its first attempt to build a much needed sewage-treatment plant. Lack of money forced the city to abandon plans in 1946, but in 1953 the company gave the city a six-acre plant site. The following year the city suggested that Carbide might build a waste-treatment plant to handle both the domestic and industrial wastes.

"Carbide found the idea feasible, since a combined plant would require lower over-all investment and would cost less to operate than two separate plants. In addition the city's waste would provide a large amount of the required nutrients for the industrial waste, thus lowering the amount and cost of chemicals necessary. Both parties then agreed that the city should own the plant. City ownership would relieve Carbide from acting as a public utility, which would eliminate legal difficulties that might arise from other towns requesting Carbide to treat their wastes. Under the agreement Carbide would conduct the necessary pilot study program, and design, build, and operate the plant. Carbide's participation in the venture enhanced the city's appeal in the bond market."

The March of Events

Two months after the staff proposals were circulated among the commissioners, but before any discussion of them took place an event occurred that could be construed as providing strong impetus for restructuring the Ohio Valley compact to create a regional association for river quality management. On February 23, 1966, the President sent a message to Congress on conservation and pollution.[8]

6. The City of South Charleston, W. Va., "Official Statement Relating to Public Offering of $8,000,000 Sewer Revenue Bonds," Feb. 1, 1961.

7. "City—Industry Cooperation Solves Pollution Problem," *Engineering News–Record,* May 9, 1963, p. 32.

8. "Preserving our Natural Heritage," message from the President of the United States, transmitting programs for controlling pollution and preserving our natural and historical heritage, 89th Cong., 2nd Sess., House Doc. No. 387, Febuary 23, 1966.

President Johnson noted that the previous session of Congress had launched a major effort "to save America's water resources," citing in this connection the Water Quality Act of 1965 and increases in federal appropriations for financing sewage-treatment plant construction and other programs. "Yet at this point," he continued, "the development of new knowledge, and *new organizations to carry on this work* [italics added], is as crucial as our dollars." He then proposed that demonstration projects be subsidized by the federal government to develop a new kind of partnership through institutional arrangements that would unite all pollution-control activities in a single river basin.

Of special significance, in view of the proposals placed before ORSANCO some months earlier, were the following statements in the President's message:

> These demonstration projects will allow experiment with new forms of organization. State and local participation may be based on an interstate compact, a river-basin commission, or even a conservancy district. The central requirement is for sufficient jurisdiction and authority to develop and carry out the long-range plan.

> These projects will enable us to curtail and control pollution in entire river basins. Broadscale planning of water standards in broad stretches of a river can achieve substantial economies. More efficient plants can be built to treat the wastes of several communities and nearby industries. Integrating the control of stream flow and treatment plant operation can reduce costs—for example, by fitting the type and amount of day-to-day treatment to varying stream conditions.

> We should continually monitor the quality of our environment, to provide a yardstick against which our progress in pollution abatement can be measured. We must apply the most modern techniques of systems analysis.

It might have been presumed, in view of what the President had suggested, that when the commissioners of ORSANCO met several weeks later in May, 1966, to discuss the future role of their interstate agency considerable enthusiasm would have been displayed for the proposal to restructure the compact. But interest in the matter had suddenly grown cold. When the chairman called for discussion, the budget committee pointed out that it would be unrealistic to talk about an expanded program unless the states were prepared to increase their appropriations. This led to agreement that additional money would be sought for a 40 per cent increase in the budget—from $130,000 (which it had been since 1954) to $182,000 for fiscal year 1967–68. But here the matter ended; further consideration of the proposals outlined in the staff memorandum was tabled.

Something of more immediate concern to the future role of the compact was on the minds of the states. The engineering committee revealed that on the day before the meeting it had obtained an advance copy of guidelines soon to be issued by the Secretary of the Interior for the setting of standards.[9] And one of the matters that troubled them was that the guidelines made no mention of using existing interstate compact agencies as the mechanism to conduct hearings and otherwise facilitate the establishment of interstate quality standards. It appeared to the committee that this could be construed either as a serious oversight or a poor understanding on the part of the federal authorities of the place and the functions of an interstate agency.

For eighteen years the ORSANCO states had relied on their interstate agency for promulgating standards. Now each state must conduct its own hearings and submit quality standards for federal approval. However, the states signatory to the Ohio Valley compact, having worked together so long in developing uniformity of policies and procedures, are in a better position than many to meet this requirement. In addition, the federal requirement for adoption of criteria has already been jointly resolved in the Ohio Valley. The undertaking was a complex one, and the ORSANCO states and advisory committees worked for several years before developing the criteria adopted by the Commission. The resulting compendium is proving useful not only to the ORSANCO states but to many others confronted with the pressing task of presenting standards for federal approval by June 30, 1967. Incidentally, the federal authorities have not yet determined what they should regard as acceptable criteria, and the Federal Water Pollution Control Administration has retained the services of an ORSANCO commissioner (Dr. B. A. Poole) for assistance in this matter.

And this brings us to the finale of the ORSANCO story as it has unfolded up to December, 1966. What emerges from this case history? Perhaps it can be summed up by saying that eight states working together have accomplished a lot and they have learned a lot. They have succeeded in converting aspirations into realities by uniting the leadership of many and inspiring the participation of all in restoring some measure of wholesomeness to waters in the Ohio Valley. And they have learned from this experience—as well as demonstrated—the potentialities of the

9. Letter of May 9, 1966, from Stewart L. Udall, Secretary of the Interior, addressed to governors of all the states enclosing copies of "Guidelines for Establishing Water Quality Standards for Interstate Waters."

interstate compact as an instrumentality for service in the practice of water-quality management.

It might be added in this connection that this regional effort has merited one of the highest honors bestowed by the engineering profession. In 1963 the American Society of Civil Engineers selected the basin-wide program for its outstanding achievement award, which is given annually to an undertaking that contributes to the well-being of mankind and whose execution has been marked by pioneering concepts. The ORSANCO project was cited as "the most effective large-scale water pollution abatement program ever undertaken in the Western Hemisphere."

As was stated in the opening theme of this story: the promise of any land lies in the streams that water it. In the Ohio Valley millions of people and thousands of industries have found their promised land. And here they have been united in reversing the trend of half a century of river degradation. "This event will interrupt no newscast," stated the editors of *Quest* magazine[10] in an appraisal of the ORSANCO program. "The rebirth of the Ohio lacks the drama of a disastrous flood. But as geographic melodrama it ranks as a major achievement in the central United States."

10. "Rebirth of the Ohio," *Quest—for Tomorrow* (Putnam Publishing Company, Chicago, Illinois), Vol. 1, No. 1 (Summer–1960), p. 30.

APPENDIX

MAJOR TRIBUTARIES OF THE OHIO RIVER AND SOME SALIENT FEATURES

Enters Ohio at mile	Length	Average slope per mile	Drainage area	Maximum discharge at mouth	Minimum discharge at mouth	Number locks and dams	Distance navigable

THE ALLEGHENY RIVER rises in north central Pennsylvania, flows northwesterly into New York, then back southwesterly to Pittsburgh, Pa., uniting with the Monongahela River to form the Ohio.

| Pitts. | 325 mi. | 2.7 feet | 11,730 sq. mi. | 300,000 cfs. | 650 cfs. | 9 | 69.5 miles to East Brady, Pa. (9 feet) |

THE BEAVER RIVER is formed by junction of Shenango and Mahoning Rivers 3 miles south of New Castle, Pa., flows southwesterly to the Ohio River at Rochester, Pa.

| 25.6 | 21 mi. | Varies 1.6 to 11.3 ft. | 3,150 sq. mi. | 136,000 cfs. | 130 cfs. | | Short distance above mouth |

THE BIG SANDY RIVER is formed at Louisa, Ky., flows northerly, empties into the Ohio River at Cattlettsburg, Ky.

| 317.1 | 27 mi. | 1.2 feet | 4,280 sq. mi. | 120,000 cfs. | 31 cfs. | | 9 miles above mouth |

THE CUMBERLAND RIVER is formed by the junction of Poor and Clover Forks in the southeastern part of Kentucky, flows southwesterly into Tennessee, northwesterly into Kentucky, empties into the Ohio River near Smithland, Ky.

| 920.6 | 687 mi. | 0.6 feet | 18,000 sq. mi. | 200,000 cfs. | 1,100 cfs. | 14 | 191 miles to Nashville, Tennessee (9 feet) |

THE GREEN RIVER rises in Casey County, Kentucky, flows westerly to the Ohio River 8 miles above Evansville, Indiana.

| 784.3 | 370 mi. | 0.5 feet | 9,430 sq. mi. | 170,000 cfs. | 250 cfs. | 6 | 198 miles to Mammoth Cave, Ky. (5.5 feet) |

THE GUYANDOT RIVER rises in southern West Virginia, flows northwesterly to the Ohio River at Huntington, W. Va.

| 305.2 | 166 mi. | 1.8–11 ft. | 1,670 sq. mi. | 42,400 cfs. | 34 cfs. | | 0.6 miles to B&O RR Bridge (small boats) |

MAJOR TRIBUTARIES—Continued

Enters Ohio at mile	Length	Average slope per mile	Drainage area	Maximum discharge at mouth	Minimum discharge at mouth	Number locks and dams	Distance navigable

THE HOCKING RIVER has its source 35 miles southeast of Columbus, Ohio, flows southeasterly, enters the Ohio River at Hockingport, Ohio.

| 199.4 | 100 mi. | 4.5–2.3 ft. | 1,185 sq. mi. | 50,000 cfs. | 10 cfs. | | 4 miles (small boats) |

THE KANAWHA RIVER is formed by the confluence of the New and Gauley Rivers in southwestern West Virginia, flows northwesterly to the Ohio at Point Pleasant, W. Va.

| 265.4 | 97 mi. | 2.8–1 ft. | 12,300 sq. mi. | 300,000 cfs. | 900 cfs. | 3 | 91 miles (9 feet) |

THE KENTUCKY RIVER is formed by the junction of its North and Middle Forks 4 miles east of Beattyville, Ky., flows northwesterly to the Ohio River at Carrollton, Ky.

| 545.8 | 259 mi. | 0.9 ft. | 6,940 sq. mi. | 90,000 cfs. | 20 cfs. | 14 | 249 miles (6 feet) |

THE LICKING RIVER rises in the mountains of eastern Kentucky, flows northwesterly to the Ohio River between Newport and Covington, Ky.

| 470.2 | 320 mi. | 1.2 ft. | 3,670 sq. mi. | 83,000 cfs. | 5 cfs. | | 18 miles |

THE LITTLE KANAWHA RIVER rises in eastern West Virginia, flows northwesterly to the Ohio River at Parkersburg, West Virginia.

| 184.7 | 160 mi. | 1.5 feet | 2,320 sq. mi. | 75,000 cfs. | 50 cfs. | 5 | 48 miles (4 feet) |

THE LITTLE MIAMI RIVER rises in the central part of Ohio, near London, flows southwesterly to the Ohio River above Cincinnati.

| 463.6 | 90 mi. | 3.5 feet | 1,760 sq. mi. | 125,000 cfs. | 40 cfs. | | 3 miles |

THE MIAMI RIVER rises in the west central part of Ohio, flows southwesterly to Dayton, Ohio, where it is joined by the Mad and Stillwater Rivers, then flows southwesterly to the Ohio River.

| 491.0 | 161 mi. | 3.6 feet | 5,390 sq. mi. | 478,000 cfs. | 275 cfs. | | |

THE MONONGAHELA RIVER is formed 1 mile south of Fairmont, W. Va., flows northerly to meet the Allegheny River, forming the Ohio at Pittsburgh.

| Pitts. | 128 mi. | 2.1–0.7 ft. | 7,390 sq. mi. | 200,000 cfs. | 160 cfs. | 14 | 130 mi. to Fairmont (7 feet) |

MAJOR TRIBUTARIES—Continued

Enters Ohio at mile	Length	Average slope per mile	Drainage area	Maximum discharge at mouth	Minimum discharge at mouth	Number locks and dams	Distance navigable

THE MUSKINGUM RIVER is formed by the confluence of Walhonding and Tuscarawas Rivers near Coshocton, Ohio, flows southeasterly to the Ohio River at Marietta.

| 172.2 | 110 mi. | 1.5 feet | 8,040 sq.mi. | 300,000 cfs. | 400 cfs. | 11 | 91 miles to Dresden, Ohio (5 feet) |

THE SCIOTO RIVER rises in north central Ohio, flows southeasterly through Columbus to the Ohio River at Portsmouth.

| 356.6 | 237 mi. | 1.7 feet | 6,510 sq. mi. | 320,000 cfs. | 230 cfs. | | 2 miles |

THE TENNESSEE RIVER is formed by junction of the Holston and French Broad Rivers in east central Tennessee near Knoxville, flows southwest, west and north through Tennessee, Alabama, and Kentucky, to the Ohio River at Paducah, Ky.

| 932.8 | 652 mi. | Total fall: 500 feet | 40,600 sq. mi. | 410,000 cfs. | 15,000 cfs. | 24 | 650 miles (9 feet) |

THE TRADEWATER RIVER rises in Christian County, Kentucky, flows northwesterly to the Ohio River.

| 873.5 | 110 mi. | 1.0 feet | 995 sq. mi. | 4,150 cfs. | 0.2 cfs. | | 3 miles (9 feet) |

THE WABASH RIVER rises in Grand Reservoir, Ohio, flows westerly to Covington, Ind., and southwesterly to the Ohio River 110 miles above Shawneetown, Ill.

| 848.1 | 475 mi. | 0.63 feet | 33,100 sq. mi. | 440,000 cfs. | 1,600 cfs. | | |

Source: Modified from Benjamin F. Klein (ed.), The Ohio River Handbook (4th ed.; Cincinnati: Young and Klein, Inc., 1958), pp. 156–59.

OHIO RIVER VALLEY WATER SANITATION COMPACT

June 30, 1948

THIS COMPACT, Made and entered into by and between the States of Indiana, West Virginia, Ohio, New York, Illinois, Kentucky, Pennsylvania, Virginia and such additional States as may join in its execution,

WITNESSETH THAT:

WHEREAS, Pursuant to authority of the 74th Congress of the United States, granted by Public Resolution 104, approved June 8, 1936, duly appointed Commissioners respectively representing the States of Indiana, West Virginia, Ohio, New York, Illinois, Kentucky, Pennsylvania and Tennessee have heretofore negotiated a proposed Compact in form as hereinafter set forth and as approved by the 76th Congress of the United States by Public Act No. 739, effective July 11, 1940; and

WHEREAS, By legislation duly enacted, each of said negotiating States, with the exception of Tennessee, has caused said Compact to be approved, ratified, adopted and enacted into law and has authorized its execution; and

WHEREAS, By legislation duly enacted, the Commonwealth of Virginia, although not participating in the original negotiation thereof, has authorized and requested its Governor to execute said Compact on behalf of the Commonwealth and thereby to bind the Commonwealth and to indicate its assent to and acceptance of the terms and conditions of the Compact; and

WHEREAS, Since all conditions upon which the effectiveness of the Compact or the ratification and approval thereof by any of the signatory States was contingent have been met and satisfied, it is now appropriate that the signatory States duly execute the OHIO RIVER VALLEY WATER SANITATION COMPACT, which, as specifically set out in the legislation hereinabove referred to, reads as follows:

WHEREAS, A substantial part of the territory of each of the signatory States is situated within the drainage basin of the Ohio River; and

WHEREAS, The rapid increase in the population of the various metropolitan areas situated within the Ohio drainage basin, and the growth in industrial activity within that area, have resulted in recent years in an increasingly serious pollution of the waters and streams within the said drainage basin, constituting a grave menace to the health, welfare and recreational facilities of the people living in such basin, and occasioning great economic loss; and

WHEREAS, The control of future pollution and the abatement of existing pollution in the waters of said basin are of prime importance to the

290

people thereof, and can best be accomplished through the cooperation of the States situated therein, by and through a joint or common agency;

Now, therefore, The States of Illinois, Indiana, Kentucky, New York, Ohio, Pennsylvania, Tennessee and West Virginia do hereby covenant and agree as follows:

ARTICLE I

Each of the signatory States pledges to each of the other signatory States faithful cooperation in the control of future pollution in and abatement of existing pollution from the rivers, streams and water in the Ohio River basin which flow through, into or border upon any of such signatory States, and in order to effect such object, agrees to enact any necessary legislation to enable each such State to place and maintain the waters of said basin in a satisfactory sanitary condition, available for safe and satisfactory use as public and industrial water supplies after reasonable treatment, suitable for recreational usage, capable of maintaining fish and other aquatic life, free from unsightly or malodorous nuisances due to floating solids or sludge deposits, and adaptable to such other uses as may be legitimate.

ARTICLE II

The signatory States hereby create a district to be known as the "Ohio River Valley Water Sanitation District," hereinafter called the District, which shall embrace all territory within the signatory States, the water in which flows ultimately into the Ohio River, or its tributaries.

ARTICLE III

The signatory States hereby create the "Ohio River Valley Water Sanitation Commission," hereinafter called the Commission, which shall be a body corporate, with the powers and duties set forth herein, and such additional powers as may be conferred upon it by subsequent action of the respective legislatures of the signatory States or by act or acts of the Congress of the United States.

ARTICLE IV

The Commission shall consist of three commissioners from each State, each of whom shall be a citizen of the State from which he is appointed, and three commissioners representing the United States Government. The commissioners from each State shall be chosen in the manner and for the terms provided by the laws of the State from which they shall be appointed, and any commissioner may be removed or suspended from office as provided by the law of the State from which he shall be appointed. The commissioners representing the

United States shall be appointed by the President of the United States, or in such other manner as may be provided by Congress. The commissioners shall serve without compensation, but shall be paid their actual expenses incurred in and incident to the performance of their duties; but nothing herein shall prevent the appointment of an officer or employee of any State or of the United States Government.

ARTICLE V

The Commission shall elect from its number a chairman and vice chairman, and shall appoint, and at its pleasure remove or discharge, such officers and legal, clerical, expert and other assistants as may be required to carrry the provisions of this Compact into effect, and shall fix and determine their duties, qualifications and compensation. It shall adopt a seal and suitable by-laws, and shall adopt and promulgate rules and regulations for its management and control. It may establish and maintain one or more offices within the District for the transaction of its business, and may meet at any time or place. One or more commissioners from a majority of the member States shall constitute a quorum for the transaction of business.

The Commission shall submit to the Governor of each State, at such time as he may request, a budget of its estimated expenditures for such period as may be required by the laws of such State for presentation to the legislature thereof.

The Commission shall keep accurate books of account, showing in full its receipts and disbursements, and said books of account shall be open at any reasonable time to the inspection of such representatives of the respective signatory States as may be duly constituted for that purpose.

On or before the first day of December of each year, the Commission shall submit to the respective governors of the signatory States a full and complete report of its activities for the preceding year.

The Commission shall not incur any obligations of any kind prior to the making of appropriations adequate to meet the same; nor shall the Commission pledge the credit of any of the signatory States, except by and with the authority of the legislature thereof.

ARTICLE VI

It is recognized by the signatory States that no single standard for the treatment of sewage or industrial wastes is applicable in all parts of the District due to such variable factors as size, flow, location, character, self-purification, and usage of waters within the District. The guiding principle of this Compact shall be that pollution by sewage or industrial wastes originating within a signatory State shall not injuriously affect the various uses of the interstate waters as hereinbefore defined.

All sewage from municipalities or other political subdivisions, public or private institutions, or corporations, discharged or permitted to flow into these portions of the Ohio River and its tributary waters which form boundaries between, or are contiguous to, two or more signatory States, or which flow from one signatory State into another signatory State, shall be so treated, within a time reasonable for the construction of the necessary works, as to provide for substantially complete removal of settleable solids, and the removal of not less than forty-five per cent of the total suspended solids; provided that, in order to protect the public health or to preserve the waters for other legitimate purposes, including those specified in Article I, in specific instances such higher degree of treatment shall be used as may be determined to be necessary by the Commission after investigation, due notice and hearing.

All industrial wastes discharged or permitted to flow into the aforesaid waters shall be modified or treated, within a time reasonable for the construction of the necessary works, in order to protect the public health or to preserve the waters for other legitimate purposes, including those specified in Article I, to such degree as may be determined to be necessary by the Commission after investigation, due notice and hearing.

All sewage or industrial wastes discharged or permitted to flow into tributaries of the aforesaid waters situated wholly within one State shall be treated to that extent, if any, which may be necessary to maintain such waters in a sanitary and satisfactory condition at least equal to the condition of the waters of the interstate stream immediately above the confluence.

The Commission is hereby authorized to adopt, prescribe and promulgate rules, regulations and standards for administering and enforcing the provisions of this article.

ARTICLE VII

Nothing in this Compact shall be construed to limit the powers of any signatory State, or to repeal or prevent the enactment of any legislation or the enforcement of any requirement by any signatory State, imposing additional conditions and restrictions to further lessen or prevent the pollution of waters within its jurisdiction.

ARTICLE VIII

The Commission shall conduct a survey of the territory included within the District, shall study the pollution problems of the District, and shall make a comprehensive report for the prevention or reduction of stream pollution therein. In preparing such report, the Commission shall confer with any national or regional planning body which may be established, and any department of the Federal Government authorized to deal with matters relating to the pollution problems of the District. The Commission shall draft and recommend to the governors of the various signatory States uniform legislation dealing with the pollution of rivers, streams and waters and other pollution problems within the District. The Commission shall consult with and advise the various States, communities, municipalities, corporations, persons, or other entities with regard to particular problems connected with the pollution of waters, particularly with regard to the construction of plants for the disposal of sewage, industrial and other waste. The Commission shall, more than one month prior to any regular meeting of the legislature of any State which is a party thereto, present to the governor of the State its recommendations relating to enactments to be made by any legislature in furthering the intents and purposes of this Compact.

ARTICLE IX

The Commission may from time to time, after investigation and after a hearing, issue an order or orders upon any municipality, corporation, person, or other entity discharging sewage or industrial waste into the Ohio River or any other river, stream or water, any part of which constitutes any part of the boundary line between any two or more of the signatory States, or into any stream any part of which flows from any portion of one signatory State through any portion of another signatory State. Any such order or orders may prescribe the date on or before which such discharge shall be wholly or partially discontinued, modified or treated or otherwise disposed of. The Commission shall give reasonable notice of the time and place of the hearing to the municipality, corporation or other entity against which such order is proposed. No such order shall go into effect unless and until it receives the assent of at least a majority of the commissioners from each of not less than a majority of the signatory States; and no such order upon a municipality, corporation, person or entity in any State shall go into effect unless and until it receives the assent of not less than a majority of the commissioners from such State.

It shall be the duty of the municipality, corporation, person or other entity to comply with any such order issued against it or him by the Commission, and any court of general jurisdiction or any United States District Court in any of the signatory States shall have the jurisdiction, by mandamus, injunction, specific performance or other form of remedy, to enforce any such order against any municipality, corporation or other entity domiciled or located within such State or whose discharge of the waste takes place within or adjoining such State, or against any employee, department or subdivision of such municipality, corporation, person or other entity; provided, however, such court may review the order and affirm, reverse or modify the same upon any of the grounds customarily applicable in proceedings for court review of administrative decisions. The Commission or, at its request, the Attorney General or other law enforcing official, shall have power to institute in such court any action for the enforcement of such order.

ARTICLE X

The signatory States agree to appropriate for the salaries, office and other administrative expenses, their proper proportion of the annual budget as determined by the Commission and approved by the Governors of the signatory States, one-half of such amount to be prorated among the several States in proportion to their population within the District at the last preceding Federal census, the other half to be prorated in proportion to their land area within the District.

ARTICLE XI

This Compact shall become effective upon ratification by the legislatures of a majority of the States located within the District and upon approval by the Congress of the United States; and shall become effective as to any additional States signing thereafter at the time of such signing.

Now, THEREFORE, IN WITNESS OF their ratification, adoption and enactment into law of the foregoing Compact, and in witness of their assent to and acceptance of the terms, conditions and obligations therein contained, the signatory States have caused this OHIO RIVER VALLEY WATER SANITATION COMPACT to be executed by their respective Governors and by their respective Compact Commissioners and have caused their respective seals to be hereunto affixed this 30th day of June, 1948.

STATEMENT OF POLICIES

(Submitted and adopted at a meeting of the Commission, October 29, 1948)

WHEREAS, on June 30, 1948, at Cincinnati, Ohio, the states of Indiana, West Virginia, Ohio, New York, Illinois, Kentucky, Pennsylvania, and Virginia, formally executed the Ohio River Valley Water Sanitation Compact, Article III of which created the Ohio River Valley Water Sanitation Commission as the instrumentality through which to accomplish the basic objectives of the Compact, namely, the control of future pollution and the abatement of existing pollution from the rivers, streams and waters in the Ohio River Basin which flow through or into or border upon any of the signatory States; and

WHEREAS, through duly appointed Commissioners of the signatory States the Commission has been activated and its organization has been completed so that it is now able to commence to function as contemplated by the Compact;

NOW, THEREFORE, the Ohio River Valley Water Sanitation Commission does hereby announce the following policies which it will follow in the exercise of the powers vested in it and in the discharge of the duties placed upon it by the provisions of the Compact:

1. The primary function of the Ohio River Valley Water Sanitation Commission is to take such action as may be within its power and to promote within the States which are signatories to the Compact the taking of such action as may be necessary in order to place and maintain the interstate waters of the Ohio River Basin in a sanitary condition satisfactory for a source of public and industrial water supplies, suitable for recreational and agricultural usage, capable of maintaining fish and other aquatic life, free from unsightly or malodorous nuisances due to floating solids or sludge deposits, and adaptable to other legitimate uses.

2. (a) In the performance of its primary function, the Commission will be guided by the principle that no sewage or industrial waste originating within one of the signatory States shall injuriously affect any of the above-defined uses of the interstate waters of the Ohio River Basin which are intended to be protected by the Compact;

(b) In performing its primary function, the Commission will take any and all action necessary and appropriate to bring about the treatment of all sewage which flows into the waters subject to its jurisdiction at least to a degree sufficient to result in substantially complete removal of all settleable solids and suitable removal of suspended solids; and, in addition, to bring about the treatment of all industrial waste discharged therein to a degree sufficient to insure the suitability of such waters for the above-defined uses.

(c) As promptly as possible, the Commission will define, after investigation, due notice and public hearings, those sections of the waters subject to its jurisdiction which may require particular standards of treatment in order to produce the above-prescribed sanitary condition.

(d) The Commission proposes to take any and all action necessary and appropriate to prevent the development or the creation of any new source of polluting waste or discharge likely to affect any of the waters which are subject to its jurisdiction.

3. The realization by the Commission of any objective will be accomplished whenever possible through the use of or through cooperation with the established regulatory agencies of the States which are signatories of the Compact, and resort by the Commission to any procedural remedy expressly made available to it by the provisions of the Compact will occur only after the efforts of the Commission to accomplish any objective through an appropriate state agency have proved unproductive, or under circumstances which clearly indicate that any such efforts would prove futile.

4. The Commission proposes to undertake a study of all legislation relating to water sanitation which is now in effect in the various States which are signatories of the Compact and based upon that study the Commission proposes, whenever deemed necessary, to submit and to encourage the adoption of recommendations for legislative additions or amendments designed to raise to a satisfactory standard the regulatory and enforcement legislation of those states pertaining to water sanitation.

5. The Commission, upon request, will assist and support state agencies or representatives seeking enactment of legislation pertinent to the accomplishment of any objective of the Commission.

6. Through cooperation with existing state regulatory agencies and industrial representatives, the Commission will formulate and promote upon an industry-wide basis, a program looking toward the establishment of minimum standards for the treatment of industrial wastes.

7. When and to the extent deemed necessary to the development of the above-prescribed sanitary condition, the Commission will adopt quality standards for the various waters which are subject to its jurisdiction.

8. Except when it may not be conducive to the satisfactory accomplishment of any of its objectives, the Commission proposes to deal with individual communities and industries through appropriate state agencies, rather than to do so directly.

9. The Commission, through cooperation with various state agencies, will establish a procedure for the filing with the Commission of engineering design data covering new or revised projects for the treatment of sewage and industrial wastes. The Commission will also establish a program whereby all such data will be reviewed in order that the adequacy of any such new or revised installations may be determined and in order that the Commission can submit and urge for adoption by the sponsors of any such project appropriate recommendations for such changes or additions as may be necessary to meet the standards of the Commission. As has heretofore been the practice, detailed plans and specifications for any such projects will be submitted directly to appropriate state agencies for their review and approval.

10. The Commission intends to promote a program of public information and education pertaining to its functions and objectives, but before any publicity is released or before any program is undertaken which has particu-

lar bearing upon any one or more of the signatory States, clearance therefore will be obtained from the appropriate agency of the State or States affected.

11. The Commission does not propose, in the immediate future, to operate a laboratory or to engage in research activities, but instead will endeavor to accomplish any necessary laboratory or research work through state agencies, the United States Public Health Service, or established research agencies.

12. The Commission will conduct studies and prepare reports as follows:

(a) All available water analyses and other technical studies relating to streams of the Ohio River Basin, including reports or surveys of the United States Public Health Service and state water pollution control agencies, will be assembled, correlated and supplemented. Based thereon a comprehensive report will be prepared covering the water pollution problems of the Ohio River Basin, and making recommendations for their correction, elimination and prevention.

(b) A study, analysis and comparison will be made of the stream pollution control policies, procedures, philosophies, limitations and accomplishments of each of the signatory States, and based thereon, recommendations for improvements will be prepared for submission to the States when deemed necessary.

(c) Surveys which the Commission may be required to make covering interstate streams, concerning which questions involving the rights and duties of two or more States may be at issue, as a consequence of which the Commission may have been called upon to act as an arbitrator.

(d) Such investigations, studies, or analyses as may be necessary or desirable to the furtherance of any of the objectives of the Commission.

ORSANCO DOCUMENTARY FILMS

Following is a list of ORSANCO films produced to illustrate various aspects of pollution abatement in the Ohio Valley. These 16 mm movies, in color and with sound, may be borrowed for group showings by request to Commission headquarters, 414 Walnut St., Cincinnati, Ohio, 45202.

GOOD RIDDANCE   This fast-moving, omnibus film depicts the progress made and the tasks that still remain in curbing water pollution in the Ohio Valley. This offers a general introduction on the regional crusade for clean streams undertaken by eight states. (29½ minutes)

BEARGRASS CREEK   The story of what can happen to a stream when people along its banks disregard their obligation to prevent pollution. Of particular interest is the work being done by the University of Louisville in conducting the ORSANCO-sponsored study of aquatic-life resources. (19½ minutes)

OIL ON THE RIVER   Beginning with the story of the discovery of oil in the Ohio Valley, this film shows the unhappy consequence of carelessness in handling, transportation, storage, and use of oil products and then depicts preventive measures. (20½ minutes)

CRISIS ON THE KANAWHA   A portrayal of industrial growth and the failure to keep pace with it in terms of river protection is the opening theme of this film. Then follows a detailed description of the remedial steps that are being taken to deal with the situation. (22 minutes)

RIVER WATCHERS   Safeguarding streams from pollution hazards calls for constant vigilance. This is the story of the sentinels in the eight states who are engaged in checking sewage plant operations, aerial surveillance, virus identification, sampling of streams, forecasting river flow and evaluating the results from robot monitors. (18½ minutes)

THE FIRST FIFTEEN YEARS   ORSANCO commissioners describe progress in the fifteen-year crusade for clean streams in the Ohio Valley. A highlight of the film is a visit to The Kettering Laboratory where toxicity studies are documented. (26 minutes)

COAL AND WATER   A penetrating look at pollution problems created by the coal industry and the steps being taken to solve those problems. Included is a description of sealing operations in an underground mine to curb acid mine-drainage. (23 minutes)

"OOPS!"   An educational film which demonstrates how careless actions within a plant may result in river pollution and steps to take to guard against such situations. Designed as an in-plant training aid to solicit employee and supervisor alertness in preventing accidental spills. (22 minutes)

Appendix 5.

ORSANCO TECHNICAL AND RESEARCH REPORTS

An annotated bibliography of publications and special reports related to investigations and research projects of the Ohio River Valley Water Sanitation Commission and its Advisory Committees (1948–1965).

Commission Publications

ACID MINE DRAINAGE, PRINCIPLES AND GUIDE TO PRACTICES

Sept. 1963—A handbook prepared by the Coal Industry Advisory Committee and published by ORSANCO, for the use of coal-mine operators and the guidance of regulatory agency personnel. It describes in simplified fashion the fundamental principles underlying control measures promulgated by ORSANCO and the manner in which they can be applied. The case histories describe how situations at various types of mines have been dealt with.

BACTERIAL-QUALITY OBJECTIVES FOR THE OHIO RIVER

June 1951—Development of recommendations on bacterial-quality objectives for waters used for potable supplies and recreational purposes. The study provides background information in support of the recommended objectives, and describes how the objectives are to be applied and interpreted.

BRINE CONTAMINATION IN THE MUSKINGUM RIVER

Aug. 1951—Determination of the nature and magnitude of brine-waste discharges from salt-processing operations and their effect on quality conditions in a river basin. (Loan copy available)

DISPOSAL OF SPENT SULFATE PICKLING SOLUTIONS

Oct. 1952—An analysis of methods for treating spent solutions resulting from sulfuric acid pickling to reduce stream pollution. Compiled by the Steel Industry Action Committee. (Loan copy available)

DUST RECOVERY PRACTICE AT BLAST FURNACES

Jan. 1958—An evaluation of settleable solids formation and recovery at mills in the Ohio Valley and a suggested procedure for defining performance of waste water clarifiers. Compiled by Steel Industry Action Committee. (Price $1.00)

FISH-KILL HANDBOOK

March 1956—A practical outline of what to do and how to do it, designed for the agency or individual charged with responsibility for investigating a fish-kill. Contains bibliography on bioassays, toxicity, and biological indicators of pollution. (Price 50¢)

METHODS FOR TREATING METAL-FINISHING WASTES

Jan. 1953—An evaluation of various disposal methods and their applicability to specific waste-control conditions. Compiled by Metal-Finishing Industry Action Committee. (Price $1.00)

MONONGAHELA RIVER SEWAGE-TREATMENT CONSIDERATIONS

Jan. 1959—Staff report outlining quality conditions in the river, the status of control facilities, and recommendations for remedial action. (Loan copy)

OHIO RIVER POLLUTION PATTERNS—1950

June 1951—Water-quality conditions and changes revealed by a simultaneous sampling of the 963-mile stretch of the Ohio River from Pittsburgh to Cairo.

OHIO RIVER POLLUTION-ABATEMENT NEEDS—CINCINNATI POOL

Jan. 1949—Investigations leading to recommended treatment standards for organic wastes discharged to the Cincinnati Pool for establishment of Treatment Standard No. 1. (Loan copy available)

OHIO RIVER POLLUTION-ABATEMENT NEEDS—
HUNTINGTON TO CINCINNATI STRETCH

Feb. 1952—Staff findings with respect to existing conditions and recommendations for remedial measures used as a basis for the conduct of a public hearing for establishment of Treatment Standard No. 2.

OHIO RIVER POLLUTION-ABATEMENT NEEDS—
PITTSBURGH TO HUNTINGTON STRETCH

March 1953—Staff findings with respect to existing conditions and recommendations for remedial measures used as a basis for the conduct of a public hearing for establishment of Treatment Standards No. 3 and 4. (Limited supply)

OHIO RIVER POLLUTION-ABATEMENT NEEDS—CINCINNATI TO CAIRO STRETCH

Nov. 1953—Staff findings with respect to existing conditions and recommendations for remedial measures used as a basis for the conduct of a public hearing for establishment of Treatment Standards No. 5, 6, and 7. (Limited supply)

OIL PIPELINE BREAKS

Sept. 1950—A guidebook prepared by the staff on the development of preventive measures and the organization of emergency crews to cope with oil pipeline breaks. Pollution control procedures are described, including methods for recovering lost oil. (Loan copy available)

PHENOL WASTES TREATMENT BY CHEMICAL OXIDATION

June 1951—Report on a co-operative research project showing how phenols can be destroyed by three methods of chemical oxidation (chlorine, ozone, and chlorine dioxide). (Price $1.00)

PLANNING AND MAKING INDUSTRIAL WASTE SURVEYS

April 1952—Detailed instructions for measuring volume of waste flow, obtaining representative samples, and calculating waste loads. Compiled by Metal-Finishing Industry Action Committee. (Price $1.00)

PLATING-ROOM CONTROLS FOR POLLUTION ABATEMENT

July 1951—A guidebook of principles and practices for curbing losses of solutions and metals that otherwise might find their way into water courses. Compiled by Metal-Finishing Industry Action Committee. (Price 50¢)

PROCEDURES FOR ANALYZING METAL-FINISHING WASTES

Aug. 1954—Methods designed to screen out interfering substances and selected for accuracy and reproducibility of results. Compiled by Metal-Finishing Industry Action Committee. (Price $1.00)

REDUCING PHENOL WASTES FROM COKE PLANTS

Jan. 1953—Sources, volumes, and concentrations of phenolic wastes and methods for reduction by process changes or treatment. Compiled by Steel Industry Action Committee. (Price $1.00)

REGULATORY ACTIONS

Jan. 1961 (revised Jan. 1963)—A compendium of regulatory actions adopted by the Commission for the control of sewage, industrial wastes, and other substances.

RESERVOIRS AND POLLUTION CONTROL BENEFITS

Jan. 1953—Description and status of the 80-unit reservoir program of the U. S. Corps of Engineers in the Ohio River Basin with reference to its present and anticipated effects on pollution abatement.

RIVER-QUALITY CONDITIONS DURING A 16-WEEK
SHUTDOWN OF UPPER OHIO VALLEY STEEL MILLS

Sept. 1961—Closure of the mills because of a labor strike presented a unique opportunity to appraise the condition of streams that were relieved of a burden of industrial effluents. Staff report includes the data and describes evaluation methods. (Loan copy available.)

SEWAGE TREATMENT WORKS

June 1952—A manual describing step-by-step engineering and financial procedures for cities or villages undertaking construction of a sewage-works project. Report issued by ORSANCO and the Ohio Health Department. (Price $1.00)

WABASH RIVER POLLUTION-ABATEMENT NEEDS

Aug. 1950—Staff findings on conditions in one stretch of the Wabash River with recommendations for remedial measures between Terre Haute, Ind., and Mt. Carmel, Ill. (Loan copy available)

WATER QUALITY AND FLOW VARIATIONS IN THE OHIO RIVER—1951–55

March 1957—A compilation of chemical and bacteriological analyses coupled with flow-discharge records from a network of monitor stations. Includes a hydrographic study of the flow-variability pattern, particularly with regard to minimum flows. (Price $2.00)

WATER QUALITY AND FLOW VARIATIONS—OHIO RIVER
AND TRIBUTARIES—1956–57

April 1959—A compilation of chemical and bacteriological analyses at 44 locations on the Ohio River and tributary streams. Included are qualigrams which show observed range and frequency of occurrence at five locations on the Ohio River for alkalinity, pH, total hardness, sulfate, chloride, dissolved solids, temperature, and turbidity; also flow duration curves for 18 of the major tributaries of the Ohio River. (Price $2.00)

Reports on Contract Investigations

ACID MINE DRAINAGE

May 1961—A report prepared by Ohio State University under Commission sponsorship for the purpose of developing guidelines for the conduct of future research on acid mine drainage control. (Loan copies available)

AQUATIC-LIFE RESOURCES OF THE OHIO RIVER

Jan. 1962—An inventory of the aquatic-life resources of the Ohio River based on a three-year study by the University of Louisville, sponsored by ORSANCO and the Kentucky Division of Fish and Wildlife Resources. (Loan copies available)

PHYSIOLOGICAL ASPECTS OF WATER QUALITY

An evaluation of information on the physiological aspects of substances in water conducted by The Kettering Laboratory of the University of Cincinnati under contract with ORSANCO. Findings, which are presented in some twenty-six reports issued by The Kettering Laboratory during the period 1952–59, are part of the Commission archives. Substances included in the study are: acrylonitrile, ammonium, arsenic, cadmium, carbon tetrachloride, chloride, chromium, cobalt, copper, cresol, cyanide, detergents, fluoride, inorganic salts, iron, lead, manganese, naphthalene, nickel, nitrate, phenol, pyridine, sodium arsenite, sulfur, tin, zinc.

PHYTOPLANKTON

A study of the composition of phytoplankton in a portion of the Ohio River and the effect of these organisms on water-quality conditions conducted in 1960 by the Potamological Institute of the University of Louisville under a contract arrangement with ORSANCO. Purpose of the work was to evaluate factors affecting phytoplankton blooms and their relationship to taste and odor occurrences.

RADIOACTIVITY

From 1959 to 1964, the Potamological Institute of the University of Louisville, under contract with ORSANCO, conducted investigations to develop information on the accumulation of radio-materials by fish, by aquatic organisms, and in river sediments at selected stations along the Ohio River; also included are evaluations on radioactivity levels revealed from monitoring data. Findings are set forth in a series of annual reports, copies of which are available on a loan basis.

TASTE AND ODOR

Examination of Ohio River samples to identify substances contributing to taste and odor problems and the development of improved techniques (e.g. chloroform extraction of carbon filter residue), for analysis of these substances. The study was conducted under contract at The Kettering Laboratory of the University of Cincinnati, April, 1957 to December, 1959.

Advisory Committee Reports Published in Technical Journals

AQUATIC-LIFE ADVISORY COMMITTEE

Findings and recommendations on quality requirements suitable for the maintenance of a harvestable fish crop. Documented in three reports published in *Sewage and Industrial Wastes*: First Report— March 1955 —page 321. Discusses influence of dissolved oxygen and hydrogen-ion concentrations and outlines bioassay procedures. 2nd Report—May 1956—page 678. Presents conclusions with regard to temperature, dissolved solids, settleable solids, color, chloride and fluoride ions. 3rd Report—January 1960—page 65. Deals with effect of radioactivity, detergents, cyanides, phenolic compounds, iron, and manganese on aquatic life.

CHEMICAL INDUSTRY ADVISORY COMMITTEE

"Current Practices in Municipal Treatment of Industrial Wastes"— *Sewage and Industrial Wastes,* June 1957, p. 672. A survey of practices at 100 sewage-treatment plants analyzed with respect to their handling of industrial wastes.

"Site Selection for Chemical Industry Plants"—*Industrial Wastes,* Jan-Feb. 1957, p. 24. Originally titled "Operation and Design Practice as Related to Pollution Control in the Chemical Industry," this report deals specifically with treatment and disposal of water-borne wastes.

"Selecting Sites for Chemical Plants"—*Industrial Wastes,* March-April 1958, p. 46. Waste disposal considerations as they relate to the location of new processing facilities.

"Detergents in Sewage and Surface Water"—*Industrial Wastes,* July-Aug. 1956, p. 212. A report on development of analytical procedures and research activities.

"Components of Household Synthetic Detergents in Water and Sewage" —*Journal of the American Water Works Association,* March, 1963, p. 369. A report on sanitary-engineering aspects of detergents.

PETROLEUM INDUSTRY COMMITTEE
(formerly Oil Refining Industry Committee)
"Foul Condensate Treatment and Disposal"—*Sewage and Industrial Wastes,* Feb. 1958, p. 185. Experiences and operating data relating to the treatment, disposal, and reuse of foul-condensate waters.

Articles and Reports of Reference Interest

"Creating Public Awareness and Motivation for Clean Streams"—by Edward J. Cleary, *American Journal of Public Health,* June 1959, p. 757. Analysis of methods used by ORSANCO to create public support to promote construction of waste-treatment facilities.

"Ohio River Water Quality and Flow"—by Edward J. Cleary and David A. Robertson, Jr., *Journal of the American Water Works Association,* March 1958, p. 399. Experiences of the Ohio River Valley Water Sanitation Commission in pioneering the establishment of a river-quality monitor program. Methods of operation, evaluation of data, and costs are discussed.

"Robot Monitor System for the Ohio Valley" by Edward J. Cleary, *Journal of the American Water Works Association,* Nov. 1962, p. 1347. Description of an electronic sentinel system designed to provide automatic and continuous surveillance of river-quality variations in the Ohio River Valley.

"Evaluation of Membrane Filter Technique for Appraising Ohio River Water Quality" by Harold W. Streeter and David A. Robertson Jr., *Sewage and Industrial Wastes,* Feb., 1960. An evaluation of a 20-month study by the Water Users Committee of the Commission comparing the membrane filter and standard dilution methods for enumerating coliform organisms in raw waters.

"Reuse of Ohio River Water"—by Edward J. Cleary, Robert K. Horton, and Robert J. Boes, *Journal of the American Water Works Association,* June 1963, p. 683. An investigation into reuse of Ohio River water, showing relationship of water used by industries and municipalities to river flow.

"An Electronic Monitor System for River-Quality Surveillance and Research" by Edward J. Cleary, *International Conference on Water Pollution Research,* London, Sept., 1962. Detailed description of design features of analyzer units, telemetry, and data-logging equipment of the ORSANCO robot-monitor system.

"Barge Transport of Hazardous Material"— *ORSANCO 1960 Annual Report.* Findings and recommendations resulting from a staff inquiry of the risks involved in barge transport of chemical compounds on the Ohio River.

"Instrumentation for Water Quality Management in the Ohio Valley," *ASTM National Forum on the Control of Water Quality,* May 12-13, 1965, Philadelphia (Wm. L. Klein). A discussion of the methods used for collecting, processing, and evaluating data obtained from the ORSANCO robot-monitor system.

NOTICE OF REQUIREMENT FOR SEWAGE TREATMENT

(Standard No. 3)

You are hereby notified that on April 29, 1953 the Ohio River Valley Water Sanitation Commission, acting in accordance with and pursuant to authority contained in Article VI of the Ohio River Valley Water Sanitation Compact, established, subject to revision as changing conditions may require, the following standard of treatment for all sewage from municipalities or other political subdivisions, public or private institutions or corporations discharged or permitted to flow into that portion of the Ohio River extending from the Allegheny County-Beaver County line in Pennsylvania, located approximately 15 miles downstream from the confluence of the Allegheny and Monongahela Rivers at Pittsburgh, to U. S. Corps of Engineers Dam No. 27, located about five miles upstream from Huntington, W. Va., and being 301.0 miles downstream from Pittsburgh, Pennsylvania:

   (a) Substantially complete removal of settleable solids; and

   (b) Removal of not less than forty-five percent of the total suspended solids; and, in addition

   (c) Reduction in coliform organisms in accordance with the following schedule:

      Not less than 80 per cent reduction during the months May through October.
      Not less than 85 per cent reduction during the months November through April.

Under the terms and provisions of the Ohio River Valley Water Sanitation Compact all sewage from municipalities or other political subdivisions, public or private institutions, or corporations, discharged or permitted to flow into the above described portion of the Ohio River will be required to be treated in accordance with the above established standard within a time reasonable for the construction of the necessary works. As one of the municipalities, subdivisions, institutions or corporations subject to the provisions of the Ohio River Valley Water Sanitation Compact, you are herewith called upon to advise the   (*name of state control agency*) as to the extent to which you are now meeting the standard of sewage treatment above set forth and, in addition, to advise as to the minimum period of time which, in your opinion, will be required in order to complete construction of works necessary to meet that standard.

Issued this   *day of*   *, 1953*   *at Cincinnati, Ohio.*

To _____

Ohio River Valley Water Sanitation Commission

_____

_____   *Chairman*

_____

        [Seal]   _____

                                   Executive Director & Chief Engineer

_____

Commissioners for (name of state)

Appendix 7.

ORSANCO RULES OF PROCEDURE FOR PUBLIC HEARINGS

I. PURPOSE AND SCOPE OF PUBLIC HEARINGS

A. *Hearings under Article VI*

By the language of Article VI of the Ohio River Valley Water Sanitation Compact, the Ohio River Valley Water Sanitation Commission is empowered to conduct public hearings with regard to either of the following matters:

1. What, if any, degree of treatment, higher than that specified in Article VI must, in specified instances, be given to sewage discharged or permitted to flow into interstate portions of the Ohio River and its tributary waters in order to protect public health and to preserve those waters for legitimate purposes.
2. What degree of modification or treatment must be given to industrial wastes discharged or permitted to flow into interstate portions of the Ohio River and its tributary waters in order to protect public health and to preserve those waters for legitimate purposes.

B. *Hearings under Article IX*

By the language of Article IX of the Ohio River Valley Water Sanitation Compact, the Ohio River Valley Water Sanitation Commission is empowered to conduct public hearings upon the basis of which it may subsequently order any municipality, corporation, person or other entity to discontinue, in whole or in part, or to modify, treat or otherwise dispose of any discharge of sewage or industrial waste permitted to flow into interstate portions of the Ohio River or its tributary waters.

II. WHEN HEARINGS ARE TO BE HELD

A. Public hearings authorized by Article VI of The Ohio River Valley Water Sanitation Compact, shall be held whenever, after full investigation by the Commission into the necessity for such a hearing, the Commission by a majority vote of the Commissioners present at a meeting duly held, shall direct, or, without a meeting, whenever, after full investigation by the Commission into the necessity for such a hearing, the Commission by a majority of Commissioners then appointed and qualified under the provisions of the Compact, may in writing direct.

B. Public hearings authorized by Article IX of The Ohio River Valley Water Sanitation Compact, shall be held whenever, after full investigation by the Commission into the necessity for such a hearing, the Commission, by a majority vote of the Commissioners present at a meeting duly held, shall direct.

308

III. NOTICE OF HEARINGS

A. *Form*. Notice of any hearing held under authority of Article VI or Article IX shall be issued over the signature of the Chairman and/or the Executive Director of the Commission in substantially the following form:

"OHIO RIVER VALLEY WATER SANITATION COMMISSION

NOTICE OF PUBLIC
HEARING

"Pursuant to authority contained in Article _____ of the Ohio River Valley Water Sanitation Compact, and pursuant to direction of the Ohio River Valley Water Sanitation Commission, a public hearing

will be held by the Commission at _____, commencing at _____ o'clock, _____M., on the _____

day of _____, 1949 _____, and continuing thereafter from day to day until completed. The purpose of said hearing

will be _____

_____.

"Any and all parties whose interests may be affected by such hearing or by any action of the Commission which may be taken as the result of such hearing are invited to be present or to be represented at the hearing to be held as above stated. All interested parties present or represented at said hearing will be given an adequate opportunity to express, either orally or in writing, their views upon the issues there to be considered.

"Interested parties who desire additional information concerning the conduct of this hearing or who desire information with regard to evidence, views or recommendations which are to be submitted at such hearing, are requested to call at the offices of the Ohio River Valley Water Sanitation Commission, 410 First National

Bank Building. On and after the _____ day of _____,

19_____, there will be on file and available for examination at the offices of the Commission, located as above stated, copies of the report of the Commission's Engineering Committee covering

its investigation of _____

_____

and including the recommendations of that Committee with regard to _____

_____

_____.

"OHIO RIVER VALLEY WATER SANITATION COMMISSION

"by _____
                                    Chairman

"_____, 19____ "

B. *Publication and Distribution.* Not less than fifteen (15) days prior to the date of any such hearing notice thereof shall be given as follows:

1. Publication as a paid advertisement or as a news item on not less than two separate dates in at least one newspaper of general circulation in the area most likely to be affected by the hearing.

2. Direct mail to any municipality, political subdivision, public or private institution, corporation or individual known to be interested in or likely to be affected by the subject matter of the hearing.

3. Direct mail to any organization or association known to represent any municipality, political subdivision, public or private institution, corporation or individual known to be interested in or likely to be affected by the subject matter of the hearing.

4. Such other and additional publication and distribution as the Chairman of the Commission may consider necessary and desirable in order to insure adequate notification to parties who may be interested in or affected by the subject matter of the hearing.

IV. CONDUCT OF HEARINGS

A. *Hearing Board.* Each hearing held under authority of Article VI or Article IX shall be conducted by a Hearing Board, the size and composition of which shall be designated by the Commission concurrently with its action directing that the hearing be held. The Hearing Board shall select a presiding officer for the hearing from among its membership.

B. *Proceedings at Hearings*

1. The presiding officer shall open the hearing by reading aloud the Notice of Hearing and the pertinent provisions of the Compact, under authority of which the hearing is being held. In addition, the presiding officer shall make such explanatory remarks as he may deem necessary in order to state clearly the purpose and scope of the hearing.

2. The presiding officer shall then announce that all present desiring to do so will be given a full opportunity to express their views and opinions with regard to the subject matter of the hearing and will be given full opportunity to present any testimony or evidence which may be relevant and material to the subject matter of the hearing.

3. Witnesses shall then be called in such order as the presiding officer may direct for the purpose of giving testimony or expressing their views or opinions with regard to the subject matter of the hearing.

4. Witnesses giving testimony before the hearing shall be subject to cross examination by or on behalf of interested parties present to whatever extent the presiding officer may deem warranted in order to insure a full and complete inquiry into the subject matter of the hearing.

5. The presiding officer in his discretion may continue the hearing from time to time for the purpose of giving any interested party the opportunity to present additional evidence or testimony relevant and material to the subject matter of the hearing which could not be properly prepared in time for the hearing or within the discretion of the presiding officer such additional but unavailable evidence or testimony may thereafter be submitted to the Hearing Board in writing subject to limitation as the presiding officer may prescribe, provided that any such evidence subsequently submitted shall be available for examination by any party interested in the subject matter of the hearing.

6. A complete stenographic record of the proceedings had at any such hearing shall be made and preserved by the Hearing Board which shall include a copy of the Notice of Hearing, a list of the persons notified, together with a statement of such other manner of publication of notice as was given and a list of all interested persons or parties attending the hearing.

V. REPORT AND RECOMMENDATIONS OF HEARING BOARD

A. As soon as practicable after the completion of any hearing held under authority of Article VI or Article IX of the Compact, the Hearing Board shall carefully review all testimony, evidence, views or opinions which may have been presented at the hearing and shall prepare for submission to the Commission recommendations with regard to the subject matter of the hearing. Copies of the record of the proceedings and the recommendations of the Hearing Board shall be transmitted to the Commission for its review and final action.

B. Final action based upon a hearing held under authority of Article VI of the Compact may be taken by the Commission upon a majority vote of the members present at any meeting duly held at which a quorum is present.

C. No order based upon a hearing held under authority of Article IX of the Compact shall be issued by the Commission unless and until, at a meeting duly held at which a quorum is present, it receives the the affirmative vote of at least a majority of the Commissioners from each of not less than a majority of the states which are signatories to the Compact, and unless and until, at a meeting duly held at which a quorum is present, it receives the affirmative vote of not less than a majority of the Commissioners from the state in which is located the municipality, corporation, person or other entity against which such order may be directed.

VI. DOCKETING AND MAINTENANCE OF RECORDS

A. The Secretary of the Commission is hereby authorized and directed to establish and maintain separate permanent dockets in which shall be maintained memoranda of any action of the Commission taken in the exercise of any of the authority granted to it under Article VI or Article IX of the Ohio River Valley Water Sanitation Compact. Each case in which action is taken by the Commission under authority of either Article shall be designated upon the appropriate docket by an identifying number and all entries with respect to each such case shall be made upon that docket under its assigned number.

B. In each case in which the Commission shall exercise any authority granted to it under Article VI or Article IX of the Compact, the order of the Commission making final disposition of the case shall be set forth in full as the final entry made with respect to that particular case in the appropriate docket to be maintained as hereby directed.

C. The Secretary of the Commission is hereby directed to maintain a permanent file covering each action which may be taken by the Commission pursuant to any of the authority contained in Article VI or Article IX of the Compact, which file shall include the original or certified copies of all papers, reports, affidavits, notices, transcripts of evidence and proceedings and other documents pertaining to the case or to the hearing held with regard thereto.

VII. AMENDMENTS

These rules may from time to time be amended by appropriate action of the Commission.

ORSANCO INDUSTRIAL-WASTE CONTROL POLICY AND PROCEDURE

(Adopted April 6, 1955; Amended September 12, 1958, and January 14, 1960)

WHEREAS, activities and experiences of the Ohio River Valley Water Sanitation Commission have now reached the point where it is desirable and necessary from administrative and other standpoints to issue a formal statement of policy and procedure in order to:

Promote the execution of provisions in the Compact for the control of industrial wastes;

Provide for the Compact states a plan of action for expediting the Commission's control program on interstate waters;

Furnish to existing industrial establishments in the Ohio Valley located on waters under jurisdiction of the Commission and to those who are about to locate on these waters information with regard to control of waste discharges; and

Establish a basis for effective and orderly conduct of staff activities;

NOW, THEREFORE, the Ohio River Valley Water Sanitation Commission does hereby declare the following principles and procedures by which it will be guided in pursuing the obligations placed upon it by the provisions of the Compact and in the exercise of powers vested in it:

I.   Requirements for the modification or restriction of industrial-waste discharges in waters as defined in Article VI of the Compact (the Ohio River and its tributary waters which form boundaries between, or are contiguous, to two or more signatory states, or which flow from one signatory state into another signatory state) shall be designed to safeguard and maintain water uses that will serve the public interest in the most beneficial and reasonable manner. However, certain minimum or basic requirements, applying to every industrial-waste discharge, will be stipulated in accordance with the directive in Article I of the Compact that all waters are to be "free from unsightly or malodorous nuisances due to floating solids or sludge deposits."

II.   In reaching conclusions on water uses to be safeguarded in various sections along streams the Commission will be guided by an evaluation of present uses, such future uses as can be reasonably foreseen and all other pertinent information. Decisions with regard to water-uses shall be subject to such review as the Commission deems necessary in accordance with changing conditions or by request from parties who may be affected. Among the legitimate uses of water to be considered by the Commission—but not necessarily restricted to them—are the following: Public and industrial supplies, maintenance of aquatic life, agricultural purposes, recreational and esthetic pursuits, navigation, power development and ultimate disposal of waste effluents.

III.   To aid in the appraisal of water suitability for various uses and for guidance in the establishment of waste-control requirements the Commission will employ quality criteria. These criteria, to be applied at point of use,

313

are not to be considered as effluent standards. The criteria will define within the boundaries of expert knowledge the respective physical, chemical, biological and bacteriological conditions of water in the stream consistent with protection of specific uses.

IV. In developing control measures for industrial-waste discharges the Commission will be guided by an examination of all local factors, including:

   a. Variations in the size, flow, location, character, self-purification characteristics and the established and proposed uses of the receiving stream;
   b. Variability of industrial operations and consequent changes in location, volume, type and combinations of waste discharges;
   c. Economic considerations.

V. Industrial-waste control measures will be promulgated on a step-by-step basis as follows:

   1st step—Establishment of basic requirements that are applicable to all industrial wastes discharged into interstate waters of the district. These basic requirements, designated as IW-1, are set forth following this statement.
   2nd step—Determination of supplementary "tailored" control requirements, through and in co-operation with appropriate state agencies, for each industrial plant based on such investigations and voluntary agreements or hearings as deemed necessary to establish the need and validity of control measures beyond those that satisfy basic requirements.

VI. It is recognized that time and circumstances will determine how quickly supplementary "tailored" requirements should and can be stipulated for each industrial plant. Meanwhile, every industrial plant that is now discharging or may seek to discharge wastes into interstate waters of the district as defined in the Compact, will be expected to comply as promptly as possible with the first-step basic requirements, designated as IW-1 and set forth following this statement.

VII. If supplementary "tailored" waste-control requirements are to be stipulated for an industrial plant, they will be based on stream surveys and continuing investigations of water use and quality conditions, the volume and characteristics of waste discharges and other factors applicable to a specific situation or area. Recommendations will be developed after consultation and in cooperation with appropriate state agencies and the industrial plants involved. Revision of supplementary "tailored" control measures may be required from time to time depending on: (a) changes in the quantity or character of industrial-waste discharges; (b) changes in conditions of stream use.

VIII. It shall be the responsibility of each state agency to supply such information and data as may be necessary to develop supplementary waste-control requirements. The states will also keep the Commission informed of new or contemplated industrial-waste discharges into those waters coming under the jurisdiction of the Commission, so that the effect of these on existing conditions can be appraised and decisions reached with regard to revised control requirements.

IX. Priority of attention by the Commission in development of supplementary "tailored" requirements shall be given to those industrial plants now discharging directly into the Ohio River; the plan shall be to proceed in an orderly manner from the head of the river to its mouth. However, on request of any state, consideration will be given to shifting investigations to any location which may best serve Commission interests.

X. The appropriate state regulatory agency will administer regulatory controls. Questions concerning compliance with requirements are to be addressed to the signatory state agency in the state in which the industrial plant is operating. The state agency will arrange for such further contact or consultation with the Commission as may be necessary or requested. Whenever, in the opinion of the Commission, satisfactory compliance with basic and supplemental requirements is not being or cannot be obtained through efforts of such state agencies, the Commission will take such action as may be necessary to transpose such requirement or requirements into treatment standards or regulations within the contemplation of Article VI of the Compact and to procure enforcement of them through use of the procedures prescribed in Article IX of the Compact.

IW-1—BASIC INDUSTRIAL WASTE REQUIREMENTS

Industrial wastes shall be treated or otherwise modified prior to discharge so as to maintain the following conditions in the receiving waters:

1. Freedom from anything that will settle to form putrescent or otherwise objectionable sludge deposits which interfere with reasonable water uses.
2. Freedom from floating debris, scum and other floating materials in amounts sufficient to be unsightly or deleterious.
3. Freedom from materials producing color or odor in such degree as to create a nuisance.
4. Freedom from substances in concentrations or combinations which are toxic or harmful to human, animal or aquatic-life.

These conditions to be maintained in the receiving waters following the discharge of industrial-waste effluents, are basic or minimum requirements. Investigations will be conducted by the Commission as time and circumstances permit to establish the need and validity of altering or adding to the above basic requirements.

Questions concerning compliance with requirements are to be addressed to the signatory state agency in the state in which the industrial plant is operating. Arrangements will be made by the state agency for such contact and consultation with the Commission as may be necessary or requested.

Appendix 9.

HYPOTHETICAL EXAMPLE OF ALLOCATIONS OF CHLORIDE CAPACITY UNDER STAFF PROPOSAL A

To illustrate application of the uniform reduction, balanced tributary drainage-basin system of allocation of chloride capacity among main-stem and tributary sources of discharge (Proposal A) some hypothetical examples are presented.

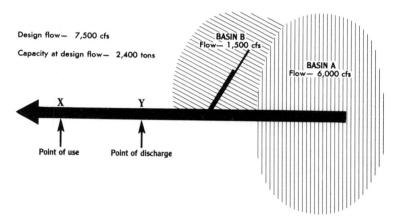

Figure A-1.

For this purpose and in the interest of simplification, a situation applicable to the Ohio River is set forth in idealized fashion. The conditions are shown in Figure A-1, and they may be stated as follows:

The main-stem river has two tributary drainage basins called A and B. At a point-of-use, called X, it has been determined that the allowable chloride loading, or capacity of the river, is 2,400 tons per day at the selected design flow of 7,500 cfs. This flow at point X is comprised of 6,000 cfs from basin A and 1,500 cfs from basin B. There are no main-stem chloride discharges, the entire load at point X being the sum of the discharges from basins A and B. These, then, are the fixed conditions.

The following demonstrates the computation of allotment using three different situations that might occur. Each demonstration is based on application of the theory of uniform reduction, balanced drainage-basin allotment, which can be stated in this form:

The chloride capacity at the control point is a function of water available, which flow is the total of the flows contributed by upstream tributaries; the main stem is not credited with any flow contribution because the amount is negligible. Consequently, upstream tributaries must share their dilution capacity for the accommodation of main-stem loads.

316

The allowable chloride loading from all sources above the control point is fixed by the dilution available at the control point. This chloride capacity will be allotted in proportion to magnitude of total load from all main-stem sources and from the tributaries on the basis of total load and contributed flow.

These relationships can be expressed in the shorthand of mathematical formulas as follows:

Main-stem allotment =

$$\frac{\text{Main-stem loads}}{\text{Total load at control point}} \times \text{Allowable capacity at control point}$$

Total tributary allotment =

$$\frac{\text{Total tributary loads}}{\text{Total load at control point}} \times \text{Allowable capacity at control point}$$

Specific tributary allotment =

$$\frac{\text{Flow contributed by tributary}}{\text{Flow at control point}} \times \text{Total tributary allotment}$$

From these relationships it becomes a simple matter to compute the allotments and required cutbacks under varying situations of loading.

Situation 1—For example, consider this situation imposed on the fixed conditions previously set forth:

Basin A contributes a load of	800 tons
Basin B contributes a load of	1,600 tons
A main-stem industry located at point Y wishes to add a load of	600 tons

Total load reaching control point X would be 3,000 tons. But, it will be recalled, the capacity at the design flow has been established as 2,400 tons. Therefore, in order to accommodate the requested addition of 600 tons, provisions for cutback must be made. To accomplish this in accordance with the principle of uniform-percentage reduction coupled with balanced drainage-basin allotments, the following apportionment would be made:

Main-stem allotment at design flow $= \dfrac{600}{3,000}$ tons $\times$ 2,400 = 480 tons.

This means that the new industry must provide for a maximum cutback of 120 tons, or 20%, of its load.

Total tributary allotment at design flow $= \dfrac{(800 \text{ tons} + 1,600 \text{ tons})}{3,000}$

$\times$ 2,400 = 1,920 tons.

This means that the existing loads from the tributaries must be cut back a maximum of 480 tons, or 20%, in order to provide capacity for the new industry load. In other words, both the existing loads and the new load have been uniformly reduced.

Basin A allotment at design flow $= \dfrac{6,000 \text{ cfs}}{7,500 \text{ cfs}} \times 1,920$ tons = 1,536 tons.

Since basin A is contributing only 800 tons, and the allotment based on flow is 1,536 tons, no reduction is required. The surplus capacity of 736 tons will be credited to basin B which is overloaded.

$$\text{Basin B allotment at design flow} = \frac{1,500 \text{ cfs}}{7,500 \text{ cfs}} \times 1,920 \text{ tons} = 384 \text{ tons.}$$

Since basin B is contributing 1,600 tons, and the allotment as related to the flow from the basin is only 384 tons, a reduction of 1,216 tons is indicated. However, a credit of 736 tons of surplus capacity from basin A decreases the reduction required to 480 tons (1,216 −736).

To summarize, the resulting requirements created by Situation 1 (where a new industry seeks accommodation of a 600-ton load) would be:

Situation 1	Existing Load	New Load	Allotment at Design Flow	Maximum Reduction Required
Basin A	800 tons		1,536 tons	None
Basin B	1,600 tons		384 tons	480 tons*
Main-stem industry		600 tons	480 tons	120 tons
	2,400 tons	600 tons	2,400 tons	600 tons

* Credit of 736 tons from Basin A applied.

OTHER SITUATIONS—Similar computations for varying conditions of loadings give the following results:

Situation 2—Fixed conditions remain the same; but new loads requested on basin A and on main stem.

	Existing Load	New Load	Allotment at Design Flow	Maximum Reduction Required
Basin A	800	600	1,600	None
Basin B	1,600		400	1,000*
Main-stem		600	400	200
	2,400	1,200	2,400	1,200

* Credit of 200 tons from Basin A applied.

Situation 3—Fixed conditions remain the same; but new loads requested in basin B and on main stem.

	Existing Load	New Load	Allotment at Design Flow	Maximum Reduction Required
Basin A	800		1,600	None
Basin B	1,600	600	400	1,000*
Main-stem		600	400	200
	2,400	1,200	2,400	1,200

* Credit of 800 tons from Basin A applied.

Distribution of "Credits"—With regard to distribution of the "credit" not needed by a tributary basin, the examples shown simply transfer the credit

APPENDIX   319

to the other basin. When the credit is to be distributed among several basins the procedure would be to proportion the credit in accordance with relative flow from each basin.

Discharge Schedules—Illustrative discharge schedules for chloride loadings under Situation 1 are shown in Figure A-2. It can be seen, for example, that the main-stem industry's proportionate share in the available capacity equals its normal load of 600 tons per day at a stream flow of 10,000 cfs.

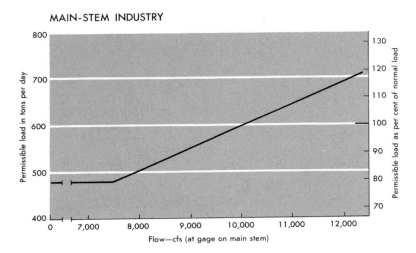

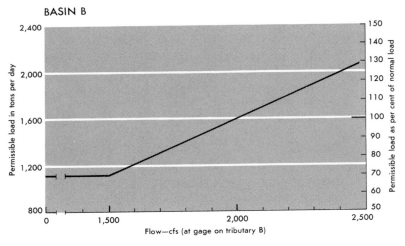

Figure A-2. Discharge schedule showing permissible chloride loadings at various flows under Situation 1.

At flows less than this the permissible loading for the industry is less than its normal load, thus requiring a cutback. The minimum permissible loading (allotment), based on the capacity at the design flow of 7,500 cfs, is 480 tons per day or 80 per cent of normal load. The maximum cutback, therefore, is 20 per cent.

Any chloride held in storage during times of cutback would be discharged in accordance with the schedule curve when the flow rises above 10,000 cfs.

ORSANCO STREAM-QUALITY CRITERIA AND MINIMUM CONDITIONS

(ORSANCO RESOLUTION No. 16–66, Adopted May 12, 1966, Amended September 8, 1966)

WHEREAS: The assessment of scientific knowledge and judgments on water-quality criteria has been a continuing effort over the years by the Commission in consultation with its advisory committees; and

WHEREAS: The Commission now finds it appropriate to consolidate viewpoints and recommendations relating to such criteria;

NOW, THEREFORE, BE IT RESOLVED: That the Ohio River Valley Water Sanitation Commission hereby adopts the following statement and specifications:

Criteria of quality are intended as guides for appraising the suitability of interstate surface waters in the Ohio Valley for various uses, and to aid decision-making in the establishment of waste-control measures for specific streams or portions thereof. Therefore, the criteria are not to be regarded as *standards* that are universally applicable to all streams. What is applicable to all streams at all places and at all times are certain minimum conditions, which will form part of every ORSANCO standard.

Standards for waters in the Ohio River Valley Water Sanitation District will be promulgated following investigation, due notice and hearing. Such standards will reflect an assessment of the public interest and equities in the use of the waters, as well as consideration of the practicability and physical and economic feasibility of their attainment.

The ORSANCO criteria embrace water-quality characteristics of fundamental significance, and which are routinely monitored and can be referenced to data that is generally available. The characteristics thus chosen may be regarded as primary indicators of water quality, with the understanding that additional criteria may be added as circumstances dictate. Unless otherwise specified, the term average as used herein means an arithmetical average.

MINIMUM CONDITIONS APPLICABLE TO ALL WATERS AT ALL PLACES AND AT ALL TIMES

1. Free from substances attributable to municipal, industrial or other discharges that will settle to form putrescent or otherwise objectionable sludge deposits;

2. Free from floating debris, oil, scum and other floating materials attributable to municipal, industrial or other discharges in amounts sufficient to be unsightly or deleterious;

3. Free from materials attributable to municipal, industrial or other discharges producing color, odor or other conditions in such degree as to create a nuisance;

321

4. Free from substances attributable to municipal, industrial or other discharges in concentrations or combinations which are toxic or harmful to human, animal, plant or aquatic life.

STREAM-QUALITY CRITERIA

FOR PUBLIC WATER SUPPLY

The following criteria are for evaluation of stream quality at the point at which water is withdrawn for treatment and distribution as a potable supply:

1. *Bacteria:* Coliform group not to exceed 5,000 per 100 ml as a monthly average value (either MPN or MF count); nor exceed this number in more than 20 percent of the samples examined during any month; nor exceed 20,000 per 100 ml in more than five percent of such samples.

2. *Threshold-odor number:* Not to exceed 24 (at 60 deg. C.) as a daily average.

3. *Dissolved solids:* Not to exceed 500 mg/l as a monthly average value, nor exceed 750 mg/l at any time. For Ohio River water, values of specific conductance of 800 and 1,200 microhms/cm (at 25 deg. C.) may be considered equivalent to dissolved-solids concentrations of 500 and 750 mg/l.

4. *Radioactive substances:* Gross beta activity (in the known absence of Strontium-90 and alpha emitters) not to exceed 1,000 micro-microcuries per liter at any time.

5. *Chemical constituents:* Not to exceed the following specified concentrations at any time:

Constituent	Concentration (mg/l)
Arsenic	0.05
Barium	1.0
Cadmium	0.01
Chromium (hexavalent)	0.05
Cyanide	0.2
Fluoride	2.0
Lead	0.05
Selenium	0.01
Silver	0.05

FOR INDUSTRIAL WATER SUPPLY

The following criteria are applicable to stream water at the point at which the water is withdrawn for use (either with or without treatment) for industrial cooling and processing:

1. *Dissolved oxygen:* Not less than 2.0 mg/l as a daily-average value, nor less than 1.0 mg/l at any time.

2. *pH:* Not less than 5.0 nor greater than 9.0 at any time.

3. *Temperature:* Not to exceed 95 deg. F. at any time.

4. *Dissolved solids:* Not to exceed 750 mg/l as a monthly average value, nor exceed 1,000 mg/l at any time. For Ohio River water, values of specific conductance of 1,200 and 1,600 microhms/cm (at 25 deg. C.) may be considered equivalent to dissolved-solids concentrations of 750 and 1,000 mg/l.

For Aquatic Life

The following criteria are for evaluation of conditions for the maintenance of a well-balanced, warm-water fish population. They are applicable at any point in the stream except for areas immediately adjacent to outfalls. In such areas cognizance will be given to opportunities for the admixture of waste effluents with river water.

1. *Dissolved oxygen:* Not less than 5.0 mg/l during at least 16 hours of any 24-hour period, nor less than 3.0 mg/l at any time;

2. *pH:* No values below 5.0 nor above 9.0, and daily average (or median) values preferably between 6.5 and 8.5.

3. *Temperature:* Not to exceed 93 deg. F. at any time during the months of May through November, and not to exceed 73 deg. F. at any time during the months of December through April.

4. *Toxic substances:* Not to exceed one-tenth of the 48-hour median tolerance limit, except that other limiting concentrations may be used in specific cases when justified on the basis of available evidence and approved by the appropriate regulatory agency.

For Recreation

The following criterion is for evaluation of conditions at any point in waters designated to be used for recreational purposes, including such water-contact activities as swimming and water skiing:

Bacteria: Coliform group not to exceed 1,000 per 100 ml as a monthly average value (either MPN or MF count); nor exceed this number in more than 20 percent of the samples examined during any month; nor exceed 2,400 per 100 ml (MPN or MF count) on any day.

For Agricultural or Stock Watering

The following criteria are for the evaluation of stream quality at the point at which water is withdrawn for use for agriculture or stock-watering purposes:

1. Free from substances attributable to municipal, industrial or other discharges that will settle to form putrescent or otherwise objectionable sludge deposits;

2. Free from floating debris, oil, scum and other floating materials attributable to municipal, industrial or other discharges in amounts sufficient to be unsightly or deleterious;

3. Free from materials attributable to municipal, industrial or other discharges producing color, odor or other conditions in such degree as to create a nuisance;

4. Free from substances attributable to municipal, industrial or other discharges in concentrations or combinations which are toxic or harmful to human, animal, plant or aquatic life.

Appendix 11.

Municipal and Institutional Sewage-Treatment Facilities—July 1, 1965

Number of communities (top number) and population served (bottom number)

Status	Ill.	Ind.	Ky.	N.Y.	Ohio	Pa.	Va.	W. Va.	Total	% of Total
Control currently acceptable	**64** 282,635	**172** 1,186,067	**226** 1,260,588	**10** 87,040	**298** 3,474,844	**283** 2,546,997	**40** 133,894	**74** 377,220	**1,167** 9,349,285	**68.5** 82.0
Treatment provided, improvements under construction	**0** 0	**7** 519,749	**5** 38,553	**0** 0	**5** 35,978	**0** 0	**0** 0	**3** 109,678	**20** 703,958	**1.2** 6.2
Treatment provided; not adequate	**4** 64,032	**14** 97,310	**10** 22,091	**4** 11,019	**30** 188,970	**13** 81,858	**20** 16,723	**17** 104,331	**112** 586,334	**6.6** 5.1
New treatment works under construction	**1** 4,370	**9** 11,009	**12** 20,370	**0** 0	**11** 13,143	**14** 35,989	**8** 15,031	**20** 56,133	**75** 156,045	**4.4** 1.4
No treatment, construction not started	**2** 2,680	**75** 85,060	**12** 13,645	**4** 11,493	**34** 50,702	**100** 249,379	**20** 23,648	**82** 161,483	**329** 598,090	**19.3** 5.3
Total	**71** 353,717	**277** 1,899,195	**265** 1,355,247	**18** 109,552	**378** 3,763,637	**410** 2,914,223	**88** 189,296	**196** 808,845	**1,703** 11,393,712	**100.0** 100.0

Status of Industrial Waste-Control Facilities—July 1, 1965

Status	Ill.	Ind.	Ky.	N.Y.	Ohio	Pa.	Va.	W. Va.	Total	% of Total
Control currently acceptable	10	216	149	18	308	510	45	194	1,450	84.2
Control facilities inadequate, improvements in progress	0	0	7	0	11	3	0	3	24	1.4
Control provided, but not adequate	8	27	14	7	49	16	3	31	155	8.9
New control facilities under construction	0	13	3	0	3	11	0	4	34	1.9
Planning treatment facilities or preparing to connect to municipal sewers	0	9	1	6	1	24	1	7	49	2.9
No action by company	0	0	0	5	0	0	1	5	11	0.7
Total number of industries	18	265	174	36	372	564	50	244	1,723	100.0
Complying with ORSANCO minimum requirements	18	251	159	20	355	511	48	198	1,560	90.5

INDEX

327